SUETONIUS
TIBERIUS

Edited with Introduction, Commentary
and Bibliography by

Hugh Lindsay

Bristol Classical Press

First published in 1995 by
Bristol Classical Press
an imprint of
Gerald Duckworth & Co. Ltd
The Old Piano Factory
48 Hoxton Square, London N1 6PB

A catalogue record for this book is available
from the British Library

ISBN 1-85399-387-5

Available in USA and Canada from:
Focus Information Group
PO Box 369
Newburyport
MA 01950

Printed in Great Britain by
Booksprint, Bristol

Contents

Preface

The entirety of Suetonius' life of Tiberius has had no modern commentator in English. This is not to say that both the Suetonian life, and the life of Tiberius himself has not attracted plentiful attention from contemporary audiences. This commentary aims to provide a guide to historical, historiographical and literary aspects of Suetonius' approach to Tiberius. I have not here attempted to provide a guide to the Latinity of Suetonius in the life of Tiberius. The commentary therefore does not try to cover the same ground as Goodyear on Tacitus or Woodman on Velleius. I have not provided help with translation, nor any discussion of grammatical peculiarities. It is to be hoped that the commentary will nevertheless be of use to students of Suetonius who have no Latin, most of whom will be depending on the Penguin translation of Robert Graves as updated by Michael Grant. Those who are just starting on a study of Tiberius may find it useful to consult Shotter's recent introductory work (Shotter [1992]). I have provided summary bibliographies on many historical issues relating to Tiberius at relevant points in the commentary.

I have inevitably incurred a great debt to my predecessors, and it will be evident that sections 1-23 of the commentary have been influenced by the commentary of Du Four (1941), while section 24-40 owe something to Rietra (1928). I hope I have acknowledged those debts adequately. The remainder of the commentary has been written without such aids, and may be the worse for that. It has been my intention to provide more detailed discussion of the structure of the life than was encompassed in either of these works. Wherever possible I have reacted to views of Tiberius expressed in the most recent modern biographies of Tiberius in English, those of Seager (1972) and Levick (1976), as well as in a large selection of other contemporary works on aspects of Tiberius. Nevertheless, the aim is not to correct their approaches, but rather to promote an awareness of how Suetonius shaped available material on the principate of Tiberius within the confines of his rather rigid biographical scheme. I hope the reader may emerge with a better idea of how Suetonius wrestled with the tradition.

One section of the introduction to this work, on the characterisation of Tiberius in this life, was first delivered at *Ancient History in a Modern University at Macquarie University* in July 1993. It appears here in slightly modified form.

I am pleased to thank Tom Hillard for helping me with some problems over the Claudian family tree. I have not tried to reconcile all the problems in the branches of the late Republican family, and simply point out here that Stemma 1 has adhered to orthodoxy. There is undoubtedly scope for improving upon the reconstructions that I have printed.

Professor Werner Eck kindly provided me with a copy of his article on the *SC de Cn. Pisone patre* and I have been able as a result to make some reference to this highly significant piece of evidense. I thank him most cordially.

This work had its origins in my work on the Suetonian life of Caligula, a work on which I started many years ago under the guidance of Brian Bosworth. Although he cannot be held directly responsible for anything in this volume, I believe that aspects of my approach to Tiberius go back to the grounding I received at University of Western Australia. I thank him, but naturally he cannot be held responsible for the shortcomings of this volume. I am pleased to thank my wife for her support while I have been completing the project.

H.M.L.
Newcastle (NSW) August 1994

Abbreviations

Standard abbreviations for Greek and Latin authors have been used, and periodicals generally follow the conventions of *L'Année philologique*. The name-date system has been used for all books cited. Full details of articles and books cited can be found in the bibliography.

AE *L'Année epigraphique* (Paris, 1888-).

AFA *Acta Fratrum Arualium quae supersunt*, ed. W. Henzen (Berlin, 1874).

ANRW *Aufstieg und Niedergang der römischen Welt*, ed. H. Temporini (Berlin, 1972-).

AUMLA *Journal of the Australasian Universities Language and Literature Association*.

BMC *Coins of the Roman Empire in the British Museum*, ed. H. Mattingly (London, 1923-40).

CAH *Cambridge Ancient History* (1923-)

CIL *Corpus Inscriptionum Latinarum* (Berlin, 1869-).

D & S *Dictionnaire des Antiquités Grecques et Romaines*, ed. Ch. Daremberg and E. Saglio (Paris, 1877-1919).

EJ^2 V. Ehrenberg & A.H.M. Jones, *Documents illustrating the Reigns of Augustus and Tiberius*, 2nd ed. (Oxford, 1976).

HA *Historia Augusta*.

HRR *Historicorum Romanorum Reliquiae*, ed. H. Peter (2 vols, Stuttgart, 1967).

IGR *Inscriptiones Graecae ad Res Romanas Pertinentes*, ed. R. Cagnat (Paris, 1906-27).

ILS *Inscriptiones Latinae Selectae*, ed. H. Dessau (Berlin, 1892-1916)

Inscr. Ital. *Incriptiones Italiae*, ed. A. Degrassi (Rome, 1937-63).

MRR *Magistrates of the Roman Republic*, ed. T.R.S. Broughton (New York, 1951).

PECS *Princeton Encyclopaedia of Classical Sites*, ed. R. Stillwell (Princeton, 1976).

PIR^1 *Prosopographia Imperii Romani Saec. I,II,III*, ed. H. Dessau, E. Krebs and P. von Rohden (Berlin, 1896-1898).

PIR^2 *Prosopographia Imperii Romani Saec. I,II,III*, ed. A. Stein and L. Petersen (Berlin, 1933-).

P. Oxy.	*The Oxyrhyncus Papyri* (1898-).
RE	*Realencyclopädie der klassischen Altertumswissenschaft*, ed. A. Pauly, G. Wissowa (Stuttgart, 1894-).
RIC^2	*Roman Imperial Coinage*, 2nd ed. C.H.V. Sutherland and R.A.G. Carson, Vol. 1 (London, 1984).
SIG^3	*Sylloge Inscriptionum Graecarum* (ed.3), 4 vols (Leipzig, 1915-1921).
St. R	*Römisches Staatsrecht*, T. Mommsen (Leipzig, 1887).

Introduction

The career of Suetonius and the publication of the *De Vita Caesarum*

1. I have recently discussed the career and background of Suetonius both in my commentary on the life of Caligula and in an article on the early history of the imperial correspondence.[1] To avoid unnnecessary duplication readers are directed to those works, but a brief summary of conclusions is included here. Since the discovery of a dedication in honour of Suetonius at Hippo Regius in Africa in the 1950s,[2] there has ensued a reassessment of the biographer's career, which has now resulted in a renewed interest in the biographies themselves. This was slow to emerge, since the tendency to isolate the courtier from his literary career was the first trend within the scholarship. Suetonius has also had a problem emerging from the shadow of his contemporary, the Senatorial historian Tacitus.[3]

2. There are numerous signs that the biographer's family had lived at Rome for some time, and he appears to have been born there in about AD 69.[4] He appears in the letters of the younger Pliny, but serious problems have emerged in interpreting that evidence.[5] Pliny was his patron, perhaps at a stage when Suetonius' role in public life was just beginning. Pliny assisted him by helping him to find a retreat from the world of the city (*Ep. 1.24*). He did discard a tribunate which was proferred to him shortly before AD 103, not, as long was thought, because of a retiring nature, but more plausibly because a superior opportunity arose in some other sphere of public life (*Ep. 3.8.1*).[6] The Hippo inscription is not a monument to a shrinking violet.

3. The *ius trium liberorum*. was obtained for Suetonius in about AD 111 (*Ep. 10.94*), by which time he may have been associated with Pliny on his posting to Bithynia.[7] The request for the *ius trium liberorum* was written while Pliny was in Bithynia, and he was never to return to Rome.[8] Suetonius soon after this emerged as a public figure, and may not have needed the patronage of Septicius Clarus, as has sometimes been argued. Clarus' role has been inflated because of the dedication of the *Caesares* to him during Clarus' term as praetorian prefect.[9] An additional factor in the exaggeration of the role of Clarus has been the tale of their joint fall from grace.[10]

4. The Hippo Inscription is probably best explained in terms of

Hadrian's visit to Africa in AD128.[11] I have recently argued that this is the right explanation for a dedication to Suetonius at Hippo.[12] Suetonius as *ab epistulis* would certainly have been in the emperor's company.[13] To support this view I have argued for the dislocation of the well known passage about the dismissal of Suetonius and Septicius Clarus in the *HA*, as first suggested by Crook.[14]

5. The inscription concentrates on positions of high status, and does little to illuminate the earliest phases of Suetonius' life. After a much debated flaminate, the pontificate of Vulcan, and a possible role amongst the *iudices selecti* under Trajan, the inscription treats his major posts.[15] There seems to be a consensus now that the posts of *a studiis* and *a bibliothecis* should be dated under Trajan. A lacuna in the first half of line 6 could have recorded the administrative post of *a libellis*.[16]

6. The role of *a studiis* brought the biographer close to the emperor with duties as the emperor's advisor on literary and scientific matters, and some supervision of his private library.[17] The position of *a bibliothecis* involved control of the public collections at Rome. Suetonius perhaps obtained this replacing freedmen procurators in about AD 112-113 when the *bibliotheca Ulpia* was completed within Trajan's new forum (dedicated in January AD 112).[18] The post might have been held at the same time as that of *a studiis* and *a libellis* soon after return from Bithynia, at a stage when his literary reputation was no longer in its infancy. The long list of publications provided by the Suda is suggestive of an industrious literary career.[19]

7. Under Hadrian Suetonius rose to the highly influential court position of *ab epistulis*,[20] thus becoming a member of the *consilium principis*.[21] The postion involved reception of embassies to the emperor as well as management of official communications throughout the empire, including military correspondence.[22] Titinius Capito was another leading equestrian who provided a precedent for the career of Suetonius under Domitian, Nerva and Trajan, and only resigned as *ab epistulis* when he obtained advancement to the prefecture of the *uigiles* under Trajan.[23] The *HA* mistakenly credits Hadrian with being the first to choose an equestrian *ab epistulis*.[24]

8. Suetonius and Septicius Clarus are both said to have been dismissed from their respective posts by Hadrian. This is recorded in the above mentioned problematic passage in the Historia Augusta.[25] I refer the reader to my detailed arguments in favour of rejecting the ostensible date of this passage (in Britain in AD 122).[26] If I am wrong, and the *HA* is to be taken at face value, then this has consequences for the date of the *De Vita Caesarum*, which will have appeared at least in part between AD 119-122, since it was dedicated to Septicius Clarus during his prefecture.

9. I have argued that the dismissal should be dated to AD 128 (or soon after). Septicius Clarus may still have been praetorian prefect at this time,

although it seems that Marcius Turbo (his colleague) accompanied Hadrian to Africa.[27] This provides a context for an honorary inscription for Suetonius at Hippo, and allows Suetonius to have written his *Caesares* some years after the publication of Tacitus' *Annales*.[28] Elements in Suetonius which may respond to Tacitus have been pointed out.[29] Suetonius' choice to start his series with Julius Caesar and Augustus may have been prompted by the gap created by Tacitus (who had chosen AD 14 as his starting point), as well as by a personal predilection for the transitional period.[30] Although it is hard to prove, Suetonius may have allowed himself to engage in some response to interpretations provided by the Senatorial historian. Their worlds were different in that the focus of Suetonius was on the personality of the emperor, while Tacitus was concerned with the interrelationship between Senate and emperor. However, any idea that Suetonius as an equestrian disapproved of the elite view has to be discarded, since it is only too clear that he himself was a member of that elite.

10. The result of this conclusion for Suetonius' *Caesares* is that at least one book of the work was dedicated to Septicius Clarus at a date after AD 119, and probably before AD 128. The sacking of Suetonius and Clarus perhaps occurred after the African visit in AD 128. A novel thesis that the lives from Galba to Domitian were composed first, at a Trajanic date was despatched by Syme.[31] It can now be assumed that all the lives appeared together if we date their publication close to AD 128.

Suetonius and Biography in the early 2nd century AD

11. Suetonius' life of Tiberius is one of the longer lives within his series. In recent years there has been considerable debate over the reasons for the variation in the depth and length of treatment of individual subjects. Much of the discussion has concerned the interrelationship between Suetonius' own life and consequent access to suitable resources on each emperor. The answer could simply be that he found the Julio-Claudian family more interesting and important for the institution of the principate than their successors the Flavians.[32] Wallace-Hadrill has shown how in the *De Viris Illustribus* concentration on the Ciceronian and Augustan period reflects Suetonius' interest in the cultural history of that period.[33] Caesar, Augustus and Tiberius bridge this interesting period, and the focus of the biographer's concerns is firmly on the manner in which each individual conducts an imperial life. His concentration within his treatment of all the emperors on the extent to which they conform to ideals about the behaviour of a sovereign can also be brought in to reinforce the idea that he thought Julio-Claudians

more important, since they actually instituted the monarchy.[34] However, any analysis demands an assessment of how Suetonius came to write about the Caesars in the first place, as well as some discussion of his predecessors in the genre.

12. Apart from his life as a courtier, Suetonius had a background in encyclopaedic compositions, probably influenced by the similar works of Varro. In the Suda we hear of works on Greek and Roman games, types of clothing, and the Roman Calendar. Although most of these are only known through fragments, occasional signs of them are to be found in the biographies. Where relevant these are noted in the commentary.[35]

13. His first biographies appear to have been the *De Viris Illustribus*, a series of literary biographies classified under 5 headings: poets, orators, historians, philosophers, grammarians and rhetoricians. Only the *De Grammaticis et Rhetoribus* has survived in any substance, although certain extant lives of poets are also ascribed to Suetonius. I have argued recently on the basis of a reference in the life Horace that the *DVI* was not completed until Suetonius attained high office under Hadrian.[36]

14. Suetonius provides the earliest example of Imperial biography in Latin. Some twenty years earlier Plutarch wrote in Greek eight lives from Augustus to Vitellius,[37] perhaps completing them soon after the death of Domitian. It is agreed that the *Caesares* preceded his series of Parallel lives.[38] The lives of Galba and Otho, which have survived, are closer to narrative history than biography, although this may be caused by the complexities of the political history of AD 68-69. Little can be deduced about the lives that have perished. Comparison between the Plutarchean and Suetonian lives of Caesar suggest ways in which Plutatch's treatment of the early emperors would have differed from the extant *Caesares* of Suetonius. However, Suetonius appears to have known neither his Greek contemporary nor his work.[39] By the time he is working on Julio-Claudian and Flavian lives a new dynasty is firmly ensconced, and it will have been relatively safe to discuss the shortcomings of those rulers.[40]

15. The genre of biography nevertheless provides some common ground in terms of the outlook of the two authors. Within his extant life of Galba Plutarch distinguishes his approach from that of the historians by noting his focus on the individual rather than his times (*Galba* 2.5). All the detail about private life is included as a guide to character (*Alex.* 1). Plutarch shares with Suetonius a lack of interest in a purely political analysis. Suetonius went further in this direction, with a very detailed review of imperial talents.[41]

16. Although it is not hard to trace the ancestry of the literary biographies written by Suetonius,[42] evidence for the popularity of political biographies in the Hellenistic age is insubstantial. Geiger put forward the theory that Nepos was the originator of the genre of political biography, and this approach has promoted some debate, but far from general acceptance.[43] It leads to the unusual conclusion that Plutarch was influenced in his choice of imperial subjects by a relatively minor Roman author who had little sympathy for Greek ideals.[44]

17. Although Suetonius started with literary lives which unquestionably had Greek models, it is more difficult to show a precise scheme which was borrowed for the *Caesares*. The picture is certainly more complex. When he started to write about political figures he appears to have adapted and expanded elements of the scheme employed on literary figures. Greek biography is then a major influence, but many indigenous elements can also be detected. These have recently been reviewed by R.G. Lewis, in a comprehensive survey of Suetonius' literary antecedents.[45] What is certain is that many of the tests applied to the Roman emperors are rooted in Roman values, even though the process of discussing virtues and vices had a long history in the rhetorical schools and elsewhere in the Greek tradition.

18. It is thus apparent that we cannot discount Hellenistic influences on Suetonius' *Caesares*,[46] but his entire background as a polymath thoroughly imbued with the Graeco-Roman tradition lies behind his approach to biography. The Suetonian scheme provides a chronological account until the *acme* of the career. In the imperial lives this was calculated as the time of accession. This is followed by a series of rubrics illustrating personal qualities.[47] This was an adaptable scheme, which allowed for individual eccentricities to be highlighted. In any biographical scheme, the earliest stages tend to be dictated by chronology. Thus ancestry and early life up to accession precede a topical approach to the individual, often as in the *Caligula* with a sharp division between phases.[48] In the *Tiberius* the emperor is portrayed as slow to take on his dominant role (33), but his decline into viciousness does not begin until his retirement to Capri (42). Virtues and vices form an important part of the scheme in the *Caesares*, and had a lengthy ancestry in the Greek and Roman tradition. The virtues of the subject had been a feature of the *encomium* and funeral *laudatio*, whereas vices (and especially tyrannical vices) were rehearsed as part of the training in *uituperatio* in the rhetorical schools.[49] The moral assessment is followed by a treatment of the emperor's physical characteristics, and his literary and artistic tastes. The treatment is brought to a close with the death scene and associated omens, which may have been influenced by the so-called *exitus* literature.[50] Each aspect is handled in such a way as to support a moralising and fixed charcterisation.[51] The scheme as a whole can be seen to be neither totally innovative nor completely dependent on a single predecessor.

The Tradition about Tiberius and the contribution of Suetonius

The Lost Historians

19. We must remember that our main sources on the Julio-Claudian period, Tacitus and Suetonius, are separated from the events they describe by at least a generation.[52] Predecessors had already formed the main lines of the tradition before these early 2nd century writers made their mark. Tacitus in a famous passage underlines some of the problems he himself encountered in dealing with these predecessors:

> Tiberii Gaique et Claudii ac Neronis res florentibus ipsis ob metum falsae, postquam occiderant, recentibus odiis compositae sunt.[53]

In relation to the sources about Tiberius the following observations are pertinent:

1) For the reign of Tiberius the adulatory tradition of which Tacitus talks is most clearly represented in the pages of Velleius Paterculus.[54] Valerius Maximus can also be cited in this context. Otherwise Suetonius alludes to the adulatory tradition only once in the context of the reign of Caligula (*Cal.* 8.2).

2) Agrippina the Younger, the mother of Nero, wrote memoirs in which she gave an account of her own life and the fortunes of her family. Evidence of the contents suggests that the work promoted the interests of herself and her ascendents quite ruthlessly. For an idea of its scope see Plin. *NH* 7.7; Tac. *Ann.* 4.53; 13.54.[55] Relevant to the age of Tiberius is her claim that Agrippina the Elder received a rebuff from Tiberius when she asked for a new husband.

3) A negative tradition dominates our sources on all four emperors mentioned. Philo and the two Senecas are extant contemporary sources who fit into Tacitus' category of those with ulterior motives (*recentibus odiis*) in their handling of imperial subjects. In the *Tiberius* Suetonius consulted the Elder Seneca on the death of Tiberius (73.2). That evidence reveals the expected problems.

4) Despite his claim to write *sine ira et studio* Tacitus himself does not escape from a hostile picture of the Julio-Claudians.

20. The earliest sources on the Julio-Claudian period on whom Tacitus and Suetonius relied have often been canvassed, but the picture remains incomplete. Quintilian names some important writers of this period (*Inst.* 10.1.101-104). Key figures are Seruilius Nonianus and Aufidius Bassus, but surviving fragments give little impression of the scope and interpretation to be expected from these writers.[56] Seruilius' writings probably covered all of Tiberius' reign, but Bassus is thought to have ended with the fall of Seianus in AD 31. The Elder Pliny took up the narrative where Bassus left off (Plin. *Ep.* 3.5.5). Quintilian avoids reference to this work, but it was used by both Tacitus and Suetonius. Suetonius names Pliny in his discussion of the birthplace of Caligula (apparently citing the *Bella Germaniae*). He must have been familiar with the *A fine Aufidi Bassi*, a work in 31 books.[57] Pliny's *Naturalis Historia* provides numerous incidental historical references, which give clues to the scope and approach in the historical works.[58] Cluuius Rufus and Fabius Rusticus, who again are omitted by Quintilian may have been important to Tacitus and particularly Suetonius.[59] Excessive schematism over the methods and dependence of Tacitus and Suetonius on earlier authorities should, however, be avoided. It is especially clear in the case of Suetonius that no single source was followed slavishly.[60]

Extant sources

21. The most important extant historical sources for the reign of Tiberius are (in chronological order) Velleius Paterculus, Josephus in the *Jewish War* and the *Jewish Antiquities*, Tacitus, Suetonius and finally Dio Cassius. Velleius provides an interesting corrective to Tacitus, but he is hard to use, and we are fortunate to have a full modern commentary by Woodman. Dio Cassius provides a chronological basis for the reign, which is absent from Suetonius because of his biographical aims. This sometimes supplements the annalistic material in Tacitus, and is occasionally useful because of the different interests of the Severan historian.[61] He does not employ radically different secondary literature from Tacitus and Suetonius. The fragmentary nature of Dio's text adds to problems created by his uncritical acceptance of his sources.

Details of sources underlying the Suetonian life

22. Suetonius gives quite extensive material on the ancestry of the Claudian gens and it is a question whether this is the product of genuine research. Some of the problems with his tally of the honours are outlined in the commentary (1.2 below). It would be interesting to know what Suetonius used as the basis for both this tally and his calculation of distinctions in the Liuian gens. The *libri annales* which contained this type of information were apparently first incorporated into an historical work by the 2nd century annalist Piso.[62] Whether Suetonius used this sort of material or made his own tally from sources like the Augustan Capitoline *fasti* must remain a subject for speculation, although a digested version of the information is surely a likely inference.[63] Suetonius might be expected to have employed a family history of the type written by Atticus and mentioned by Cornelius Nepos.[64]

Archival materials and Suetonius

23. Suetonius' role as *ab epistulis* was already known from the *HA* before the discovery of the Hippo inscription revealed other aspects of his employment in court circles.[65] It was inevitable that speculation would ensue over whether he was *ab epistulis* at the moment when he published the *De Vita Caesarum*, and over the extent to which this might have resulted in unusual opportunities for research.[66] In fact the critical passage in the *HA* suggests that his career came to a sudden end, and there has been modern speculation since the time of Macé over the biographer's access to resources. Most evidence of the use of documents in the *Caesares* dates from the late Republican or early imperial period. Macé noted the brevity of the Flavian lives as well as a decline in the use of so-called archival materials.[67] He explained this by suggesting that the early lives were written with all this detail as a reflection of a deeper interest in the earlier period, but rejected the decline as a direct result of his exclusion from court. It is only since the appearance of the Hippo inscription that it has been fashionable to suggest a direct link between the dismissal and the slighter documentation of the later lives.

24. Syme pointed to various detailed references in the later lives which suggested a date in the late 120s AD,[68] and this approach encouraged Townend to place some of the biographies before the disgrace (the *Diuus Iulius* and the *Augustus*), while pointing to signs of bitterness in the later lives which he felt ill suited a man still in the imperial service under Hadrian.[69] Townend felt that this new tone could already be detected in the life of Tiberius. Coninck points out some of the flaws in this argument.[70] Most important is consideration of why even in disgrace Suetonius should have been deprived of access to the public collections at Rome as well as to archives on the Palatine. *Curiosa* represent another type of evidence in decline as the work progresses.

25. Syme thought that disgrace need not be the only method of explaining this decline, and in an important article explored the extent to which an *ab epistulis* might have been expected to accompany the emperor on his travels.[71] He thus provides a better explanation for the unevenness of coverage than Townend, but a truly convincing solution has yet to be reached. Coninck thought that Suetonius was influenced by Tacitus when he employed the *acta senatus* on the *initia imperii* of Tiberius.[72] This approach tends to direct attention to the reason for ceasing to employ the superior technique. We are forced back to the position of Macé, who related the change of treatment to Suetonius' own cultural and intellectual interests, an approach now espoused by Wallace-Hadrill.[73]

8

The use of the acta diurna and the acta senatus in the life of Tiberius

26. The principal collection of documents available comprised the *acta diurna*, a daily record of events in the city, which was published both at home and abroad. The original was stored in archives, and it is well known that both Pliny and Tacitus in addition to Suetonius made use of this source.[74]

27. Suetonius frequently produces utterances of Tiberius which he claims were delivered in the Senate. On many occasions these appear to be verbatim reports, but scholars have been suspicious of their authenticity. It can never be proved that Suetonius had constant recourse to the *acta senatus*, nor to the more widely available *acta diurna*. As Talbert points out an author like Tacitus (who also claims to have used the *acta senatus*) actively shunned verbatim quotation as out of keeping with the elevated style, but Suetonius was not so constrained.[75] It seems possible that Suetonius did seek out authentic material, even if it is agreed that his approach was not primarily archival. Some of the relatively numerous quotations of the emperor's words clearly could not have originated in prepared speeches, and it may be that we have to look further afield than the *acta senatus* in such instances.[76] However, in the life of Tiberius quotations of Tiberius words are unusually abundant, and on two occasions the biographer is claiming to be able to cite the actual words employed by the emperor when he objected to individual *senatus consulta*. See notes at *Tib.* 24.1; 27-29 (esp. 28); 50.2; 57.2; 67.2; 71.

Official letters

28. Quite a number of apparently official letters are cited in the life. In some instances there are parallels elsewhere in the tradition. See *Tib.* 26.2; cf. Dio 57.2.1; 8.1-2; *Tib.* 32.1 (Tac. *Ann.* 3.2); 32.2 (Dio 57.10.5); *Tib.* 34.1 (cf. Tac. *Ann.* 2.33; 3.52-4); *Tib.* 67.1 (Tac. *Ann.* 6.6).

Detailed knowledge of wills

29. The will of Tiberius is the last private document of which Suetonius claims to have special knowledge, with the exception of poems of Nero which had come into his possession and clearly are not a product of research in the archives (Suet. *Nero* 52.2). In the life of Tiberius he also mentions the will of Augustus on which he gives fuller comment at Suet. *Aug.* 101. See *Tib.* 23.33-4; 50.2; 76.

Letters of Augustus

30. These are cited on 18 occasions directly and a further six times indirectly in the lives from Augustus to Claudius.[77] Suetonius shows in the life of Augustus some knowledge of the actual script of Augustus.[78] It was suggested by Townend that this was privileged information such as might be found in an imperial *scrinium*. Letters of Augustus are mentioned at *Tib*. 11.8; 21.6-10; 10.2-3; 11.7-8; 12.5.

Tiberian sermones in the Senate
31. 6 passages are relevant: 24.3; 28.1-2 [2 passages]; 29.2-3 [2 passages]; 67.3-4. It is easiest to assume that these derive either from direct or indirect contact with the *acta senatus*.

The commentarii of Tiberius
32. Suetonius quotes a *commentarius de uita sua* in an important passage. In this work the aged Tiberius is supposed to have recorded that Seianus had been punished for persecuting his children and those of his adoptive heir Germanicus (*Tib*. 61.1). The papers enjoyed by the emperor Domitian appear to be quite separate (Suet. *Dom*. 20: *commentarii*).[79]

The possible influence of Tacitus on Suetonius
33. In quite a few places in the Suetonian life of Tiberius there are close parallels between Suetonius and Tacitus over the interpretation of events.[80] These have been noted in the commentary, and some important comparisons are listed below. It is always hard to clarify whether these similarities are a product of the use of common sources or rather direct knowledge of the other's text. If arguments presented above over Suetonius' career are accepted, it will be clear that influence could only have flowed in one direction - Suetonius could have borrowed from Tacitus, but not *vice versa*. It is difficult to know how important this may be. Some authorities have thought Suetonius critical of Tacitus on some issues (e.g. Suet. *Cal*. 8),[81] but often he seems simply to run through a range of possible interpretations of Tiberian behaviour or even to adhere to a view very close to that of Tacitus. If Tacitus was only one of a number of sources Suetonius was using on the Julio-Claudian emperors, he will hardly have bothered to react to every interpretative detail.

34. I note in particular the following passages:
21.1. Goodyear (1972) 135 notes close wording between the account of whether Augustus was still breathing when Tiberius arrived at his death-bed. See Tac. *Ann*. 1.5.3: *spirantem adhuc Augustum reppererit*; cf. Suet. *Tib*. 21.1: *spirantem adhuc Augustum repperit*.
21.2. On the *diritas* of Tiberius. Augustus is supposed to have hoped to improve his own posthumous reputation by appointing Tiberius. See Tac. *Ann*. 1.10.7; Dio 56.45.3.

22. *renuntianti tribuno factum esse quod imperasset*; this is very close to the wording of Tacitus (*Ann.* 1.6.5: *nuntianti centurioni, ut mos militiae, factum esse quod imperasset*; cf. Suet. *Claud.* 29.2: *renuntiante centurione factum esse quod imperasset negaret quicquam se imperasse*).

24.1. The theme is Tiberian hypocrisy which is underlined by showing the discrepancy between words and actions; cf. Tac. *Ann.* 1.7.4-5; Dio 57.2.1.

43.1. *secessu uero Caprensi etiam sellaria excogitauit*; cf. Tac. *Ann.* 6.1: *tumque primum ignota ante uocabula reperta sunt sellariorum et spintriarum ex foeditate loci ac multiplici patientia*. This is a Suetonian passage which could derive from Tacitus (see notes ad loc.).

58. *exercendas esse leges respondit*. Compare Tac. *Ann.* 1.72.3ff., who reports the same words. Here is an example where the exact quotation is more likely to have enterted the tradition rather than been copied from Tacitus.

Characterisation in the Suetonian life of Tiberius[82]

35. Two articles in 1971 (Bringmann) and 1972 (Döpp) took up the debate started by Steidle over the structure and effectiveness of the Suetonian biographical scheme with specific reference to the life of Tiberius[83]. Steidle had argued against 19th century views, particularly that of Leo, who maintained that Suetonius forced his lives into a mould that had been set by Alexandrian literary biography.[84] Against that thesis Steidle pointed to the mixture of topical and chronological elements as a commonplace feature in ancient biographical writing, and emphasised the flexibility of the scheme which in Suetonius showed the impact of specifically Roman interests and questions. He believed that this flexibility enabled Suetonian biography to be adjusted to suit the peculiarities of an individual life. Bringmann and Döpp both argue that the scheme was by its very nature inflexible, and that the conflict between the chronological and the topical approaches led to discrepancies and contradictions which are particularly noticeable in the life of Tiberius. A more positive view of the biography has been taken by Guia (1978) who believed that both Tacitus and Suetonius were confronted with a pre-existing contradictory tradition about Tiberius.[85] This had already been formed in the light of both political and ideological prejudices. There are instances where Suetonius does however appear to respond to the ambiguities in Tacitus. In short, Suetonius cannot be blamed for all the contradictions and dislocations to be found in the life, since many of them were already entrenched in the tradition when he approached his subject.

11

36. Here the aim is to examine the problem of fixity of character as confronted by both Tacitus and Suetonius in relation to Tiberius, while underlining both the similarities and differences in their treatment of this controversial character. While few will be convinced that the Suetonian Tiberius is one of his better lives, this will show how Suetonius wrestled with the problem of the contradictions he found in his sources. Suetonius never seriously questioned the entire tradition, but in this respect he seems no less critical than Tacitus. The hostility of Tacitus to Tiberius has been attributed by some authorities to his experiences under Domitian, and there are occasional glimmers of a more favourable view of the emperor. However, the tyrannical portrait is more likely to be a product of the hostility of the underlying tradition about Tiberius, something from which Tacitus was no more capable of escaping than his contemporary Suetonius.

37. The Suetonian life of Tiberius divides Claudii into two groups, those who did positive services to the state (*egregia merita*) and another category who had behaved rather badly (*sequius admissa*).[86] These morally assessed categories are very important for Suetonius' characterisation of the emperor Tiberius, who is admitted to be a Claudian on both sides of his family.[87] Suetonius never openly discusses heredity, but it is clear that he believes it of some importance. Although the debit side is to predominate, this double inheritance seems to be intended to allow Suetonius some flexibility in the treatment of a controversial character. Nevertheless in the main part of the biography Suetonius adheres to the notion of fixity of character.

38. Before proceeding to examine the emphases in the Suetonian treatment it is important to realise that negative characterisation of the Claudian *gens* had a long history before the age of Trajan and Hadrian when Tacitus and Suetonius were writing. A Livy writing soon after Actium could portray Appius Claudius the *decemuir* in tyrannical terms, but like a Tiberius, the *decemuir* did not immediately show his colours.[88] A process of unmasking had to occur before the *saeuitia* and *libido* of the tyrant were openly acknowledged.[89] This treatment, which emphasises fixity of character, had an important influence on the Tacitean Tiberius,[90] but it is perhaps of more importance to ask where Livy got it from, and in general how ancient the tradition of Claudian arrogance, duplicity, and savagery may be.

39. Ogilvie in his commentary on the Livian passages suggests that political conditions of the 80s are being evoked.[91] The decemviral seizure of property must certainly remind us of late republican proscriptions, and Ogilvie notes that the whole atmosphere of Livy's narrative is charged with the rhetorical clichés of the late Republic. In the introduction to his edition of Books 1-5 he suggests that two main sources lie behind Livy's account of the early city.[92] The first of these was a *popularis* and Marian supporter, Licinius

Macer. He took a strong line against popular indifference to Sulla's attack on the tribunate, and is thought to have written under the influence of the history of Cn. Gellius (c. 130 BC), but with additions corresponding to his prejudices. It is not impossible that his view of Sulla lurks behind Livy's portrait of the decemvir, although the pseudo-*popularis* nature of the masked tyrant has led to doubts.[93] Did Sulla ever behave like a *popularis*, whether deceptively or not? Would Livy himself ever have used a source with *popularis* sympathies?[94] Valerias Antias, on the other hand, was pro-Sullan. But one of Sulla's staunchest allies was Ap. Claudius Pulcher and it would be strange indeed if a pro-Sullan historian were to give such a hostile interpretation of the *gens Claudia*. Nevertheless Ogilvie and several other modern critics have accepted this.[95]

40. Vasaly thinks there is more of Livy in this picture of the *decemuir* than these critics will allow.[96] While some will be sympathetic to her approach, and it is true that Livy had lived through the proscriptions of 43 BC, there is no doubt that the tradition of Claudian arrogance and tyranny pre-dated Livy, since it is also found in Dionysius of Halicarnassus with some variations of detail.[97] Others have tried to associate the hostility to the Claudii with the political fortunes of Clodius, who certainly had a sufficiently controversial career to polarise political interpretation. The tradition may in fact be much older. Although it has often been remarked that Cicero makes no use of the hostile view of the Claudii in the *Pro Caelio*,[98] there could be political reasons for this,[99] and he does allude to the Appius-Verginia story in the later *De Finibus*.[100] This latter reference could be seen as a product of Cicero's antagonism to Clodius and Clodia, but it is surely more likely that the story was one learnt in his childhood. If so, we must look for a 2nd century authority. The very early involvement of the Claudian family in the political life of Rome suggests that they would have been thoroughly embroiled in factional disputes throughout. It may be appropriate to return to the older view that stories such as that of Appius-Verginia derive ultimately from Fabius Pictor.[101] One of the early annalists is another possibility.

41. Whatever we make of the origin of the dual tradition about the Claudii, this background shows that Suetonius cannot have conflated the negative and positive traditions about Tiberius and used the theory of hypocrisy to cover over the contrast between the early and the late years. Such a view of the life might hold that Suetonius only underlines the imperfect concealment of Tiberius' vices in his early years as a further method of concealing the inconsistencies of his portrait.[102] But we must rather imagine that Tacitus, Suetonius, and their sources, were strongly influenced by previous literary handling of the character of members of the *gens*, and could not escape the theme of the unmasking of the tyrant. Once a decision had been made that Tiberius belonged in the camp of the negative portrayals this approach became inevitable.

42. Naturally the straight-jacket of the tyrant theme created problems for authors like Suetonius and Tacitus faced with the considerable amount of information on Tiberius available to them. It is true that the treatment of the reign by rubrics in the biographical format tended to highlight these difficulties. Nevertheless it is not hard to perceive elements of a more reasonable man lurking under both treatments, especially as a soldier,[103] and in various stories which illustrate his *ciuilitas*.[104] Since Suetonius and Tacitus believed that character was fixed from birth they were forced to suppose that he was a tyrant from the beginning, and merely managed to disguise this fact initially.[105] I shall examine some of the main themes related to the tyrannical character of Tiberius to illustrate the problem.

Hypocrisy

43. One of the most persistent elements in the tradition about Tiberius is the theme of his hypocrisy. The handling of this is similar to the handling of Appius Claudius in Livy. Eventually the tyrant is to be exposed. This is not merely a feature of the Suetonian treatment, but also one of the most notorious aspects of the Tacitean version. The accession debate in Tacitus is portrayed as a farce in which Tiberius will not openly admit the unlimited nature of his power; he treats the senate as though its role was unchanged from republican times. Suetonius also handles the accession in the same light, and we can notice that at a particular point Suetonius indicates the end of Tiberian hypocrisy over who is in charge of affairs (33). At this moment Tiberius shows himself puritanical over both sexual and other matters (33-5), and this comes to seem a further level of hypocrisy when we find out about his own excesses on Capri.

44. When he retired to Capri in AD 26 (42), we are told that the mask dropped. Even before this time he had not been able to conceal all his vices, and Suetonius also provides numerous instances of duplicity and treachery which can be dated later than AD 26.[106] This probably does not amount to an inconsistency in the characterisation since hypocrisy itself is seen as part of his make-up. It is the mask of *civilitas* that goes by the board in AD 26; after that time he was no longer able to keep up the pretence of *moderatio*.

Stinginess

45. Stinginess is not immediately obvious as a tyrannical characteristic. Suetonius illustrates it in sections 46-8. The main emphasis is on his unwillingness to spend money on large public projects.[107] But stinginess is not seen as a static attribute. Eventually it turned into rapacity. It represents a further stage in the unmasking of the tyrant. The case of Hortalus mentioned in section 47 may be used to demonstrate the unreliability of the tradition of stinginess. It seems probable that disbursements were actually made and that Suetonius has it wrong (see notes ad loc.).

46. Some modern analysts have thought that the financial crisis in AD 33 was brought about by a shortage of money in circulation caused by Tiberius' failure to spend sufficiently, but it is unlikely that Frank is right in his assessment that the volume of coinage put into circulation had undergone a continuing decline from about 10 BC.[108] Rodewald has shown some of the fallacies in his argument.[109] We can hardly therefore say that this attribute of the emperor is proved to be historical. After the destruction of the twelve cities in Asia Minor in AD 17 his *liberalitas* is well known. But for Suetonius this only rates a throw away line at the end of his segment on imperial benefactions.[110]

Saeuitia

47. The handling of tyrannical *saeuitia* begins at section 51. Already in the early part of the life there are hints of it in the masked tyrant. Unlike his fully revealed counterpart the duplicitous character manifests his unpleasant character through sternness or *diritas*.[111] Once the mask is pulled off his capacity for *saeuitia* is demonstrated by instances exhibiting everything from cruelty through to bloodthirstiness.

48. The first instances are an attack on his relations with his immediate family, and in particular his mother. Initially a pattern of stubborn dealings with Liuia is illustrated, and this is said to have developed into hostility and finally non-attendance at her funeral. Her will was annulled and after her death Tiberius persecuted her friends.[112]

49. There are however problems with the whole tradition about Tiberius' relationship with Liuia. When Liuia dies in AD 29 the Tacitean account suggests that Tiberius dismissed the matter as of little consequence. It is registered as a negative point that her funeral was simple and that her will long remained unexecuted.[113] This latter issue was settled by Caligula as one of his initial popular measures, and it can be suspected that Caligulan propaganda had developed the theme of the duteous Caligula as compared with the unfilial Tiberius.[114] It is credible that this approach could have had some currency when we remember that Caligula's *laudatio* for Liuia at the funeral represented one of his first important steps in public life.[115] Tacitus proceeds to moralise about Tiberius' continuation of a life of debauchery, and lists his failure to attend Liuia's funeral as though this represented a deliberate slight of a sloughed off and no longer relevant relative.[116] As evidence for his lack of respect is listed his moderation in accepting honours in her favour from the Senate. The account is given specious plausibility by the implication that Tacitus himself has seen the letter to the Senate in which Tiberius handled the matter of his mother's death.[117] But even if he had seen the letter it is clear that a malicious interpretation has been put upon it. Tiberius was habitually hesitant about accepting honours either for himself or for Liuia for policy reasons which are not directly related to his relationship with his mother.[118] The imputation is furthered by Tacitus' discussion of the career of Fufius Geminus, allegedly covertly criticised by Tiberius through a reference to the power of feminine friendship. His career had advanced through the influence of Liuia, and Tacitus believed his sharp tongue was resented by the emperor. This is a manifestation of the Tacitean theme that the outspoken and individualistic senator had the capacity to curb through criticism the worst excesses of imperial despotism. As he is quick to point out in his introduction to the *Annals*, this was a class in decline in the face of increasing imperial adulation.[119] But the hostile approach to the relationship between Liuia and Tiberius must pre-date Tacitus, who has only put his own emphases on it.

50. Tiberius' attitude to his family is further exemplified in section 52 by his behaviour after the death of Drusus. Suetonius illustrates his callousness through an anecdote about his reaction to condolences delivered by a Trojan delegation some months after the death of Drusus. He is supposed to have replied 'May I condole with you, in return, on the death of your eminent fellow-citizen Hector'.[120] Tacitus also pillories Tiberius for his lack of conspicuous grieving. It is taken as a negative point that he continued to attend the senate when Drusus became ill, and an unfavourable contrast is drawn between his restraint and the open display of grief by the consuls. Again, when they sit in the ordinary benches to display their grief, Tiberius is seen to be haughty in his request for them to take thought of behaviour appropriate to their rank.[121] Nevertheless his actual quoted words reveal leadership rather than any less favourable characteristics.[122] It is notable that Drusus' funeral itself is treated summarily by Tacitus,[123] since he did actually participate in it, and delivered the funeral speech in his honour.[124] Tacitus clearly could not attack the emperor for his absence as he does later with the death of Liuia.

51. The trial of Piso is developed as a further illustration of his familial dealings. It is supposed by Suetonius that Tiberius, who had already had a confrontation with Germanicus over his intrusion into the imperial domain of Egypt, set up Piso to dispose of Germanicus, and then had Piso tried and executed after destroying the proof of imperial involvement.[125] The Tacitean version of these same events is more subtle than this, but it is clear that he too was faced with a confusing tradition which was very hostile to Tiberius.

52. In section 53 Tiberian dealings with Agrippina provide the next stage in the increasing *saeuitia*. It seems to be indisputable that a very bad relationship did exist between Tiberius and Agrippina, although the story of the poisoned apple has close links with the tyrant theme. Stories of physical abuse and forced feeding during her exile are also suspect. Her children are said to have fared little better; they were declared public enemies, and starved to death. Tacitus shares the story that Drusus was so hungry that he was forced to eat the stuffing from his mattress.[126]

53. Suetonius next covers the dealings of Tiberius with the senate, and makes generalisations which are suggestive of a blood bath. We are told, for instance, that hardly any of his *consilium* met natural deaths. Sejanus' treatment is seen as a betrayal after being given powers for specious purposes.[127] Greek favourites were further victims. This is even more disreputable since they offend through their knowledge of the emperor's pet interest.[128]

54. At this point (57) Suetonius returns to the early life of the emperor and explains that his subject always had the tendencies which were ultimately revealed. This had first been verbalised by his boyhood teacher of rhetoric Theodorus of Gadara who had described him as 'mud kneaded with blood'.[129] After he became emperor, even while the pretence of *moderatio* was still in place, Suetonius can find anecdotal evidence of Tiberian *saeuitia*. This leads into his discussion of *maiestas* (58), which is clearly to represent a consolidation of the tyrannical behaviour after the mask has gone. Naturally the tyrant becomes the subject of lampoons which celebrate his bloodthirsty nature (59). The whole treatment culminates with his ungrateful treatment of the fisherman who brought him a mullet on Capri (60) and section 61 gives a detailed description of individual cruelties. Amongst other alllegations we find that every crime became capital under Tiberius. He is said to have had a particularly savage reaction to the discovery that Drusus had died at the hands of Liuia and Sejanus. It resulted in an obsessive stage in his *saeuitia* in which he tortured individuals indiscriminately to ascertain the truth (62).

55. One of the most extreme examples of tyrannical *saeuitia* cited by Suetonius is in the section where his physical build is outlined (68). As elsewhere in Suetonius the physical description has a moral dimension. It is no surprise to discover that Tiberius is left handed when the moral connotations of that fact are taken into account. It is seen as a sign of waywardness and homosexuality;[130] in addition we discover that his left hand is so strong that he can poke a finger through a sound newly plucked apple, or into the skull of a boy or young man, a point surely containing an innuendo about his sexual tastes, as well as the suggestion of regular gratuitous *saeuitia*.

56. The final demonstration of his *saeuitia* is provided by popular reactions to his death (75). These are quite extreme, and include the suggestion that his body should only be given half a burning. This appears to be a reflection of his perceived tyrannical status, since it was notorious that a tyrant's body could not be totally consumed by the flames.

Superstition

57. Superstition is another feature of Tiberius' personality. At first sight this should have been something of which Suetonius approved,[131] but it soon emerges that Tiberian superstition has unpleasant overtones. Perhaps this is because Suetonius thought that Tiberius did not have sincere belief in the gods. He says that Tiberius' astrological interests had persuaded him that the world was wholly ruled by fate. Suetonius seems to see this as hypocrisy, since the emperor was frightened by thunder (69). When he returned from Rhodes Tiberius is said to have been confident because of prophecies that had been in his mind since childhood. Already his mother Liuia had subscribed to belief in this lore (14). In this early passage Suetonius seems to approve of what he believes are infallible signs. But the consultation of soothsayers is said to have been banned during his reign except in the presence of witnesses, and he also attempted to suppress oracles near Rome. While both of these moves can be appreciated as having political overtones, Suetonius cites them as a sign of the terror under which he lived, and says that he gave up on the oracles after a miracle with the sacred lots which he had removed from temple of Fortuna at Praeneste (63). This is consistent with the general view taken by Suetonius that those who are hubristic enough to interefere with godly matters meet an inevitable nemesis.

Cultural interests

58. Even cultural interests do not redeem the emperor. The story of the picture of Atlanta engaged in *fellatio* with Meleager is modelled in such a way as to bring discredit on Tiberius; he is portrayed as choosing a picture with a subject of this type when he had the choice of a cash inheritance instead (44). Yet it may well be that Tiberius' interest in erotic art of one sort or another in conjunction with speculation over his activities on Capri combined to create the hostile tradition representing him as a sexual pervert.

59. It is allowed that he became deeply devoted to Greek and Latin literature in his youth, and later on Rhodes (11). He is said to have modelled his rhetoric on that of Messalla Coruinus, but he was considered affected when he produced prepared speeches, and was better as an *ex tempore* performer (70). This may reflect the realities but it is important to be cautious, since we learn also in Tacitus of the *Claudiana superbia* and its impact on public utterance.[132] Even the interpretation of topics of this sort may have been

influenced by what was expected in the case of wicked Claudii. His interest in Euphorion, Rhianus and Parthenius again relates to his interest in the erotic, and criticism is probably intended. The obscure Homeric questions in which he is said to have been interested are also introduced as an attack on his scholarly interests.

Lechery and drink

60. Lechery and drinking are tyrannical vices.[133] Although Suetonius appears to exaggerate, the stories about alcohol may have some substance. Tiberius' drinking probably started when he was on campaign in Spain in 26-5 BC. Suetonius talks of him developing the habit as a *tiro* (42.1). Suetonius follows contemporary trends with his interest in and criticism of imperial taste, but there are serious chronological objections with the story of the drinking bout once he had become *princeps*. The elder Pliny already knew of this clearly hostile tradition, and it must be another element owed to the lost Julio-Clauidan historians. The charges of lechery on Capri are likewise suspect, and may reflect the changing political environment more than the social realities (41ff.).

61. All the points raised above show that Suetonius tries to give an overall picture of Tiberius which will explain his diverse characteristics within the limitations of his presentation as a hypocritical tyrant. This allows the biographer a certain level of inconsistency in the portrait, since he can show that Tiberius was actually misunderstood before he revealed his real character with its tyrannical tendencies. Even more positive attributes tend to be clouded by his actions as emperor. The totality has been influenced very strongly by earlier portraits of the Claudian *gens*, which in turn had suffered at the hands of the traditions of rhetorical *uituperatio*. The net result is that Suetonius does not mean to ignore the evidence, but he is often trapped by the presumptions under which he is operating. Instances can be found where the Suetonian version is highly implausible historically, and these may represent areas where the biographer was attempting to model his character rather than engage in a minute analysis of the evidence. Sometimes the problem lies in the pre-existing tradition. The entire achieves a level of cohesion, even if a modern audience inevitably finds that the unmasking of a fixed tyrannical figure unconvincing.

Notes to the Introduction

1. See Lindsay (1993) 1-6; *Historia* 43 (1994) 454-68.

2. *AE* 1953, 73: *C Suetoni[o] Tran[quillo f]lami[ni adlecto] int[er selectos a Di]uo Tr[aiano Parthico] Pont. Volca[nal]i [a] studiis a byblio[thecis ab e]pistulis [Imp. Caes. Trai]ani Hadriani [Hipponenses Re]gi DDPP.* Useful contributions on this much discussed inscription include E. Marec and H.-G. Pflaum, *CRAI* (1952) 76-85; G.B. Townend, *Historia* 10 (1961) 99-109; C. Baurain, *LEC* 44 (1976) 124-144.

3. Suetonius has been best served by A.F. Wallace-Hadrill (1983). B. Baldwin (1983) appeared at about the same time, but was too heavily influenced by earlier scholarship. See A.R. Birley, *JRS* 74 (1984) 245-251; K.R. Bradley, *CPh* 80 (1985) 254-265. Gascou's major 1984 work on Suetonius as an historian is reviewed by Wallace-Hadrill in *CR* 36 (1986) 243-245. Cizek (1977) also examines Suetonius' career, although he is more interested in structural questions. R.C. Lounsbury (1987) reviews earlier approaches to the career, and shows some of the trends in the scholarship.

4. Suetonius' grandfather appears to have lived in Rome (Suet. *Cal.*19.3). His equestrian father, Suetonius Laetus, fought for Otho on the losing side at the battle of Bedriacum under the legate Vedius Aquila (Suet. *Otho* 10.1; Tac. *Hist.* 2.44.1; 3.7). Suetonius himself was educated educated at Rome (Suet. *Gramm.* 4); his birth date has been estimated within the range AD 62-72. AD 69 is an accepted compromise.

5. Plin. *Ep.* 1.18 shows him shrinking from a court appearance because of a dream. This has led to modern suppositions that Suetonius was a shy scholar who lurked in the background. On this see Lounsbury, op.cit. 4ff. The timid Suetonius has developed psychological problems in T.F. Carney, *PACA* 11(1968) 7-21; R.F. Newbold, *Latomus* 43 (1984) 118-132.

6. The tribunate was in Britain under L. Neratius Marcellus (*CIL* XVI 48,19th January AD 103; Syme [1958] 91). Suetonius requested that the office be transferred to a relative, Caesennius Silvanus (Plin. *Ep.* 3.8.1). On the operation of patronage see H.M. Cotton, *Chiron* 11 (1981) 229-238, esp. 235f. For the date of Pliny's letter see A. Birley (1981) 88. The letter in which Pliny issues a mild rebuke to Suetonius for slowness in publishing a work has also been over stressed (*Ep.* 5.10).

7. First proposed by Syme, (1958) 660; 779; see *Hermes* 109 (1981) 107.

8 He died in his second year of office. His tenure of Bithynia-Pontus is to be dated AD 110-112. See W. Eck *Chiron* 12 (1982) 349-351.

9. Lydus *De Mag.* 2.6.

10. *HA Hadr.* 11.3. E. Cizek (1977) 181ff. took an extreme view of the

patronage situation, and his approach is easily dismissed. See Lounsbury (1987) 14ff.

11. For Hadrian's visit to Africa in AD 128 see R.H. Chowen, *CJ* 65 (1969-70) 323-324.

12. See *Historia* 43 (1994) 454-68.

13. First suggested by Syme, (1958) 779.

14. J.A. Crook, *PCPhS* n.s. 4 (1956-57) 18-22.

15. More fully discussed in Lindsay (1993) 2.

16. A later example of this career pattern is the case of L. Volusius Maecanius, under Antoninus Pius (*CIL* XIV 5347; *AE* 1955,179). See van't Dack, *Historia* 12 (1963) 179. Notice also the inaccurate statement at HA *Hadr*. 22.8: *ab epistulis et a libellis primus equites Romanos habuit*. On the actual role of the *a libellis* see Millar (1977) 249-251. The evidence shows that dealing with *libelli* could fall within the scope of the duties of the *a studiis*, at least when freedmen held these posts.

17. His precise sphere is unknown. For discussion see E. van't Dack, *Historia* 12 (1963) 177-184; F. Millar (1977) 90f.

18. The idea of using a leading intellectual for this type of post may have had a. precedent if we accept that Tacitus had been a librarian to Titus. See N. Reed, *CQ* 26 (1976) 309-314; R.P. Oliver, *CQ* 29 (1979) 224-225. Various freedmen held posts controlling libraries, both public and imperial. The title *procurator bibliothecarum* seems to have been interchangeable with *a bibliothecis* . See E. van't Dack, op. cit. 177-184.

19. Suda s.v. Τράγκυλλος.

20. See G.B. Townend, *Historia* 10 (1961) 375-381; Millar, op.cit. 224-228.

21. Lounsbury (1987) 11-12 rightly emphasises the favour involved, and points out that the appointment of Suetonius under Trajan, and his continuation under Hadrian represent the beginning of the regular advance of equestrians into the *officia palatina*.

22. Statius *Siluae* 5.1.86ff.

23. See Pflaum, op.cit. (1960-61) no. 60, and discussion in Lounsbury (1987) 9-11.

24. HA *Hadr*. 22.8.

25. HA *Hadr*. 11.3.

26. In the works mentioned in n. 1 above.

27. *ILAf*. 421, discussed by Lindsay (1993) 5.

28. Dated by Syme to AD 123 ([1958] 473; 782). It should be noted, however, that a date under Trajan has strong support, with Tacitus possibly dying c. AD 116, before he completed the Annals. See R.P. Oliver, *ICS* 2 (1977) 289-314. Compare Goodyear (1981) 387-93 who thought that Tacitus might have started work on the *Annales* in about AD 109 and brought the project to completion in about AD 118. G.W. Bowersock has recently added support for the early date in T.J. Luce & A. J. Woodman (eds) (1993) 3-10.

29. See Lindsay (1993) on Suet. *Cal.* 8.1ff, discussing D.W. Hurley, *AJPh* 110 (1989) 316-338; for apparent responses by Suetonius to allegations in the later books of the Annals see J. Beaujeu, *REL* 38 (1960) 234-235, accepted by J. Gascou, *Latomus* 37 (1978) 443. On echoes of Tacitus in the life of Tiberius see below.

30. As suggested by Birley, *JRS* 74 (1984) 249.

31. See G.W. Bowersock, *Hommages à Marcel Renard* I (1969) 119-125, and compare K.R. Bradley, *JIES* 1 (1972) 257-263. There is a reference in the life of Titus which in fact supports the proposed later Hadrianic date: Suet. *Tit.* 10.2. Domitia Longina is referred to as though she were no longer alive, and her death is to be placed in AD 126: *CIL* XV 554; see *PIR*^{2} D 181; Syme, *JRS* 60 (1970) 39.

32. We do not need to follow the extreme view of Townend that he grew weary of the project, as outlined in T.A. Dorey (ed.), *Latin Biography* (1967) 90-91.

33. See A. Wallace-Hadrill (1983) 50-72.

34. The point is made by C. Murison (1992) vi.

35. The best modern overview is that of Wallace-Hadrill (1983) 50-72.

36. On the *De Grammaticis et Rhetoribus* see T. Viljamaa, *ANRW* II.33.5 (1991) 3826-51. I have recently discussed the life of Horace in some detail. See H.M. Lindsay, 'Suetonius on the character of Horace' *AUMLA* 83 (1995) 69-82 and for discussion of the date of the *De Viris Illustribus see Historia* 43 (1994) 459-64.

37. Lamprias Catalogue nos 26, 27, 29-33.

38. On the chronology of Plutarch's works see C.P. Jones, *JRS* 56 (1966) 61-74; he discusses the lives of the Caesars in *Plutarch and Rome* (1971) 72-80, arguing for a Flavian date. Syme has preferred to date the work under Nerua. See *MH* 37 (1980) 104-128, esp. 105-110.

39. An unconvincing attempt to show that Suetonius reacts to Plutarch was made by Baldwin (1983) 88; 526-546. Common sources can account for all similarities.

40. T.F. Carney believed that Suetonius was being critical of Hadrian, but he has had few followers. See *PACA* 11 (1968) 7-21.

41. What is described as 'informatory' material by D.R. Stuart (1928) 251-252.

42. I have discussed this in Lindsay (1993) 6-7.

43. See J. Geiger (1985); for criticism see J.L. Moles, *CR* 39 (1989) 229-233. Recent research has focussed on the relationship between Nepos' biographies and the contemporary political scene. See F. Millar, *G&R* 35 (1988) 40-55; A.C. Dionisotti, *JRS* 78 (1988) 35-49.

44. See now the edition by N. Horsfall (1989).

45. R.G. Lewis, *ANRW* 2.33.5 (1991) 3623-3674.

46. Momigliano (1971) 86-88 is sensible on this subject, in contrast to Leo (1901) who is confident that Greek influences predominate.

47. See the well known passage at Suet. *Aug.* 9: *proposita uitae eius uelut summa, partes singillatim neque per tempora sed per species exsequar, quo distinctius demonstrari cognoscique possint.*

48. Suet. *Cal.* 22: *hactenus ... reliqua ut de monstro.* Cf. *Nero* 19.3: *Haec partim nulla reprehensione, partim etiam non mediocri laude digna in unum contuli, ut secernerem a probris ac sceleribus eius, de quibus dehinc dicam.*

49. On Suetonian virtues and vices see Mouchova (1968) 42-51; and especially A. Wallace-Hadrill (1983) 142-174, following earlier articles in *Historia* 30 (1981) 298-325; *JRS* 72 (1982) 32-48. For discussion of the tyrant's attributes as rehearsed in the rhetorical schools see J.R. Dunkle, *TAPhA* 98 (1967) 151-171; *CW* 65 (1971) 12-20.

50. This has often been suggested, but there is little evidence to support it. On the *exitus* literature see F.A. Marx, *Philologus* 92 (1937) 83-103.

51. Character-development in the ancient world is best discussed by C.J. Gill, *CQ* 33 (1983) 469-487; of some interest is L.R. Cochran, *Biography* 3 (1980) 189-201.

52. I have already given an account of the Julio-Claudian tradition as it relates to Caligula in Lindsay (1993) 8-12.

53. Tac. *Ann.* 1.2.

54. See A.J. Woodman (1977), (1983) for a full commentary.

55. The work is dated to her retirement from politics between AD 54-9 by Furneaux ad *Ann.* 4.53. for fragments see *HRR* II CXXIII; 94.

56. See H. Peter, *HRR* II CXXV-CXVIIII; 96-98..

57. On fragments of Pliny's historical works see Peter, *HRR* II CXXXXVI-CLXII; 109-12.

58. See Suet. *Cal.* 8.1ff. On the lost Julio-Claudian historians the best survey is that of J.J. Wilkes, *CW* 65 (1972) 177-192; 197-203. On Seruilius Nonianus see Syme (1970) 91-109.

59. T.P. Wiseman (1991) xii ff; Appendix 2, 111-118.

60. Note cautions of Wilkes, op. cit 180 on the operation of 'Nissen's law'.

61. See F. Millar (1964) for an analysis of those interests.

62. See analysis of T. P. Wiseman [1979] 9-26

63. On the location of the Capitoline *fasti* see now C.J. Simpson, *Historia* 42 (1993) 61-81.

64. Nepos *Atticus* 18.2-4. See N. Horsfall (1989) ad loc.

65. HA *Hadr*. 11.3.

66. The area has been recently surveyed by L. de Coninck, *ANRW* 2.33.5 (1991) 3675-3700.

67. A. Macé (1900) 180-85. In passing one can note the now discredited view that the Flavian lives appeared before the remainder. See G.W. Bowersock, *Hommages à M. Renard* I (1969) 119-25, refuted by K.R. Bradley, *JIES* 1 (1973) 257-63.

68. R. Syme (1958) 779-80. See especially Suet. *Tit*. 4.1.

69. G.B. Townend, *CQ* n.s. 9 (1959) 285-93; *Latin Biography* (ed. T.A. Dorey) [1967] 86-91.

70. Op.cit. 3698ff.

71. R. Syme, *Hermes* 109 (1981) 109-17.

72. Op.cit. 3699; cf. A.R. Birley, *JRS* 74 (1984) 249.

73. A. Wallace-Hadrill (1983) 53; 56-7.

74. See B. Baldwin, *Chiron* 9 (1979) 189-203. Coninck advises caution over authenticity of such materials (op.cit. 3677).

75. On the *acta senatus* see R.J.A. Talbert (1984) 322-37. For Tacitus and the avoidance of verbatim quotation see ibid. 324. On the *acta diurna* see B. Baldwin, *Chiron* 9 (1979) 189-203.

76. See discussion by N.P. Miller, *AJPh* 89 (1968) 1-19; M. Benner (1975).

77. See Coninck, op.cit. 3684-85.

78. Suet. *Aug.* 87.1-88.2.

79. Wilkes, op.cit. 181.

80. Syme did not believe these were numerically significant. See Syme (1958) 782; Goodyear (1972) 168.

81. This has been thought to be a corrective of Tac. *Ann.* 1.42.2. See Goodyear (1972) 286.

82. An earlier version of this segment of the introduction was delivered at *Ancient History in a Modern University* at Macquarie University (July 8-13 1993).

83. K. Bringmann, *RhM* 114 (1971) 268-85; S. Döpp, *Hermes* 100 (1972) 444-60, replying to W. Steidle (1963) 13ff.

84. F. Leo (1901).

85. M. Guia, *Athenaeum* 56 (1978) 329-45; see also M. Guia, *Athenaeum* 53 (1975) 352-63; M. Guia, *ANRW* 2.33.5 (1991) 3733-47.

86. Suet. *Tib.* 2.1.

87. Suet. *Tib.* 3.1.

88. For the date as between 27-5 BC see Ogilvie (1965) 2. On the *decemuir* see recent discussion by A. Vasaly, *TAPhA* 117 (1987) 203-26.

89. On the unmasking of Appius see Livy 3.36.

90. It is Livy who first uses the term *insita superbia* in relation to the Claudii (2.27.1). Cf. Tac. *Ann.* 1.4: *uetere atque insita Claudiae familiae superbia.*

91. R.M. Ogilvie (1965) 467.

92. Ogilvie, op.cit. 5-17.

93. Mommsen was a believer in the impact of Licinius Macer on the tradition. He suggested that the Claudii were in fact champions of the plebeians, but that Licinius Macer or some other annalist deliberately falsified the picture. See Mommsen, *Römische Forschungen* (1864) 287ff. The discussion of G.C. Fiske *HSCPh* 13 (1902) 1-59, although out-dated, is of some value.

94. A negative answer is reached by R. Seager *CQ* 27 (1977) 377-90, but for some doubts over his approach see Vasaly, op.cit. 208 n. 17.

95. Argued forcefully by T.P. Wiseman (1979) 113ff.

96. Op.cit. 225-6.

97. e.g. Dion. Hal. *Ant.* 5.40.3; 6.24.1ff; 6.38 etc. Dionysius had first arrived in Italy in 30 BC. See Dion. Hal. *Ant.* 1.7.2.

98. As discussed by T.P. Wiseman (1979) 104-39.

99. This is suggested by Vasaly op. cit. 214.

100. *De Finibus* 2.20.66: *tenuis L. Verginius unusque de multis sexagesimo anno post libertatem receptam uirginem filiam sua manu occidit potius quam ea Ap. Claudi libidini, qui tum erat summo in imperio, dederetur.*

101. This is the approach of A. Alföldi (1963) 163, following Hermann Peter. However, none of the extant fragments of Pictor in Peter's *HRR* cover this period.

102. For early evidence of his 'true' nature see 22 (concealment of his involvement in the death of Agrippa Postumus); 24 (immediate control over praetorians, but slow acceptance of the title of emperor); 25 (hypocritical reliance on Libo); 30 (pretence of restoring powers to the senate and magistrates); 38 (pretence of interest in the provinces); .

103 Note concern for his troops in Suet. *Tib.*16; 17; 18.

104 These can be explained as part of the mask worn by the tyrant, but the argument wears a little thin. See Suet. *Tib.*10; 11; 20; 24; 26; 31; 32.

105. On character development see above all C. Gill, *CQ* 33 (1983) 469-87. In exceptional circumstances Plutarch does allow for a radical change in a man's character. See S. Swain, *Phoenix* 43 (1989) 62-8. On some of the problems in determining the true personality of a subject see L.R. Cochran, *Biography* 3 (1980) 189-201.

106. 54 (hypocrisy in his dealings with Nero and Drusus); 55 (hypocritical exploitation of Sejanus for whom he had no affection); 56 (zeal for study, but hostile reaction when a Greek professor came prepared); 57 (initial popularity through a pretence of moderation [no date]); 61 (hypocrisy in claiming that Sejanus was killed for persecuting Nero and Drusus [AD31]); 65 (duplicitous dealings with Sejanus).

107. For his building programme see chapter on Tiberius in F.C. Bourne (1946).

108. See T. Frank, *AJPh 56* (1935) 336-41; see also in *ESAR Vol.V* (1940) 32ff; R. Newbold, *Athenaeum* 52 (1974) 110-43, esp. 110-11.

109. See C. Rodewald (1976) 1-17.

110. For the earthquake in AD 17 see Suet. *Tib.* 48.2; Tac. *Ann.* 2.47; Dio 57.17..7; Oros. 7.4.13.

111. See K. Scott, *AJPh* 53 (1932) 139-51.

112. Suet. *Tib.* 51

113. Tac. *Ann.* 5.1.

114. For the payment of Liuia's legacies see Suet. *Cal.* 16.3; Suet. *Tib.* 51; *Galba* 5; Dio 58.2.3a; 59.2.3-4.

115. Tac. *Ann.* 5.1.6; Suet. *Cal.* 10.2.

116. Tac. *Ann.* 5.2.

117. Tac. *Ann.* 5.2.

118. Of course Tacitus elswhere also implies that Tiberius has a troubled relationship with his mother over the business of honours, and was constantly trying to whittle down recognition. See Tac. *Ann.* 1.14, where Tacitus suggests that Tiberius saw excessive honours for women as a slight to himself. Honours for Liuia have been discussed by H.W. Ritter, *Chiron* 2 (1972) 313-38.

119. Tac. *Ann.* 1.2.

120. Suet. *Tib.* 52 (Penguin translation).

121. Tac. *Ann.* 4.8.

122. Tac. *Ann.* 4.8.

123. Tac. *Ann.* 4.9. Although he says that the funeral was on a considerable scale only the funerary procession and the presence of imagines is discussed.

124. See n. 4 and Tac. *Ann.* 4.12.

125. Suet. *Tib.* 52.

126. Suet. *Tib.* 54; Tac. *Ann.* 6.23; cf. Dio 58.25.4.

127. Suet. *Tib.* 55.

128. Suet. *Tib.* 56.

129. Suet. *Tib.* 57 (Penguin translation).

130. See G. Maranon (1956) 50-1.

131. On his superstition see Plin. *Ep.* 1.18.

132. Tac. *Ann.* 1.4.3; 1.33.

133. For the related theme of the tyrant at the table see now J. Goddard in J. Elsner and J. Masters (eds), (1994) 67-82.

Analysis of the *species*

Textual variants

This edition follows the text of the Teubner edition of M. Ihm (Leipzig 1908) with the minor variations listed below. Short notes in the commentary explain more controversial alterations: spelling variants, punctuation, or expansions of abbreviations are not listed.

Reference	Ihm	This edition
2.1	+ Tibus	+ Claudius
2.2	+ Drusus	+ Russus
21.4	+ μουισασαιστ	+ Μούσαις

Suetonius Tiberius

Text

Patricia gens Claudia (fuit enim et alia plebeia, nec potentia minor nec 1.1
dignitate) orta est ex Regillis oppido Sabinorum. inde Romam recens condi-
tam cum magna clientium manu commigrauit auctore Tito Tatio consorte
Romuli, uel, quod magis constat, Atta Claudio gentis principe, post reges
exactos sexto fere anno; atque in patricias cooptata agrum insuper trans
Anienem clientibus locumque sibi ad sepulturam sub Capitolio publice accepit. deinceps procedente tempore duodetriginta consulatus, dictaturas quin- 1.2
que, censuras septem, triumphos sex, duas ouationes adepta est. cum
praenominibus cognominibusque uariis distingueretur, Luci praenomen con-
sensu repudiauit, postquam e duobus gentilibus praeditis eo alter latrocinii,
caedis alter conuictus est. inter cognomina autem et Neronis assumpsit, quo[d]
significatur lingua Sabina fortis ac strenuus.

Multa multorum Claudiorum egregia merita, multa etiam sequius admissa 2.1
in rem p. extant. sed ut praecipua commemorem, Appius Caecus societatem
cum rege Pyrro ut parum salubrem iniri dissuasit. Claudius Caudex primus
freto classe traiecto Poenos Sicilia expulit. + Claudius Nero aduenientem ex
Hispania cum ingentibus copiis Hasdrubalem, prius quam Hannibali fratri
coniungeretur, oppressit. contra Claudius Regillianus, decemuir legibus 2.2
scribendis, uirginem ingenuam per uim libidinis gratia in seruitutem asserere
conatus causa plebi fuit secedendi rursus a patribus. Claudius + Russus statua
sibi diademata ad Appi Forum posita Italiam per clientelas occupare temptauit. Claudius Pulcher apud Siciliam non pascentibus in auspicando pullis ac
per contemptum religionis mari demersis, quasi *ut biberent quando esse
nollent*, proelium nauale iniit; superatusque, cum dictatorem dicere a senatu
iuberetur, uelut iterum inludens discrimini publico Glycian uiatorem suum
dixit.

Extant et feminarum exempla diuersa aeque, siquidem gentis eiusdem 2.3
utraque Claudia fuit, et quae nauem cum sacris Matris deum Idaeae obhaer-
entem Tiberino uado extraxit, precata propalam, *ut ita demum se sequeretur,
si sibi pudicitia constaret*; et quae nouo more iudicium maiestatis apud
populum mulier subiit, quod in conferta multitudine aegre procedente car-
pento palam optauerat, *ut frater suus Pulcher reuiuisceret atque iterum
classem amitteret, quo minor turba Romae foret*. praeterea notatissimum est, 2.4
Claudios omnis, excepto dum taxat P. Clodio, qui ob expellendum urbe

Ciceronem plebeio homini atque etiam natu minori in adoptionem se dedit, optimates adsertoresque unicos dignitatis ac potentiae patriciorum semper fuisse atque aduersus plebem adeo uiolentos et contumaces, ut ne capitis quidem quisquam reus apud populum mutare uestem aut deprecari sustinuerit; nonnulli in altercatione et iurgio tribunos plebi pulsauerint. etiam uirgo Vestalis fratrem iniussu populi triumphantem ascenso simul curru usque in Capitolium prosecuta est, ne uetare aut intercedere fas cuiquam tribunorum esset.

3.1   Ex hac stirpe Tiberius Caesar genus trahit, e<t> quidem utrumque: paternum a Tiberio Nerone, maternum ab Appio Pulchro, qui ambo Appi Caeci filii fuerunt. insertus est et Liuiorum familiae adoptato in eam materno auo. quae familia, quanquam plebeia, tamen et ipsa admodum floruit octo consulatibus, censuris duabus, triumphis tribus, dictatura etiam ac magisterio equitum honorata; clara et insignibus uiris ac maxime Salinatore

3.2 Drususque. Salinator uniuersas tribus in censura notauit leuitatis nomine, quod, cum se post priorem consulatum multa inrogata condemnassent, consulem iterum censoremque fecissent. Drusus hostium duce Drauso comminus trucidato sibi posterisque suis cognomen inuenit. traditur etiam pro praetore ex prouincia Gallia ret<t>ulisse aurum Senonibus olim in obsidione Capitolii datum nec, ut fama est, extortum a Camillo. eius abnepos ob eximiam aduersus Gracchos operam patronus senatus dictus filium reliquit, quem in simili dissensione multa uarie molientem diuersa factio per fraudem interemit.

4.1   Pater Tiberi, Nero, quaestor C. Caesaris Alexandrino bello classi praepositus, plurimum ad uictoriam contulit. quare et pontifex in locum P. Scipionis substitutus et ad deducendas in Galliam colonias, in quis Narbo et Arelate erant, missus est. tamen Caesare occiso, cunctis turbarum metu abolitionem facti decernentibus, etiam de praemiis tyrannicidarum refer-

4.2 endum censuit. praetura deinde functus, cum exitu anni discordia inter triumuiros orta esset, retentis ultra iustum tempus insignibus L. Antonium consulem triumuiri fratrem ad Perusiam secutus, deditione a ceteris facta, solus permansit in partibus ac primo Praeneste, inde Neapolim euasit

4.3 seruisque ad pilleum frustra uocatis in Siciliam profugit. sed indigne ferens nec statim se in conspectum Sexti Pompei admissum et fascium usu prohibitum, ad M. Antonium traiecit in Achaiam. cum quo breui reconciliata inter omnis pace Romam redit uxoremque Liuiam Drusillam et tunc grauidam et ante iam apud se filium enixam petenti Augusto concessit. nec multo post diem obiit, utroque liberorum superstite, Tiberio Drusoque Neronibus.

5   Tiberium quidam Fundis natum existimauerunt secuti leuem coniecturam, quod materna eius auia Fundana fuerit et quod mox simulacrum Felicitatis ex s.c. publicatum ibi sit. sed ut plures certioresque tradunt, natus

est Romae in Palatio XVI Kal. Dec. M. Aemilio Lepido iterum L. Munatio
Planco conss. per bellum Philippense. sic enim in fastos actaque in publica
relatum est. nec tamen desunt, qui partim antecedente anno, Hirti ac Pansae,
partim insequenti, Seruili Isaurici <L.>que Antoni[i] consulatu, genitum eum
scribant.

Infantiam pueritiamque habuit laboriosam et exercitatam, comes usque 6.1
quaque parentum fugae; quos quidem apud Neapolim sub inruptionem hostis
nauigium clam petentis uagitu suo paene bis prodidit, semel cum a nutricis
ubere, ite<ru>m cum a sinu matris raptim auferretur ab iis, qui pro necessitate temporis mulierculas leuare onere temptabant. per Siciliam quoque et per 6.2
Achaiam circumductus ac Lacedaemoniis publice, quod in tutela Claudiorum
erant, demandatus, digrediens inde itinere nocturno discrimen uiae adiit
flamma repente e siluis undique exorta adeoque omnem comitatum circum-
plexa, ut Liuiae pars uestis et capilli amburerentur. munera, quibus a Pompeia, 6.3
Sex. Pompei sorore in Sicilia donatus est, chlamys et fibula, item bullae
aureae, durant ostendunturque adhuc Bais. post reditum in urbem a M. Gallio
senatore testamento adoptatus hereditate adita mox nomine abstinuit, quod
Gallius aduersarum Augusto partium fuerat.

Nouem natus annos defunctum patrem pro rostris laudauit. dehinc pubes- 6.4
cens Actiaco triumpho currum Augusti comitatus est sinisteriore funali equo,
cum Marcellus Octauiae filius dexteriore ueheretur. praesedit et asticis ludis
et Troiam circensibus <lusit> ductor turmae puerorum maiorum.

Virili toga sumpta adulescentiam omnem spatiumque insequentis aetatis 7.1
usque ad principatus initia per haec fere transegit. munus gladiatorium in
memoriam patris et alterum in aui Drusi dedit, diuersis temporibus ac locis,
primum in foro, secundum in amphitheatro, rudiaris quoque quibusdam
reuocatis auctoramento centenum milium; dedit et ludos, sed absens: cuncta
magnifice, impensa matris ac uitrici.

Agrippinam, Marco Agrippa genitam, neptem Caecili Attici equitis R., ad 7.2
quem sunt Ciceronis epistulae, duxit uxorem; sublatoque ex ea Druso, quanquam bene conuenientem rursusque grauidam dimittere ac Iuliam Augusti
filiam confestim coactus est ducere non sine magno angore animi, cum et
Agrippinae consuetudine teneretur et Iuliae mores improbaret, ut quam sens-
isset sui quoque sub priore marito appetentem,quod sane etiam uulgo existi-
mabatur. sed Agrippinam et abegisse post diuortium doluit et semel omnino 7.3
ex occursu uisam adeo contentis et [t]umentibus oculis prosecutus est, ut
custoditum sit ne umquam in conspectum ei posthac ueniret. cum Iulia primo
concorditer et amore mutuo uixit, mox dissedit et aliquanto grauius, ut etiam
perpetuo secubaret, intercepto communis fili pignore, qui Aquileiae natus
infans extinctus est. Drusum fratrem in Germania amisit, cuius corpus pedibus
toto itinere praegrediens Romam usque peruexit.

8   Ciuilium officiorum rudimentis regem Archelaum Trallianos et Thessalos, uaria quosque de causa, Augusto cognoscente defendit; pro Laodicenis Thyatirenis Chiis terrae motu afflictis opemque implorantibus senatum deprecatus est; Fannium Caepionem, qui cum Varrone Murena in Augustum conspirauerat, reum maiestatis apud iudices fecit et condemnauit. interque haec duplicem curam administrauit, annonae quae artior inciderat, et repurgandorum tota Italia ergastulorum, quorum domini in inuidiam uenerant quasi exceptos supprimerent non solum uiatores sed et quos sacramenti metus ad eius modi latebras compulisset.

9.1   Stipendia prima expeditione Cantabrica tribunus militum fecit, dein ducto ad Orientem exercitu regnum Armeniae Tigrani restituit ac pro tribunali diadema imposuit. recepit et signa, quae M. Crasso ademerant Parthi. post hoc Comatam Galliam anno fere rexit et barbarorum incursionibus et principum discordia inquietam. exin Raeticum Vindelicumque

9.2   bellum, inde Pannonicum, inde Germanicum gessit. Raetico atque Vindelico gentis Alpinas, Pannonico Breucos et Dalmatas subegit, Germanico quadraginta milia dediticiorum traiecit in Galliam iuxtaque ripam Rheni sedibus adsignatis conlocauit. quas ob res et ouans et curru urbem ingressus est, prius, ut quidam putant, triumphalibus ornamentis honoratus, nouo nec antea cuiquam tributo genere honoris.

9.3   Magistratus et maturius incohauit et paene iunctim percucurrit, quaesturam praeturam consulatum; interpositoque tempore consul iterum etiam

10.1   tribuniciam potestatem in quinquennium accepit. tot prosperis confluentibus integra aetate ac ualitudine statuit repente secedere seque e medio quam longissime amouere: dubium uxorisne taedio, quam neque criminari aut dimittere auderet neque ultra perferre posset, an ut uitato assiduitatis fastidio auctoritatem absentia tueretur atque etiam augeret, si quando indiguisset sui res p. quidam existimant, adultis iam Augusti liberis, loco et quasi possessione usurpati a se diu secundi gradus sponte cessisse exemplo M. Agrippae, qui M. Marcello ad munera publica admoto Mytilenas abierit,

10.2   ne aut obstare aut obtrectare praesens uideretur. quam causam et ipse, sed postea, reddidit. tunc autem honorum satietatem ac requiem laborum praetendens commeatum petit; neque aut matri suppliciter precanti aut uitrico deseri se etiam in senatu conquerenti ueniam dedit. quin et pertinacius retinentibus, cibo per quadriduum abstinuit. facta tandem abeundi potestate, relictis Romae uxore et filio confestim Ostiam descendit, ne uerbo quidem cuiquam prosequentium reddito paucosque admodum in digressu

11.1   exosculatus. ab Ostia oram Campaniae legens inbecillitate Augusti nuntiata paulum substitit. sed increbrescente rumore quasi ad occasionem maioris spei commoraretur, tantum non aduersis tempestatibus Rhodum enauigauit, amoenitate et salubritate insulae iam inde captus cum ad eam ab Armenia rediens appulisset. hic modicis contentus aedibus nec multo laxiore suburbano genus uitae ciuile admodum instituit, sine lictore aut uiatore gymnasio interdum obambulans mutuaque cum Graeculis officia usurpans prope ex aequo.

Forte quondam in disponendo die mane praedixerat, quidquid aegrorum in ciuitate esset uisitare se uelle; id a proximis aliter exceptum iussique sunt omnes aegri in publicam porticum deferri ac per ualitudinum genera disponi. perculsus ergo inopinata re diuque quid ageret incertus, tandem singulos circuit excusans factum etiam tenuissimo cuique et ignoto. unum hoc modo neque praeterea quicquam notatum est, in quo exeruisse ius tribuniciae potestatis uisus sit: cum circa scholas et auditoria professorum assiduus esset, moto inter antisophistas grauiore iurgio, non defuit qui eum interuenientem et quasi studiosiorem partis alterius conuicio incesseret. sensim itaque regressus domum repente cum apparitoribus prodiit citatumque pro tribunali uoce praeconis conuiciatorem rapi iussit in carcerem. **11.2** **11.3**

Comperit deinde Iuliam uxorem ob libidines atque adulteria damnatam repudiumque ei suo nomine ex auctoritate Augusti remissum; et quamquam laetus nuntio, tamen officii duxit, quantum in se esset, exorare filiae patrem frequentibus litteris et uel utcumque meritae, quidquid umquam dono dedisset, concedere. transacto autem tribuniciae potestatis tempore, confessus tandem, nihil aliud secessu deuitasse se quam aemulationis cum C. Lucioque suspicionem, petit ut sibi securo iam ab hac parte, conroboratis his et secundum locum facile tutantibus, permitteretur reuisere necessitudines, quarum desiderio teneretur. sed neque impetrauit ultroque etiam admonitus est, *dimitteret omnem curam suorum, quos tam cupide reliquisset.* remansit igitur Rhodi contra uoluntatem, uix per matrem consecutus, ut ad uelandam ignominiam quasi legatus Augusto abesset. **11.4** **11.5** **12.1**

Enimuero tunc non priuatum modo, sed etiam obnoxium et trepidum egit mediterraneis agris abditus uitansque praeternauigantium officia, quibus frequentabatur assidue, nemine cum imperio aut magistratu tendente quoquam quin deuerteret Rhodum. et accesserunt maioris sollicitudinis causae. namque priuignum Gaium Orienti praepositum, cum uisendi gratia traiecisset Samum, alieniorem sibi sensit ex criminationibus M. Lolli comitis et rectoris eius. uenit etiam in suspicionem per quosdam beneficii sui centuriones a commeatu castra repetentis mandata ad complures dedisse ambigua et quae temptare singulorum animos ad nouas res uiderentur. de qua suspicione certior ab Augusto factus non cessauit efflagitare aliquem cuiuslibet ordinis custodem factis atque dictis suis. equi quoque et armorum solitas exercitationes omisit redegitque se deposito patrio habitu ad pallium et crepidas atque in tali statu biennio fere permansit, contemptior in dies et inuisior, adeo ut imagines eius et statuas Nemausenses subuerterint ac familiari quondam conuiuio mentione eius orta extiterit qui Gaio polliceretur, confestim se, si iuberet, Rhodum **12.2** **12.3** **13.1**

13.2 nauigaturum caputque exulis – sic enim appellabatur – relaturum. quo praecipue non iam metu sed discrimine coactus est, tam suis quam matris impensissimis precibus reditum expostulare, impetrauitque adiutus aliquantum etiam casu. destinatum Augusto erat, nihil super ea re nisi ex uoluntate maioris fili statuere; is forte tunc M. Lollio offensior, facilis exorabilisque in uitricum fuit. permittente ergo Gaio reuocatus est, uerum sub condicione ne quam partem curamue rei p. attingeret.

14.1 Rediit octauo post secessum anno, magna nec incerta spe futurorum, quam et ostentis et praedictionibus ab initio aetatis conceperat.

14.2 Praegnans eo Liuia cum an marem editura esset, uariis captaret ominibus, ouum incubanti gallinae subductum nunc sua nunc ministrarum manu per uices usque fouit, quoad pullus insigniter cristatus exclusus est. ac de infante Scribonius mathematicus praeclara spopondit, etiam regnaturum quandoque, sed sine regio insigni, ignota scilicet tunc adhuc Caesarum potestate.

14.3 et ingresso primam expeditionem ac per Macedoniam ducente exercitum in Syriam, accidit ut apud Philippos sacratae olim uictricium legionum arae sponte subitis conlucerent ignibus; et mox, cum Illyricum petens iuxta Patauium adisset Geryonis oraculum, sorte tracta, qua monebatur ut de consultationibus in Aponi fontem talos aureos iaceret, euenit ut summum

14.4 numerum iacti ab eo ostenderent; hodieque sub aqua uisuntur hi tali. ante paucos uero quam reuocaretur dies aquila numquam antea Rhodi conspecta in culmine domus eius assedit; et pridie quam de reditu certior fieret, uestimenta mutanti tunica ardere uisa est. Thrasyllum quoque mathematicum, quem ut sapientiae professorem contubernio admouerat, tum maxime expertus est affirmantem naue prouisa gaudium afferri; cum quidem illum durius et contra praedicta cadentibus rebus ut falsum et secretorum temere conscium, eo ipso momento, dum spatiatur una, praecipitare in mare destinasset.

15.1 Romam reuersus deducto in forum filio Druso statim e Carinis ac Pompeiana domo Esquilias in hortos Maecenatianos transmigrauit totumque se ad quietem contulit, priuata modo officia obiens ac publicorum munerum expers.

15.2 Gaio et Lucio intra triennium defunctis adoptatur ab Augusto simul cum fratre eorum M. Agrippa, coactus prius ipse Germanicum fratris sui filium adoptare. nec quicquam postea pro patre familias egit aut ius, quod amiserat, ex ulla parte retinuit. nam neque donauit neque manumisit, ne hereditatem quidem aut legata percepit ulla aliter quam ut peculio referret accepta. nihil ex eo tempore praetermissum est ad maiestatem eius augendam ac multo magis, postquam Agrippa abdicato atque seposito certum erat, uni spem

16.1 successionis incumbere; data rursus potestas tribunicia in quinquennium, delegatus pacandae Germaniae status, Parthorum legati mandatis Augusto

Romae redditis eum quoque adire in prouincia iussi. sed nuntiata Illyrici defectione transiit ad curam noui belli, quod grauissimum omnium externorum bellorum post Punica, per quindecim legiones paremque auxiliorum copiam triennio gessit in magnis omnium rerum difficultatibus summaque frugum inopia. et quanquam saepius reuocaretur, tamen perseuerauit, metuens 16.2 ne uicinus et praeualens hostis instaret ultro cedentibus. ac perseuerantiae grande pretium tulit, toto Illyrico, quod inter Italiam regnumque Noricum et Thraciam et Macedoniam interque Danuuium flumen et sinum maris Hadriatici patet, perdomito et in dicionem redacto. cui gloriae amplior adhuc ex oppor- 17.1 tunitate cumulus accessit. nam sub id fere tempus Quintilius Varus cum tribus legionibus in Germania periit, nemine dubitante quin uictores Germani iuncturi se Pannoniis fuerint, nisi debellatum prius Illyricum esset. quas ob res triumphus ei decretus est multi <que> et magni honores. censuerunt etiam 17.2 quidam ut Pannonicus, alii ut Inuictus, nonnulli ut Pius cognominaretur. sed de cognomine intercessit Augustus, eo contentum repromittens, quod se defuncto suscepturus esset. triumphum ipse distulit maesta ciuitate clade Variana; nihilo minus urbem praetextatus et laurea coronatus intrauit positumque in Saeptis tribunal senatu astante conscendit ac medius inter duos consules cum Augusto simul sedit; unde populo consalutato circum templa deductus est.

Proximo anno repetita Germania cum animaduerteret Varianam cladem 18.1 temeritate et neglegentia ducis accidisse, nihil non de consilii sententia egit; semper alias sui arbitrii contentusque se uno, tunc praeter consuetudinem cum compluribus de ratione belli communicauit. curam quoque solito exactiorem praestitit. traiecturus Rhenum commeatum omnem ad certam formulam adstrictum non ante transmisit, quam consistens apud ripam explorasset uehiculorum onera, ne qua deportarentur nisi concessa aut necessaria. trans Rhenum 18.2 uero eum uitae ordinem tenuit, ut sedens in caespite nudo cibum caperet, saepe sine tentorio pernoctaret, praecepta sequentis diei omnia, et si quid subiti muneris iniungendum esset, per libellos daret; addita monitione ut, de quo quisque dubitaret, se nec alio interprete quacumque uel noctis hora uteretur. disciplinam acerrime exegit animaduersionum et ignominiarum generibus ex 19 antiquitate repetitis atque etiam legato legionis, quod paucos milites cum liberto suo trans ripam uenatum misisset, ignominia notato. proelia, quamuis minimum fortunae casibusque permitteret, aliquanto constantius inibat, quotiens lucubrante se subito ac nullo propellente decideret lumen et extingueretur, confidens, ut aiebat, ostento sibi a maioribus suis in omni ducatu expertissimo. sed re prospere gesta non multum afuit quin a Bructero quodam occideretur, cui inter proximos uersanti et trepidatione detecto tormentis expressa confessio est cogitati facinoris. a Germania in urbem post biennium 20 regressus triumphum, quem distulerat, egit prosequentibus etiam legatis, quibus triumphalia ornamenta impetrarat. ac prius quam in Capitolium flect- eret, descendit e curru seque praesidenti patri ad genua summisit. Batonem Pannonium ducem ingentibus donatum praemiis Rauennam transtulit, gratiam referens, quod se quondam cum exercitu iniquitate loci circumclusum passus es<se>t euadere. prandium dehinc populo mille mensis et congiarium trecenos nummos uiritim dedit. dedicauit et Concordiae aedem, item Pollucis

21.1 et Castoris suo fratrisque nomine de manubiis. ac non multo post lege per consules lata, ut prouincias cum Augusto communiter administraret simulque censum a[u]geret, condito lustro in Illyricum profectus est. et statim ex itinere reuocatus iam quidem adfectum, sed tamen spirantem adhuc Augustum repperit fuitque una secreto per totum diem.

21.2 Scio uulgo persuasum quasi egresso post secretum sermonem Tiberio uox Augusti per cubicularios excepta sit: *miserum populum R., qui sub tam lentis maxillis erit.* ne illud quidem ignoro aliquos tradidisse. Augustum palam nec dissimulanter morum eius diritatem adeo improbasse, ut nonnumquam remissiores hilarioresque sermones superueniente eo abrumperet; sed expugnatum precibus uxoris adoptionem non abnuisse, uel etiam ambitione tractum, ut tali successore desiderabilior ipse quandoque fieret.

21.3 adduci tamen nequeo quin existimem, circumspectissimum et prudentissimum principem in tanto praesertim negotio nihil temere fecisse; sed uitiis Tiberi[i] uirtutibusque perpensis potiores duxisse uirtutes, praesertim cum et rei p. causa adoptare se eum pro contione iurauerit et epistulis aliquot ut peritissimum rei militaris utque unicum p. R. praesidium prosequatur. ex quibus in exemplum pauca inde subieci.

21.4 *Vale iucundissime Tiberi, et feliciter rem gere,* ἐμοὶ καὶ ταῖς + Μούσαις στρατηγῶν. *iucundissime et ita sim felix, uir fortissime et dux* νομιμώτατε, *uale.*

21.5 *Ordinem aestiuorum tuorum ego uero <laudo>, mi Tiberi, et inter tot rerum difficultates* καὶ τοσαύτην ἀποθυμ[ε]ίαν τῶν στρατευομένων *non potuisse quemquam prudentius gerere se quam tu gesseris, existimo. [h]ii quoque qui tecum fuerunt omnes confitentur, uersum illum in te posse dici:*

> *unus homo nobis uigilando restituit rem.*

21.6 *Siue quid incidit de quo sit cogitandum diligentius, siue quid stomachor, ualde medius Fidius Tiberium meum desidero succurritque uersus ille Homericus:*

> τούτου γ' ἑσπ<ο>μένοιο καὶ ἐκ πυρὸς αἰθομένοιο
> ἄμφω νοστήσαιμεν, ἐπ<ε>ὶ περίοιδε νοῆσαι.

Attenuatum te esse continuatione laborum cum audio et lego, di me perdant 21.7
nisi cohorrescit corpus meum; teque oro ut parcas tibi, ne si te languere
audierimus, et ego et mater tua expiremus et summa imperi sui populus R.
periclitetur.
Nihil interest ualeam ipse necne, si tu non ualebis.
Deos obsecro, ut te nobis conseruent et ualere nunc et semper patiantur,
si non p. R. perosi sunt.

Excessum Augusti non prius palam fecit, quam Agrippa iuuene interempto. 22
hunc tribunus militum custos appositus occidit lectis codicillis quibus ut id
faceret iubebatur; quos codicillos dubium fuit, Augustusne moriens reliquisset, quo materiam tumultus post se subduceret; an nomine Augusti Liuia et ea
conscio Tiberio an ignaro, dictasset. Tiberius renuntianti tribuno, factum esse
quod imperasset, *neque imperasse se et redditurum eum senatui rationem*
respondit, inuidiam scilicet in praesentia uitans. nam mox silentio rem oblit-
erauit. iure autem tribuniciae potestatis coacto senatu incohataque adlocutione 23
derepente uelut impar dolori congemuit, utque non solum uox sed et spiritus
deficeret optauit ac perlegendum librum Druso filio tradidit. inlatum deinde
Augusti testamentum, non admissis signatoribus nisi senatorii ordinis, ceteris
extra curiam signa agnoscentibus, recitauit per libertum. testamenti initium
fuit: *quoniam atrox fortuna Gaium et Lucium filios mihi eripuit, Tiberius*
Caesar mihi ex parte dimidia et sextante heres esto. quo et ipso aucta suspicio
est opinantium successorem ascitum eum necessitate magis quam iudicio,
quando ita praefari non abstinuerit.

Principatum, quamuis neque occupare confestim neque agere dubitasset, 24.1
et statione militum, hoc est ui et specie dominationis assumpta, diu tamen
recusauit, impudentissimo mimo nunc adhortantis amicos increpans ut *ig-*
naros, quanta belua esset imperium, nunc precantem senatum et procumbentem sibi ad genua ambiguis responsis et callida cunctatione suspendens, ut
quidam patientiam rumperent atque unus in tumultu proclamaret: *aut agat aut*
desistat! alter coram exprobraret ceteros, quod polliciti sint tarde praestare,
se<d> ipsum, quod praestet tarde polliceri. tandem quasi coactus et querens 24.2
miseram et onerosam iniungi sibi seruitutem, recepit imperium; nec tamen
aliter, quam ut depositurum se quandoque spem faceret. ipsius uerba sunt:
dum ueniam ad id tempus, quo uobis aequum possit uideri dare uos aliquam
senectuti meae requiem.

Cunctandi causa erat metus undique imminentium discriminum, ut saepe 25.1
lupum se auribus tenere diceret. nam et seruus Agrippae Clemens nomine non
contemnendam manum in ultionem domini comparara et L. Scribonius Libo
uir nobilis res nouas clam moliebatur et duplex seditio militum in Illyrico et
in Germania exorta est. flagitabant ambo exercitus multa extra ordinem, ante 25.2
omnia ut aequarentur stipendio praetoriani<s>. Germaniciani quidem etiam

principem detractabant non a se datum summaque ui Germanicum, qui tum iis praeerat, ad capessendam rem p. urgebant, quamquam obfirmate resistentem. quem maxime casum timens, partes sibi quas senatui liberet, tuendas in re p. depoposcit, quando uniuersae sufficere solus nemo posset nisi

25.3 cum altero uel etiam cum pluribus. simulauit et ualitudinem, quo aequiore animo Germanicus celerem successionem uel certe societatem principatus opperiretur. compositis seditionibus Clementem quoque fraude deceptum redegit in potestatem. Libonem, ne quid in nouitate acerbius fieret, secundo demum anno in senatu coarguit, medio temporis spatio tantum cauere contentus; nam et inter pontifices sacrificanti simul pro secespita plumbeum cultrum subiciendum curauit et secretum petenti non nisi adhibito Druso filio dedit dextramque obambulantis ueluti incumbens, quoad perageretur sermo, continuit.

26.1 Verum liberatus metu ciuilem admodum inter initia ac paulo minus quam priuatum egit. ex plurimis maximisque honoribus praeter paucos et modicos non recepit. natalem suum plebeis incurrentem circensibus uix unius bigae adiectione honorari passus est. templa, flamines, sacerdotes decerni sibi prohibuit, etiam statuas atque imagines nisi permittente se poni; permisitque ea sola condicione, ne inter simulacra deorum sed inter ornamenta aedium

26.2 ponerentur. intercessit et quo minus in acta sua iuraretur, et ne mensis September Tiberius, October Liuius uocarentur. praenomen quoque imperatoris cognomenque patris patriae et ciuicam in uestibulo coronam recusauit; ac ne Augusti quidem nomen, quanquam hereditarium, nullis nisi ad reges ac dynastas epistulis addidit. nec amplius quam mox tres consulatus, unum paucis diebus, alterum tribus mensibus, tertium absens usque in Idus Maias gessit.

27 Adulationes adeo auersatus est, ut neminem senatorum aut officii aut negotii causa ad lecticam suam admiserit, consularem uero satisfacientem sibi ac per genua orare conantem ita suffugerit, ut caderet supinus; atque etiam, si quid in sermone uel in continua oratione blandius de se diceretur, non dubitaret interpellare ac reprehendere et commutare continuo. dominus appellatus a quodam denuntiauit, ne se amplius contumeliae causa nominaret. alium dicentem sacras eius occupationes et rursus alium, auctore eo senatum se a[u]disse, uerba mutare et pro auctore suasorem, pro sacris

28 laboriosas dicere coegit. sed et aduersus conuicia malosque rumores et famosa de se ac suis carmina firmus ac patiens subinde iactabat *in ciuitate libera linguam mentemque liberas esse debere;* et quondam senatu cognitionem de eius modi criminibus ac reis flagitante: *non tantum,* inquit, *otii habemus, ut implicare nos pluribus negotiis debeamus; si hanc fenestram aperueritis, nihil aliud agi sinetis: omnium inimicitiae hoc praetexto ad uos deferentur.* extat et sermo eius in senatu perciuilis: *siquidem locutus aliter*

fuerit, dabo operam ut rationem factorum meorum dictorumque reddam; si perseuerauerit, in uicem eum odero.

Atque haec eo notabiliora erant, quod ipse in appellandis uenerandisque et 29 singulis et uniuersis prope excesserat humanitatis modum. dissentiens in curia a Q. Haterio: *ignoscas,* inquit, *rogo, si quid aduersus te liberius sicut senator dixero.* et deinde omnis adloquens: *dixi et nunc et saepe alias, p.c., bonum et salutarem principem, quem uos tanta et tam libera potestate instruxistis, senatui seruire debere et uniuersis ciuibus saepe et plerumque etiam singulis; neque id dixisse me paenitet, et bonos et aequos et fauentes uos habui dominos et adhuc habeo.*

Quin etiam speciem libertatis quandam induxit conseruatis senatui ac 30 magistratibus et maiestate pristina et potestate. neque tam paruum quicquam neque tam magnum publici priuatique negotii fuit, de quo non ad patres conscriptos referretur: de uectigalibus ac monopoliis, de extruendis reficiendisue operibus, etiam de legendo uel exauctorando milite ac legionum et auxiliorum discriptione, denique quibus imperium prorogari aut extraordinaria bella mandari, quid et qua[m] forma[m] regum litteris rescribi placeret. praefectum alae de ui et rapinis reum causam in senatu dicere coegit. numquam curiam nisi solus intrauit; lectica quondam intro latus aeger comites a se remouit. quaedam aduersus sententiam suam decerni ne questus quidem 31.1 est. negante eo destinatos magistratus abesse oportere, ut praesentes honori adquiescerent, praetor designatus liberam legationem impetrauit. iterum censente, ut Trebianis legatam in opus noui theatri pecuniam ad munitionem uiae transferre concederetur, optinere non potuit quin rata uoluntas legatoris esset. cum senatus consultum per discessionem forte fieret, transeuntem eum in alteram partem, in qua pauciores erant, secutus est nemo.

Cetera quoque non nisi per magistratus et iure ordinario agebantur, tanta 31.2 consulum auctoritate, ut legati ex Africa adierint eos querentes, trahi se a Caesare ad quem missi forent. nec mirum, cum palam esset, ipsum quoque eisdem et assurgere et decedere uia. corripuit consulares exercitibus praepo- 32.1 sitos, quod non de rebus gestis senatui scriberent quodque de tribuendis quibusdam militaribus donis ad se referrent, quasi non omnium tribuendorum ipsi ius haberent. praetorem conlaudauit, quod honore inito consuetudinem antiquam ret<t>ulisset de maioribus suis pro contione memorandi. quorundam illustrium exequias usque ad rogum frequentauit.

Parem moderationem minoribus quoque et personis et rebus exhibuit. cum 32.2 Rhodiorum magistratus, quod litteras publicas sine subscriptione ad se dederant, euocasset, ne uerbo quidem insectatus ac tantum modo iussos subscribere remisit. Diogenes grammaticus, disputare sabbatis Rhodi solitus, uenientem eum, ut se extra ordinem audiret, non admiserat ac per seruolum suum in septimum diem distulerat; hunc Romae salutandi sui causa pro foribus adstantem nihil amplius quam ut post septimum annum rediret admonuit. praesidibus onerandas tributo prouincias suadentibus rescripsit *boni pastoris esse tondere pecus, non deglubere.*

33   Paulatim principem exercuit praestititque etsi uarium diu, commodiorem tamen saepius et ad utilitates publicas proniorem. ac primo eatenus interueniebat, ne quid perperam fieret. itaque et constitutiones senatus quasdam rescidit et magistratibus pro tribunali cognoscentibus plerumque se offerebat consiliarium assidebatque iuxtim uel exaduersum in parte primori; et si quem reorum elabi gratia rumor esset, subitus aderat iudicesque aut e plano aut e quaesitoris tribunali legum et religionis et noxae, de qua cognoscerent, admonebat; atque etiam, si qua in publicis moribus desidia aut mala con

34.1   suetudine labarent, corrigenda suscepit. ludorum ac munerum impensas corripuit mercedibus scaenicorum recisis paribusque gladiatorum ad certum numerum redactis. Corinthiorum uasorum pretia in immensum exarsisse tresque mul<l>os triginta milibus nummum uenisse grauiter conquestus, adhibendum supellectili modum censuit annonamque macelli senatus arbitratu quotannis temperandam, dato aedilibus negotio popinas ganeasque usque eo inhibendi, ut ne opera quidem pistoria proponi uenalia sinerent. et ut parsimoniam publicam exemplo quoque iuuaret, sollemnibus ipse cenis pridiana saepe ac semesa obsonia apposuit dimidiatumque aprum, affirmans *omnia eadem habere, quae totum.*

34.2   Cotidiana oscula edicto prohibuit, item strenarum commercium ne ultra Kal. Ian. exerceretur. consuerat quadriplam stren[u]am, et de manu, reddere; sed offensus interpellari se toto mense ab iis qui potestatem sui die festo non

35.1   habuissent, ultra non tulit. matronas prostratae pudicitiae, quibus accusator publicus deesset, ut propinqui more maiorum de communi sententia coercerent auctor fuit. eq(uiti) R(omano) iuris iurandi gratiam fecit, uxorem in stupro generi compertam dimitteret, quam se numquam repudiaturum ante

35.2   iurauerat. feminae famosae, ut ad euitandas legum poenas iure ac dignitate matronali exoluerentur, lenocinium profiteri coeperant, et ex iuuentute utriusque ordinis profligatissimus quisque, quominus in opera scaenae harenaeque edenda senatus consulto teneretur, famosi iudicii notam sponte subibant; eos easque omnes, ne quod refugium in tali fraude cuiquam esset, exilio adfecit. senatori latum clauum ademit, cum cognosset sub Kal. Iul. demigrasse in hortos, quo uilius post diem aedes in urbe conduceret. alium e quaestura remouit, quod uxorem pridie sortitionem ductam postridie

36   repudiasset. externas caerimonias, Aegyptios Iudaicosque ritus compescuit, coactis qui superstitione ea tenebantur religiosas uestes cum instrumento omni comburere. Iudaeorum iuuentutem per speciem sacramenti in prouincias grauioris caeli distribuit, reliquos gentis eiusdem uel similia sectantes urbe summouit, sub poena perpetuae seruitutis nisi obtemperassent. expulit

et mathematicos, sed deprecantibus ac se artem desituros promittentibus
ueniam dedit.

In primis tuendae pacis a grassaturis ac latrociniis seditionumque licentia 37.1
curam habuit. stationes militum per Italiam solito frequentiores disposuit.
Romae castra constituit, quibus praetorianae cohortes uagae ante id tempus
et per hospitia dispersae continerentur.

Populares tumultus et ortos grauissime coercuit et ne orerentur sedulo 37.2
cauit. caede in theatro per discordiam admissa capita factionum et histriones,
propter quos dissidebatur, relegauit, nec ut reuocaret umquam ullis populi
precibus potuit euinci. cum Pollentina plebs funus cuiusdam primipilaris non 37.3
prius ex foro misisset quam extorta pecunia per uim heredibus ad gladiatorium
munus, cohortem ab urbe et aliam a Cotti regno dissimulata itineris causa
detectis repente armis concinentibusque signis per diuersas portas in oppidum
immisit ac partem maiorem plebei ac decurionum in perpetua uincula coiecit.
aboleuit et ius moremque asylorum, quae usquam erant. Cyzicenis in ciues
R. uiolentius quaedam ausis publice libertatem ademit, quam Mithridatico
bello meruerant.

Hostiles motus nulla postea expeditione suscepta per legatos compescuit, 37.4
ne per eos quidem nisi cunctanter et necessario. reges infestos suspectosque
comminationibus magis et querelis quam ui repressit; quosdam per blanditias
atque promissa extractos ad se non remisit, ut Marobodum Germanum,
[t]Rhascuporim Thracem, Archelaum Cappadocem, cuius etiam regnum in
formam prouinciae redegit.

Biennio continuo post adeptum imperium pedem porta non extulit; se- 38
quenti tempore praeterquam in propinqua oppida et, cum longissime, Antio
tenus nusquam afuit, idque perraro et paucos dies; quamuis prouincias quoque
et exercitus reuisurum se saepe pronuntiasset et prope quotannis profectionem
praepararet, uehiculis comprehensis, commeatibus per municipia et colonias
dispositis, ad extremum uota pro itu et reditu suo suscipi passus, ut uulgo iam
per iocum Callip<p>ides uocaretur, quem cursitare ac ne cubiti quidem
mensuram progredi prouerbio Graeco notatum est. sed orbatus utroque filio, 39
quorum Germanicus in Syria, Drusus Romae obierat, secessum Campaniae
petit; constanti et opinione et sermone paene omnium quasi neque rediturus
umquam et cito mortem etiam obiturus. quod paulo minus utrumque euenit;
nam neque Romam amplius rediit [s]et paucos post dies iuxta Tarracinam in
praetorio, cui Speluncae nomen est, incenante eo complura et ingentia saxa
fortuito superne dilapsa sunt, multisque conuiuarum et ministrorum elisis
praeter spem euasit.

Peragrata Campania, cum Capuae Capitolium, Nolae templum Augusti, 40
quam causam profectionis praetenderat, dedicasset, Capreas se contulit,
praecipue delectatus insula, quod uno paruoque litore adiretur, saepta undique

praeruptis immensae altitudinis rupibus et profundo mari[s]. statimque reuo-
cante assidua obtestatione populo propter cladem, qua apud Fidenas supra
uiginti hominum milia gladiatorio munere amphitheatri ruina perierant, transiit in continentem potestatemque omnibus adeundi sui fecit: tanto magis,
quod urbe egrediens ne quis se interpellaret edixerat ac toto itinere adeuntis
submouerat.

41   Regressus in insulam rei p. quidem curam usque adeo abiecit, ut postea
non decurias equitum umquam supplerit, non tribunos militum praefec-
tosque, non prouinciarum praesides ullos mutauerit, Hispaniam et Syriam
per aliquot annos sine consularibus legatis habuerit, Armeniam a Parthis
occupari, Moesiam a Dacis Sarmatisque, Gallias a Germanis uastari ne-

42.1   glexerit: magno dedecore imperii nec minore discrimine. ceterum secreti
licentiam nanctus et quasi ciuitatis oculis remotis, cuncta simul uitia male
diu dissimulata tandem profudit: de quibus singillatim ab exordio referam.
in castris tiro etiam tum propter nimiam uini auiditatem pro Tiberio
Biberius, pro Claudio *Caldius* pro Nerone *Mero* uocabatur. postea princeps in
ipsa publicorum morum correctione cum Pomponio Flacco et L. Pisone
noctem continuumque biduum epulando potandoque consumpsit, quorum
alteri Syriam prouinciam, alteri praefecturam urbis confestim detulit, codicil-

42.2   lis quoque iucundissimos et omnium horarum amicos professus. Cestio
Gall[i]o, libidinoso ac prodigo seni, olim ab Augusto ignominia notato et
a se ante paucos dies apud senatum increpito cenam ea lege condixit, ne
quid ex consuetudine immutaret aut demeret, utque nudis puellis minis-
trantibus cenaretur. ignotissimum quaesturae candidatum nobilissimis anteposuit ob epotam in conuiuio propinante se uini amphoram. Asellio
Sabino sestertia ducenta donauit pro dialogo, in quo boleti et ficedulae et
ostreae et turdi certamen induxerat. nouum denique officium instituit a

43.1   uoluptatibus, praeposito equite R. T. Caesonio Prisco. secessu uero
Caprensi etiam sellaria excogitauit, sedem arcanarum libidinum, in quam
undique conquisiti puellarum et exoletorum greges monstrosique concubitus repertores, quos spintrias appellabat, triplici serie conexi, in uicem

43.2   incestarent coram ipso, ut aspectu deficientis libidines excitaret. cubicula
plurifariam disposita tabellis ac sigillis lasciuissimarum picturarum et
figurarum adornauit librisque Elephantidis instruxit, ne cui in opera
edenda exemplar impe[t]ratae schemae deesset. in siluis quoque ac nemori-
bus passim Venerios locos commentus est prost[r]antisque per antra et cauas
rupes ex utriusque sexus pube Paniscorum et Nympharum habitu, quae
palam iam et uulgo nomine insulae abutentes *Caprineum* dictitabant.

44.1   Maiore adhuc ac turpiore infamia flagrauit, uix ut referri audiriue, nedum
credi fas sit, quasi pueros primae teneritudinis, quos pisciculos uocabat,
institueret, ut natanti sibi inter femina uersarentur ac luderent lingua morsuque

sensim adpetentes; atque etiam quasi infantes firmiores, necdum tamen lacte depulsos, inguini ceu papillae admoueret, pronior sane ad id genus libidinis et natura et aetate. quare Parrasi quoque tabulam, in qua Meleagro Atlanta 44.2 ore morigeratur, legatum sibi sub condicione, ut si argumento offenderetur decies pro ea sestertium acciperet, non modo praetulit, sed et in cubiculo dedicauit. fertur etiam in sacrificando quondam captus facie ministri acerram praeferentis nequisse abstinere, quin paene uixdum re diuina peracta ibidem statim seductum constupraret simulque fratrem eius tibicinem; atque utrique mox, quod mutuo flagitium exprobrarant, crura fregisse. feminarum quoque, 45 et quidem illustrium, capitibus quanto opere solitus sit inludere, euidentissime apparuit Malloniae cuiusdam exitu, quam perductam nec quicquam amplius pati constantissime recusantem delatoribus obiecit ac ne ream quidem interpellare desiit, ecquid paeniteret; donec ea relicto iudicio domum se abripuit ferroque transegit, obscaenitate[m] oris hirsuto atque olido seni clare exprobrata. unde mora in Atellanico exhodio proximis ludis adsensu maximo excepta percrebruit, *hircum uetulum capreis naturam ligurire.*

Pecuniae parcus ac tenax comites peregrinationum expeditionumque 46 numquam salario, cibariis tantum sustentauit, una modo liberalitate ex indulgentia uitrici prosecutus, cum tribus classibus factis pro dignitate cuiusque, primae sescenta sestertia, secundae quadringenta distribuit, ducenta tertiae, quam non amicorum sed Graecorum appellabat.

Princeps neque opera ulla magnifica fecit - nam et quae sola susceperat, 47 Augusti templum restitutionemque Pompeiani theatri, imperfecta post tot annos reliquit - neque spectacula omnino edidit; et iis, quae ab aliquo ederentur, rarissime interfuit, ne quid exposceretur, utique postquam comoedum Actium coactus est manumittere. paucorum senatorum inopia sustentata, ne pluribus opem ferret, negauit se aliis subuenturum, nisi senatui iustas necessitatium causas probassent, quo pacto plerosque modestia et pudore deterruit, in quibus Hortalum, Quinti Hortensi oratoris nepotem, qui permodica re familiari auctore Augusto quattuor liberos tulerat.

Publice munificentiam bis omnino exhibuit, proposito milies sestertium 48.1 gratuito in trienni tempus et rursus quibusdam dominis insularum, quae in monte Caelio deflagrarant, pretio restituto. quorum alterum magna difficultate nummaria populo auxilium flagitante coactus est facere, cum per senatus consultum sanxisset, ut faeneratores duas patrimonii partes in solo collocarent, debitores totidem aeris alieni statim soluerent, nec res expediretur; alterum ad mitigandam temporum atrocitatem. quod tamen beneficium tanti aestimauit ut montem Caelium appellatione mutata uocari Augustum iusserit. militi post duplicata ex Augusti testamento legata nihil umquam largitus est, 48.2 praeterquam singula milia denariorum praetorianis, quod Seiano se non accommodassent, et quaedam munera Syriacis legionibus, quod solae nullam

Seiani imaginem inter signa coluissent. atque etiam missiones ueteranorum rarissimas fecit, ex senio mortem, ex morte compendium captans. ne prouincias quidem liberalitate ulla subleuauit, excepta Asia, disiectis terrae motu ciuitatibus.

49.1 Procedente mox tempore etiam ad rapinas conuertit animum. satis constat, Cn. Lentulum Augurem, cui census maximus fuerit, metu et angore ad fastidium uitae ab eo actum et ut ne quo nisi ipso herede moreretur; condemnatam et generosissimam feminam Lepidam in gratiam Quirini consularis praediuitis et orbi, qui dimissam eam e matrimonio post uicen-

49.2 simum annum ueneni olim in se comparati arguebat; praeterea Galliarum et Hispaniarum Syriaeque et Graeciae principes confiscatos ob tam leue ac tam impudens calumniarum genus, ut quibusdam non aliud sit obiectum, quam quod partem rei familiaris in pecunia haberent; plurimis etiam ciuitatibus et priuatis ueteres immunitates et ius metallorum ac uectigalium adempta; sed et Vononem regem Parthorum, qui pulsus a suis quasi in fidem p. R cum ingenti gaza Antiochiam se receperat. spoliatum perfidia et occisum.

50.1 Odium aduersus necessitudines in Druso primum fratre detexit, prodita eius epistula, qua secum de cogendo ad restituendam libertatem Augusto agebat, deinde et in reliquis. Iuliae uxori tantum afuit ut relegatae, quod minimum est, offici aut humanitatis aliquid impertiret, ut ex constitutione patris uno oppido clausam domo quoque egredi et commercio hominum frui uetuerit; sed et peculio concesso a patre praebitisque annuis fraudauit, per speciem publici iuris, quod nihil de his Augustus testamento cauisset.

50.2 matrem Liuiam grauatus uelut partes sibi aequas potentiae uindicantem, et congressum eius assiduum uitauit et longiores secretioresque sermones, ne consiliis, quibus tamen interdum et egere et uti solebat, regi uideretur. tulit etiam perindigne actum in senatu, ut titulis suis quasi Augusti, ita et *Liuiae*

50.3 *filius* adiceretur. quare non *parentem patriae* appellari, non ullum insignem honorem recipere publice passus est; sed et frequenter admonuit, maioribus nec feminae conuenientibus negotiis abstineret, praecipue ut animaduertit incendio iuxta aedem Vestae et ipsam interuenisse populumque et milites,

51.1 quo enixius opem ferrent, adhortatam, sicut sub marito solita esset. dehinc ad simultatem usque processit hac, ut ferunt, de causa. instanti saepius, ut ciuitate donatum in decurias adlegeret, negauit alia se condicione adlecturum, quam si pateretur ascribi albo *extortum id sibi a matre*. at illa commota ueteres quosdam ad se Augusti codicillos de acerbitate et intolerantia morum eius a sacrario protulit atque recitauit. hos et custoditos tam diu et exprobratos tam infeste adeo grauiter tulit, ut quidam putent inter causas secessus

51.2 hanc ei uel praecipuam fuisse. toto quidem triennio, quo uiuente matre afuit, semel omnino eam nec amplius quam uno die paucissimis uidit horis; ac mox neque aegrae adesse curauit defunctamque et, dum aduentus sui spem facit, complurium dierum mora corrupto demum et tabido corpore funeratam prohibuit consecrari, quasi id ipsa mandasset. testamentum quoque eius pro irrito habuit omnisque amicitias et familiaritates, etiam quibus ea funeris sui curam moriens demandauerat, intra breue tempus afflixit, uno ex iis, equestris ordinis uiro, et in antliam condemnato.

Filiorum neque naturalem Drusum neque adoptiuum Germanicum patria 52.1 caritate dilexit, alterius uitiis infensus. nam Drusus fluxioris remissiorisque uitae erat. itaque ne mortuo quidem perinde adfectus est, sed tantum non statim a funere ad negotiorum consuetudinem rediit iustitio longiore inhibito. quin et Iliensium legatis paulo serius consolantibus, quasi obliterata iam 52.2 doloris memoria, irridens *se quoque* respondit *uicem eorum dolere, quod egregium ciuem Hectorem amisissent.* Germanico usque adeo obtrectauit, ut et praeclara facta eius pro superuacuis eleuarit et gloriosissimas uictorias ceu damnosas rei p. increparet. quod uero Alexandream propter immensam et repentinam famem inconsulto se adisset, questus est in senatu. etiam causa 52.3 mortis fuisse ei per Cn. Pisonem legatum Syriae creditur, quem mox huius criminis reum putant quidam mandata prolaturum, nisi ea secreto ostentant <....> quae multifariam inscriptum et per noctes celeberrime adclamatum est: *redde Germanicum!* quam suspicionem confirmauit ipse postea coniuge etiam ac liberis Germanici crudelem in modum afflictis.

Nurum Agrippinam post mariti mortem liberius quiddam questam manu 53.1 apprehendit Graecoque uersu: *si non dominaris,* inquit, *filiola, iniuriam te accipere existimas?* nec ullo mox sermone dignatus est. quondam uero inter cenam porrecta a se poma gustare non ausam etiam uocare desiit, simulans ueneni se crimine accersi; cum praestructum utrumque consulto esset, ut et ipse temptandi gratia offerret et illa quasi certissimum exitium caueret. nouissime calumniatus modo ad statuam Augusti modo ad exercitus con- 53.2 fugere uelle, Pandatariam relegauit conuiciantique oculum per centurionem uerberibus excussit. rursus mori inedia destinanti per uim ore diducto infulciri cibum iussit. sed et perseuerantem atque ita absumptam criminosissime insectatus, cum diem quoque natalem eius inter nefastos referendum suasisset, imputauit etiam, quod non laqueo strangulatam in Gemonias abiecerit: proque tali clementia interponi decretum passus est, quo sibi gratiae agerentur et Capitolino Ioui donum ex auro sacraretur.

Cum ex Germanico tres nepotes, Neronem et Drusum et Gaium, ex Druso 54.1 unum Tiberium haberet, destitutus morte liberorum maximos natu de Germanici filiis, Neronem et Drusum, patribus conscriptis commendauit diemque utriusque tirocinii congiario plebei dato celebrauit. sed ut comperit ineunte anno pro eorum quoque salute publice uota suscepta, egit cum senatu, *non debere talia praemia tribui nisi expertis et aetate prouectis.* atque ex eo 54.2 patefacta interiore animi sui nota omnium criminationibus obnoxios reddidit

uariaque fraude inductos, ut et concitarentur ad conuicia et concitati proder-
entur, accusauit per litteras amarissime congestis etiam probris et iudicatos
hostis fame necauit, Neronem in insula Pontia, Drusum in ima parte Palatii.
putant Neronem ad uoluntariam mortem coactum, cum ei carnifex quasi ex
senatus auctoritate missus laqueos et uncos ostentaret, Druso autem adeo
alimenta subducta, ut tomentum e culcita temptauerit mandere; amborum
sic reliquias dispersas, ut uix quandoque colligi possent.

55 Super ueteres amicos ac familiares uiginti sibi e numero principum
ciuitatis depoposcerat uelut consiliarios in negotiis publicis. horum omnium
uix duos anne tres incolumis praestitit, ceteros alium alia de causa perculit,
inter quos cum plurimorum clade Aelium Seianum; quem ad summam
potentiam non tam beniuolentia prouexerat, quam ut esset cuius ministerio
ac fraudibus liberos Germanici circumueniret, nepotemque suum ex Druso
filio naturalem ad successionem imperii confirmaret.

56 Nihilo lenior in conuictores Graeculos, quibus uel maxime adquiescebat,
Xenonem quendam exquisitius sermocinantem cum interrogasset, *quaenam
illa tam molesta dialectos esset,* et ille respondisset *Doridem,* relegauit
Cinariam, existimans exprobratum sibi ueterem secessum, quod Dorice
Rhodii loquantur. item cum soleret ex lectione cotidiana quaestiones super
cenam proponere comperissetque Seleucum grammaticum a ministris suis
perquirere quos quoque tempore tractaret auctores, atque ita praeparatum
uenire, primum a contubernio remouit, deinde etiam ad mortem compulit.

57.1 Saeua ac lenta natura ne in puero quidem latuit; quam Theodorus
Gadareus rhetoricae praeceptor et perspexisse primus sagaciter et assimi-
lasse aptissime uisus est, subinde in obiurgando appellans eum πηλὸν
αἵματι πεφυραμένον, id est lutum a sanguine maceratum. sed aliquanto
magis in principe eluxit, etiam inter initia cum adhuc fauorem hominum

57.2 moderationis simulatione captaret. scurram, qui praetereunte funere clare
mortuo mandarat, ut nuntiaret Augusto *nondum reddi legata quae plebei
reliquisset,* adtractum ad se recipere debitum ducique ad supplicium imperauit et patri suo uerum referre. nec multo post in senatu Pompeio cuidam
equiti R. quiddam perneganti, dum uincula minatur, affirmauit fore ut *ex
Pompeio Pompeianus fieret,* acerba cauillatione simul hominis nomen

58 incessens ueteremque partium fortunam. sub idem tempus consulente praetore an iudicia maiestatis cogi iuberet, *exercendas esse leges* respondit et
atrocissime exercuit. statuae quidam Augusti caput dempserat, ut alterius
imponeret; acta res in senatu et, quia ambigebatur, per tormenta quaesita est.
damnato reo paulatim genus calumniae eo processit, ut haec quoque capi-
talia essent: circa Augusti simulacrum seruum cecidisse, uestimenta mu-
tasse, nummo uel anulo effigiem impressam latrinae aut lupanari intulisse,

dictum ullum factumue eius existimatione aliqua laesisse. perit denique et is, qui honorem in colonia sua eodem die decerni sibi passus est, quo decreti et Augusti olim erant.

Multa praeterea specie grauitatis ac morum corrigendorum, sed et magis   59.1 naturae optemperans, ita saeue et atrociter factitauit, ut nonnulli uersiculis quoque et praesentia exprobrarent et futura denuntiarent mala:

Asper et immitis, breuiter uis omnia dicam?
   dispeream, si te mater amare potest.

Non es eques; quare? non sunt tibi milia centum;
   omnia si quaeras, et Rhodus exilium est.

Aurea mutasti Saturni saecula, Caesar:
   incolumi nam te ferrea semper erunt.

Fastidit uinum, quia iam sitit iste cruorem:
   tam bibit hunc auide, quam bibit ante merum.

Aspice felicem sibi, non tibi, Romule, Sullam   59.2
   et Marium, si uis, aspice, sed reducem,
nec non Antoni ciuilia bella mouentis
   non semel infectas aspice caede manus,
et dic: Roma perit! regnauit sanguine multo,
   ad regnum quisquis uenit ab exilio.

quae primo, quasi ab impatientibus remedi<or>um ac non tam ex animi sententia quam bile et stomacho fingerentur, uolebat accipi dicebatque identidem: *oderint, dum probent.* dein uera plane certaque esse ipse fecit fidem.

In paucis diebus quam Capreas attigit piscatori, qui sibi secretum agenti 60 grandem mullum inopinanter obtulerat, perfricari eodem pisce faciem iussit, territus quod is a tergo insulae per aspera et deuia erepsisset ad se; gratulanti autem inter poenam, quod non et lucustam, quam praegrandem ceperat, obtulisset, lucusta quoque lacerari os imperauit. militem praetorianum ob subreptum e uiridiario pauonem capite puniit. in quodam itinere lectica, qua uehebatur, uepribus impedita exploratorem uiae, primarum cohortium centurionem, stratum humi paene ad necem uerberauit. mox in omne genus 61.1 crudelitatis erupit numquam deficiente materia, cum primo matris, deinde nepotum et nurus, postremo Seiani familiares atque etiam notos persequeretur; post cuius interitum uel saeuissimus extitit. quo maxime apparuit, non tam ipsum ab Seiano concitari solitum, quam Seianum quaerenti occasiones sumministrasse; etsi commentario, quem de uita sua summatim breuiterque composuit, ausus est scribere *Seianum se punisse, quod comperisset furere aduersus liberos Germanici filii sui;* quorum ipse alterum suspecto iam, alterum oppresso demum Seiano interemit.

61.2 Singillatim crudeliter facta eius exequi longum est; genera, uelut exemplaria saeuitiae, enumerare sat erit. nullus a poena hominum cessauit dies, ne religiosus quidem ac sacer; animaduersum in quosdam ineunte anno nouo. accusati damnatique multi cum liberis atque etiam a liberis suis. interdictum ne capite damnatos propinqui lugerent. decreta accusatoribus praecipua praemia, nonnumquam et testibus. nemini delatorum fides abro-

61.3 gata. omne crimen pro capitali receptum, etiam paucorum simpliciumque uerborum. obiectum est poetae, quod in tragoedia Agamemnonem probris lacessisset; obiectum et historico, quod Brutum Cassiumque ultimos Romanorum dixisset; animaduersum statim in auctores scriptaque abolita, quamuis probarentur ante aliquot annos etiam Augusto audiente recitata.

61.4 quibusdam custodiae traditis non modo studendi solacium ademptum, sed etiam sermonis et colloqui usus. citati ad causam dicendam partim se domi uulnerauerunt certi damnationis et ad uexationem ignominiamque uitandam, partim in media curia uenenum hauserunt; et tamen conligatis uulneribus ac semianimes palpitantesque adhuc in carcerem rapti. nemo punitorum non in Gemonias abiectus uncoque tractus, uiginti uno die abiecti tractique,

61.5 inter eos feminae et pueri. immaturae puellae, quia more tradito nefas esset uirgines strangulari, uitiatae prius a carnifice, dein strangulatae. mori uolentibus uis adhibita uiuendi. nam mortem adeo leue supplicium putabat, ut cum audisset unum e reis, Carnulum nomine, anticipasse eam, exclamauerit: *Carnulus me euasit.* et in recognoscendis custodiis precanti cuidam poenae

61.6 maturitatem respondit: *nondum tecum in gratiam redii.* annalibus suis uir consularis inseruit, frequenti quodam conuiuio, cui et ipse affuerit, interrogatum eum subito et clare a quodam nano astante mensae inter copreas, cur Paconius maiestatis reus tam diu uiueret, statim quidem petulantiam linguae obiurgasse, ceterum post paucos dies scripsisse senatui, ut de poena Paconi quam primum statueret.

62.1 Auxit intenditque saeuitiam exacerbatus indicio de morte filii sui Drusi. quem cum morbo et intemperantia perisse existimaret, ut tandem ueneno interemptum fraude Liuillae uxoris atque Seiani cognouit, neque tormentis neque supplicio cuiusquam pepercit, soli huic cognitioni adeo per totos dies deditus et intentus, ut Rhodiensem hospitem, quem familiaribus litteris Romam euocarat, aduenisse sibi nuntiatum torqueri sine mora iusserit, quasi aliquis ex necessariis quaestioni adesset, deinde errore detecto et occidi, ne

62.2 uulgaret iniuriam. carnificinae eius ostenditur locus Capreis, unde damnatos post longa et exquisita tormenta praecipitari coram se in mare iubebat, excipiente classiariorum manu et contis atque remis elidente cadauera, ne cui residui spiritus quicquam inesset. excogitauerat autem *inter genera cruciatus* etiam, ut larga meri potione per fallaciam oneratos, repente ueretris deligatis, fidicularum simul urinaeque tormento distenderet. quod nisi eum et mors 62.3 praeuenisset et Thrasyllus consulto, ut aiunt, differre quaedam spe longioris uitae compulisset. plures aliquanto necaturus ac ne reliquis quidem nepotibus parsurus creditur, cum et Gaium suspectum haberet et Tiberium ut ex adulterio conceptum aspernaretur. nec abhorret a uero; namque identidem *felicem Priamum* uocabat, *quod superstes omnium suorum extitisset.*

Quam inter haec non modo inuisus ac detestabilis, sed praetrepidus quoque 63.1 atque etiam contumeliis obnoxius uixerit, multa indicia sunt. haruspices secreto ac sine testibus consuli uetuit. uicina uero urbi oracula etiam dis[s]icere conatus est, sed maiestate Praenestinarum sortium territus destitit, cum obsignatas deuectasque Romam non repperisset in arca nisi relata rursus ad templum. unum et alterum consulares oblatis prouinciis non ausus a se 63.2 dimittere usque eo detinuit, donec successores post aliquot annos praesentibus daret, cum interim manente officii titulo etiam delegaret plurima assidue, quae illi per legatos et adiutores suos exequenda curarent. nurum ac nepotes 64 numquam aliter post damnationem quam catenatos obsutaque lectica loco mouit, prohibitis per militem obuiis ac uiatoribus respicere usquam uel consistere.

Seianum res nouas molientem, quamuis iam et natalem eius publice 65.1 celebrari et imagines aureas coli passim uideret, uix tandem et astu magis ac dolo quam principali auctoritate subuertit. nam primo, ut a se per speciem honoris dimitteret, collegam sibi assumpsit in quinto consulatu, quem longo interuallo absens ob id ipsum susceperat. deinde spe affinitatis ac tribuniciae potestatis deceptum inopinantem criminatus est pudenda miserandaque oratione, cum inter alia patres conscriptos precaretur, *mitterent alterum e consulibus, qui se senem et solum in conspectum eorum cum aliquo militari praesidio perduceret.* sic quoque diffidens tumultumque metuens Drusum 65.2 nepotem, quem uinculis adhuc Romae continebat, solui, si res posceret, ducemque constitui praeceperat. aptatis etiam nauibus ad quascumque legiones meditabatur fugam, speculabundus ex altissima rupe identidem signa, quae, ne nuntii morarentur, tolli procul, ut quidquid factum foret, mandauerat. uerum et oppressa coniuratione Seiani nihilo securior aut constantior per nouem proximos menses non egressus est uilla, quae uocatur Ionis.

Vrebant insuper anxiam mentem uaria undique conuicia, nullo non dam- 66 natorum omne probri genus coram uel per libellos in orchestra positos ingerente. quibus quidem diuersissime adficiebatur, modo ut prae pudore ignota et celata cuncta cuperet, nonnumquam eadem contemneret et proferret ultro atque uulgaret. quin et Artabani Parthorum regis laceratus est litteris parricidia et caedes et ignauiam et luxuriam obicientis monentisque, ut uoluntaria morte maximo iustissimoque ciuium odio quam primum satis

67.1 faceret. postremo semet ipse pertaesus, tali[s] epistulae principio tantum non summam malorum suorum professus est: *quid scribam uobis, p. c., aut quo modo scribam, aut quid omnino non scribam hoc tempore, dii me deaeque peius perdant quam cotidie perire sentio, si scio.*

67.2 Existimant quidam praescisse haec eum peritia futurorum ac multo ante, quanta se quandoque acerbitas et infamia maneret, prospexisse; ideoque, ut imperium inierit, et patris patriae appellationem et ne in acta sua iuraretur obstinatissime recusasse, ne mox maiore dedecore impar tantis honoribus

67.3 inueniretur. quod sane ex oratione eius, quam de utraque re habuit, colligi potest; uel cum ait: *similem se semper sui futurum nec umquam mutaturum mores suos, quam diu sanae mentis fuisset; sed exempli causa cauendum esse, ne se senatus in acta cuiusquam obligaret, quia aliquo casu mutari posset.* et rursus:

67.4 *Si quando autem,* inquit, *de moribus meis deuotoque uobis animo dubitaueritis, - quod prius quam eueniat, opto ut me supremus dies huic mutatae uestrae de me opinioni eripiat - nihil honoris adiciet mihi patria appellatio, uobis autem exprobrabit aut temeritatem delati mihi eius cognominis aut inconstantiam contrarii de me iudicii.*

68.1 Corpore fuit amplo atque robusto, statura quae iustam excederet; latus ab umeris et pectore, ceteris quoque membris usque ad imos pedes aequalis et congruens; sinistra manu agiliore ac ualidiore, articulis ita firmis, ut recens et integrum malum digito terebraret, caput pueri uel etiam adules-

68.2 centis talitro uulneraret. colore erat candido, capillo pone occipitium summissiore ut ceruicem etiam obtegeret, quod gentile in illo uidebatur; facie honesta, in qua tamen crebri et subiti tumores, cum praegrandibus oculis et qui, quod mirum esset, noctu etiam et in tenebris uiderent, sed ad breue et

68.3 cum primum e somno patuissent; deinde rursum hebescebant. incedebat ceruice rigida et obstipa, adducto fere uultu, plerumque tacitus, nullo aut rarissimo etiam cum proximis sermone eoque tardissimo, nec sine molli quadam digitorum gesticulatione. quae omnia ingrata atque arrogantiae plena et animaduertit Augustus in eo et excusare temptauit saepe apud

68.4 senatum ac populum professus *naturae uitia esse, non animi.* ualitudine prosperrima usus est, tempore quidem principatus paene toto prope inlaesa, quamuis a tricesimo aetatis anno arbitratu eam suo rexerit sine adiumento consilioue medicorum.

69 Circa deos ac religiones neglegentior, quippe addictus mathematicae plenusque persuasionis cuncta fato agi, tonitrua tamen praeter modum expauescebat et turbatiore caelo numquam non coronam lauream capite gestauit, quod fulmine afflari negetur id genus frondis.

Artes liberales utriusque generis studiosissime coluit. in oratione Latina 70.1
secutus est Coruinum Messalam, quem senem adulescens obseruarat. sed
adfectatione et morositate nimia obscurabat stilum, ut aliquanto ex tempore
quam a cura praestantior haberetur. composuit et carmen lyricum, cuius est 70.2
titulus *conquestio de morte L. Caesaris.* fecit et Graeca poemata imitatus
Euphorionem et Rhianum et Parthenium, quibus poetis admodum delectatus
scripta omnium et imagines publicis bibliothecis inter ueteres et praecipuos
auctores dedicauit; et ob hoc plerique eruditorum certatim ad eum multa de
his ediderunt. maxime tamen curauit notitiam historiae fabularis usque ad 70.3
ineptias atque derisum; nam et grammaticos, quod genus hominum praecipue,
ut diximus, appetebat, eius modi fere quaestionibus experiebatur: *quae mater*
Hecubae, quod Achilli nomen inter uirgines fuisset, quid Sirenes cantare sint
solitae. et quo primum die post excessum Augusti curiam intrauit, quasi pietati
simul ac religioni satis facturus Minonis exemplo ture quidem ac uino uerum
sine tibicine supplicauit, ut ille olim in morte filii. sermone Graeco quamquam 71
alioqui promptus et facilis, non tamen usque quaque usus est abstinuitque
maxime in senatu; adeo quidem, ut monopolium nominaturus ueniam prius
postularet, quod sibi uerbo peregrino utendum esset. atque etiam cum in
quodam decreto patrum ἔμβλημα recitaretur, commutandam censuit uocem
et pro peregrina nostratem requirendam aut, si non reperiretur, uel pluribus et
per ambitum uerborum rem enuntiandam. militem quoque Graece testimo-
nium interrogatum nisi Latine respondere uetuit.

Bis omnino toto secessus tempore Romam redire conatus, semel triremi 72.1
usque ad proximos naumachiae hortos subuectus est disposita statione per
ripas Tiberis, quae obuiam prodeuntis submoueret, iterum Appia usque ad
septimum lapidem; sed prospectis modo nec aditis urbis moenibus rediit,
primo incertum qua de causa, postea ostento territus. erat ei in oblectamentis 72.2
serpens draco, quem ex consuetudine manu sua cibaturus cum consumptum
a formicis inuenisset, monitus est ut uim multitudinis caueret. rediens ergo
propere Campaniam Asturae in languorem incidit, quo paulum leuatus Cer-
ceios pertendit. ac ne quam suspicionem infirmitatis daret, castrensibus ludis
non tantum interfuit, sed etiam missum in harenam aprum iaculis desuper
petit; statimque latere conuulso et, ut exaestuarat, afflatus aura in grauiorem
recidit morbum. sustentauit tamen aliquamdiu, quamuis Misenum usque 72.3
deuectus nihil ex ordine cotidiano praetermitteret, ne conuiuia quidem aut
ceteras uoluptates partim intemperantia partim dissimulatione. nam Chariclen
medicum, quod commeatu afuturus e conuiuio egrediens manum sibi oscu-
landi causa apprehendisset, existimans temptatas ab eo uenas, remanere ac
recumbere hortatus est cenamque protraxit. nec abstinuit consuetudine quin
tunc quoque instans in medio triclinio astante lictore singulos ualere dicentis
appellaret. interim cum in actis senatus legisset dimissos ac ne auditos quidem 73.1

quosdam reos, de quibus strictim et nihil aliud quam nominatos ab indice scripserat, pro contempto se habitum fremens repetere Capreas quoquo modo destinauit, non temere quicquam nisi ex tuto ausurus. sed tempestatibus et ingrauescente ui morbi retentus paulo post obiit in uilla Lucullana octauo et septuagesimo aetatis anno, tertio et uicesimo imperii, XVII. Kal. Ap. Cn. Acerronio Proculo C. Pontio Nigr<in>o conss.

73.2   Sunt qui putent uenenum ei a Gaio datum lentum atque tabificum; alii in remissione fortuitae febris cibum desideranti negatum; nonnulli, puluinum iniectum, cum extractum sibi deficienti anulum mox resipiscens requisisset. Seneca eum scribit intellecta defectione exemptum anulum quasi alicui traditurum parumper tenuisse, dein rursus aptasse digito et compressa sinistra manu iacuisse diu immobilem; subito uocatis ministris ac nemine respondente consurrexisse nec procul a lectulo deficientibus uiribus concidisse.

74   Supremo natali suo Apollinem Temenitem et amplitudinis et artis eximiae, aduectum Syracusis ut in bibliotheca templi noui poneretur, uiderat per quietem affirmantem sibi non posse se ab ipso dedicari, et ante paucos quam obiret dies, turris Phari terrae motu Capreis concidit. ac Miseni cinis e fauilla et carbonibus ad calficiendum triclinium inlatis, extinctus iam et diu frigidus, exarsit repente prima uespera atque in multam noctem pertinaciter luxit.

75.1   Morte eius ita laetatus est populus, ut ad primum nuntium discurrentes pars: *Tiberium in Tiberim!* clamitarent, pars Terram matrem deosque Manes orarent, ne mortuo sedem ullam nisi inter impios darent, alii uncum et Gemonias cadaueri minarentur, exacerbati super memoriam pristinae crude- **75.2** litatis etiam recenti atrocitate. nam cum senatus consulto cautum esset, ut poena damnatorum in decimum semper diem differretur, forte accidit ut quorundam supplicii dies is esset, quo nuntiatum de Tiberio erat. hos implorantis hominum fidem, quia absente adhuc Gaio nemo extabat qui adiri interpellarique posset, custodes, ne quid aduersus constitutum facerent, **75.3** strangulauerunt abieceruntque in Gemonias. creuit igitur inuidia, quasi etiam post mortem tyranni saeuitia permanente. corpus ut moueri a Miseno coepit, conclamantibus plerisque Atellam potius deferendum et in amphitheatro semiustilandum, Romam per milites deportatum est crematumque publico funere.

76   Testamentum duplex ante biennium fecerat, alterum sua, alterum liberti manu, sed eodem exemplo, obsignaueratque etiam humillimorum signis. eo testamento heredes aequis partibus reliquit Gaium ex Germanico et Tiberium ex Druso nepotes substituitque in uicem; dedit et legata plerisque, inter quos uirginibus Vestalibus, sed et militibus uniuersis plebeique Romanae uiritim atque etiam separatim uicorum magistris.

Commentary

1-4 Ancestry: the *gens Claudia*

This account of the ancestry of Tiberius serves an important biographical role, since it shows that Suetonius has some belief in the importance of heredity as a factor in personality. Other influences are also important in the decision to deal with the emperor's forebears. It had been traditional in the funeral *laudatio* at aristocratic funerals to expose the distinguished ancestors of the subject as an object for emulation, particularly for the benefit of the younger generation (cf. Polyb. 6.53-4). Thus the procedure of reviewing family history was very characteristic of the Roman scene. Biography takes a different direction from the *laudatio*, and does not restrict itself to the handling of positive examples. It is clear that the mixture of positive and negative examples from the Claudian *gens* is intended to have relevance to the interpetation of Tiberius. Suetonius makes deliberate choices from the available stock of stories about the Claudians.

1.1

Patricia gens Claudia – fuit enim et alia plebeia: Suetonius alerts his readers to the existence of a plebeian as well as a patrician branch of the *gens Claudia*. We learn from Cicero that the patrician branch was that of the Pulchri, and the plebeians were represented by the Marcelli. The Claudii Marcelli were supposed to be descended from a freedman of the patrician *gens* (Cic. *Orat.* 1.176; Ascon. *Scaur.* 22).

orta est ex Regillis: Suetonius subscribes to the tradition that the Claudii came from the Sabine town of Regili. He knows of two versions of the story, the first of which is ignored by other writers, namely that the migration took place in the time of the kings at the request of Titus Tatius. Perhaps Suetonius rejects this as the less well attested version because of doubts about the place of Titus Tatius in the list of the kings. He prefers the version which has the Claudians arriving about six years after the expulsion of the kings (504 BC) under the leadership of the man whom Suetonius calls Atta Claudius. The absorption of the Claudii as outsiders was unusual in that, according to tradition, they were granted patrician status and an estate beyond the Anio, and an entitlement to a family burial ground at the foot of the Capitoline hill. The *tribus Claudia* based on land beyond the Anio was one of the original 16 rural tribes under a system supposedly created by Seruius Tullius (Wiseman [1979] 59). The distinction of the patrician branch of the family is enumerated by Suetonius in terms of high office held, and their consciousness of their own importance by their censorship of discreditable *praenomina*. 'Proof' of their Sabine origin is adduced in the form of their arrogation of the *cognomen* Nero.

There has been a modern debate over the origin of the Claudii which has explored the possibility that the Suetonian story is fictional, and that the true origin of the family was in Etruria. This has been based on the discovery of a family tomb and inscriptions from Cervetri in honour of a family called CLAVTIE, (first published by M. Pallottino, *Studi Etruschi* 37 (1969) 79-91; L.C. Vanoni, ibid. 317-23), and doubts about the authenticity of the Sabine strand of the foundation myth, particularly the story of the Sabine rape. A.W.J. Holleman has argued forcefully that other Etruscan families faked a descent for themselves from the Sabine Numa in the aftermath of the patrician revolution at Rome, and that the Claudian material fits this pattern. See *Historia* 33 (1984) 504-8; *Historia* 35 (1986) 377-8. Nevertheless, the story of a Sabine origin for the *gens*, and a very early advent to Rome is persistent in the tradition, and linguistic arguments have been brought into the debate to buttress the ancient sources. See B.J. Kavanagh, *AHB* 4.6 (1990) 129-32.

For the Sabine tradition see Livy 2.16.4-5; Verg. *Aen.* 7.707-22; Dion.Hal. *Ant.* 5.40.1-5; Appian *Reg.* 12; Plut. *Publ.* 21.2-6. The Claudii are not the only foreign *gens* said to have been granted admission to the senate at this early stage. The chief men of Alba were also included, according to Livy (1.30.2).

Atta Claudio gentis principe: this man is normally called Att(i)us Clausus in Latin authors, and both legend and the Augustan consular *fasti* attribute very early involvment in the consulate to the *gens*, perhaps even to Attus Clausus himself. See Wiseman (1979) 60 n. 13. For variants in the tradition see ibid. 62-4. Already with this earliest representative of the Claudian *gens* a hostile and tyrannical image of the man can be set against a picture of him as great founder figure, escaping from harsh persecution. These stereotypes emerged from the political in-fighting of the late Republic. See introduction 38-42.

locumque sibi ad sepulturam sub Capitolio: under the Law of theTwelve Tables there had been a prohibition on burial or cremation within the city. This was based on ideas about death pollution. Gradually some relaxation of the rules took place, permitting exceptions for those whom the state wished to honour in an extraordinary manner. By the late Republic a Cicero could seriously misunderstand issues relating to death pollution (Cic. *De Leg.* 2.22-23).

The burial ground of the Claudian *gens* was at the foot of the Capitol in the vicinity of the still visible monument of Bibulus. This was outside the *Porta Carmentalis*. Near this location have been discovered fragments of a square mausoleum which has been attributed to the Claudian family. See Platner/Ashby (1929) 478. According to Livy there had been early Sabine settlements on the Capitoline (1.33.2). As early as 296 BC Ap. Claudius Caecus built the temple of Bellona there during the Etruscan wars, a sign of his family's entitlements in the region; an alabaster urn of Augustan date which contained the ashes of P. Clodius' son Pulcher Claudius has survived from the destroyed tomb (*CIL* VI 1282; discussed by Wiseman [1979] 59). Ap. Claudius Pulcher (cos. 79 BC) had the record of his ancestors' achievements set up on shields on the wall of the temple of Bellona (Plin. *NH* 35.12; see Wiseman [1979] 60). Surviving inscriptional *elogia* of the patrician branch of the Claudian *gens* appear to derive from this source.

1.2

This section gives a calculation of the number of distinctions achieved by the Claudian *gens*, but there are some difficulties in the figures. In some cases it is clear that both patrician and plebeian honours have been tallied, but the list of consulships appears to exclude those held by the plebeian Claudii Marcelli (see below). In other instances not all offices appear on the official *fasti*. On sources available to Suetonius see introduction **22**.

duodetriginta consulatus: only twenty two consulships are epigraphically attested for the patrician Claudii, perhaps because of the exclusion of the plebeian Claudii Marcelli (Du Four [1941] 9).

dictaturas quinque: only two dictatorships are known from the epigraphic record (*CIL* 1² p. 20). However, three more are mentioned by Livy, and Suetonius may be relying on either Livy or sources used by Livy (Livy 8.15.5; 22.53.4; 25.2.3).

censuras septem: the Capitoline *fasti* indicate six censorships within the *gens*. Of these only five are from the patrician branch; the remaining censorship was plebeian (*CIL* 1² pp. 16-29). Dio records a 7th censorship (40.63.2)

triumphos sex: of these two were held by the patricians, and four by plebeians (*CIL* 1² pp. 43-50).

duas ouationes: only one of these is epigraphically attested (*CIL* 1² p. 48), but the other one is recorded by Livy and Valerius Maximus (Livy 28.9.10; Val. Max. 4.1.9). The latter resulted from the refusal of the conqueror of Hasdrubal, C. Claudius Nero, to accept a triumph granted to himself and his colleague M. Liuius Salinator.

praenominibus cognominibusque uariis...Luci praenomen...repudiauit: repudiation of a particular *praenomen* is not without precedent. See Cic. *Phil.* 1.32; Livy 6.20.14; Quint. 3.7.20 on the Manlian *gens*. In 30 BC it was decreed that thereafter no Antonius should be named Marcus (Dio 51.19.3). In the age of Tiberius itself the son of Cn. Piso was forced to change his *praenomen* after his father's trial (Tac. *Ann.* 3.17.4). On a similar principle no member of the Liuian *gens* was allowed to hold the cognomen Drusus after the Tiberian trial of Libo Drusus (Tac. *Ann.* 2.32.1; see Goodyear [1981] 282).

The date of the elimination of the name Lucius is unknown, but it has been presumed that a reference in Cicero to a *L. Claudius rex sacrorum* must be corrupt (*Har. Resp.* 6.12 [56 BC]; Du Four [1941] 9). Aulus Gellius attributes the removal of *praenomina* to *antiqui Romanorum* (Aul. Gell. *NA* 9.2.11).

Praenomina used by the Claudii were Appius, Gaius, Decimus, and Tiberius. The topic is discussed by Th. Mommsen, *RhM* 15 (1860) 169-210 = *Rom. Forsch.* 1.1-68.

alter latrocinii, caedis alter conuictus est: Gellius confirms that the motive for excluding certain *praenomina* was conviction for a capital crime (*NA* 9.2.11).

inter cognomina...Neronis...lingua Sabina fortis et strenuus: see also Aul. Gell. *NA* 13.23.7-9. Ner or Nero is found in Oscan as title/*cognomen* and in Umbrian as a *praenomen* (Du Four [1941] 10).

2.1

Multa...egregia merita, multa etiam sequius admissa: it is important to keep in mind this segment of the life on the contrasting character of the Claudians for two reasons:

> 1. It shows that heredity did play a part in the Roman conception of characterisation.

> 2. It gives one of our strongest Suetonian statements about the contradictory nature of Tiberius, who is seen as an amalgam of these diverging strands of the family.

Male examples of excellence (*egregia merita*) are followed by the discreditable (*sequius admissa*); each group is handled chronologically. Similarly the virtuous Claudian women are followed by their inverse. The patrician arrogance (*superbia Claudiana*) of the family is underlined; Clodius is seen as an arrogant political opportunist in his decision to adopt plebeian status. Various examples of Claudian hubris follow.

To examine the male *egregia merita* first :
Appius Caecus societatem cum rege Pyrro...dissuasit: a reference to Appius Claudius Caecus' speech advising against a settlement with Pyrrhus in 279/8 BC. See *RE* s.v. Claudius no. 91, cols 2681-5.

Claudius Caudex...Poenos Sicilia expulit: Appius Claudius Caudex' command of the first Roman army to cross over to Sicily in 264 BC was a truly critical stage in the development of Roman imperialism. See *RE* s.v. Claudius no. 102, cols 2692-4.

+ Claudius Nero...Hasdrubalem...oppressit: C. Nero's defeat of Hasdrubal at the Metaurus in 207 BC. Suetonius appears to have given the *praenomen* as Tiberius (Tibus), incorrectly. The Capitoline Fasti show that the consul of 207 BC had the *praenomen* Caius (*CIL* 1^2 p.23). See *RE* s.v. Claudius no. 246.

Next the *sequius admissa*; there has been recent debate over the antiquity of the tradition of *superbia Claudiana*. See introduction **38-42.**

2.2
Claudius Regillianus, decemuir...causa plebi fuit secedendi: the allusion is to Appius Claudius Decemvir's attempt to enslave the free-born Verginia. This was in 449 BC, best known from the account in Livy (3.33-58.11). For the decemuir see *RE* s.v. Claudius no. 123, cols 2698-2702.

Stemma 1: The Appii Claudii Crassus and The Claudii Pulchri

Notes: (to next page)
All dates are BC. Numbers in bold type refer to *RE* s.v. Claudius. Those actually mentioned by Suetonius are also shown in bold type.
1. A major aim of this chart is to show how Liuia's father could claim relationship to the Claudii Pulchri. It is not comprehensive on the Claudii Pulchri of the late Republic.
2. It is likely that Claudius Pulcher (= *RE* s.v. Claudius no. 290) was adopted into the Liuii to become M. Liuius Drusus Claudianus.

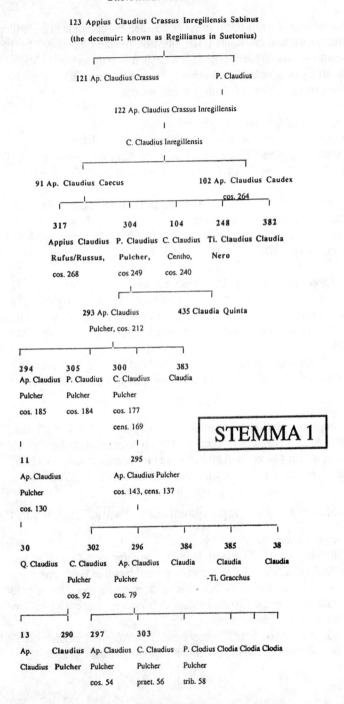

123 Appius Claudius Crassus Inregillensis Sabinus

(the decemuir: known as Regillianus in Suetonius)

121 Ap. Claudius Crassus   P. Claudius

122 Ap. Claudius Crassus Inregillensis

C. Claudius Inregillensis

91 Ap. Claudius Caecus   102 Ap. Claudius Caudex

cos. 264

317	304	104	248	382
Appius Claudius	P. Claudius	C. Claudius	Ti. Claudius	Claudia
Rufus/Russus,	Pulcher,	Centho,	Nero	
cos. 268	cos 249	cos. 240		

293 Ap. Claudius   435 Claudia Quinta

Pulcher, cos. 212

294	305	300	383
Ap. Claudius	P. Claudius	C. Claudius	Claudia
Pulcher	Pulcher	Pulcher	
cos. 185	cos. 184	cos. 177	
		cens. 169	

STEMMA 1

11	295
Ap. Claudius	Ap. Claudius Pulcher
Pulcher	cos. 143, cens. 137
cos. 130	

30	302	296	384	385	38
Q. Claudius	C. Claudius	Ap. Claudius	Claudia	Claudia	Claudia
	Pulcher	Pulcher		-Ti. Gracchus	
	cos. 92	cos. 79			

13	290	297	303			
Ap.	Claudius	Ap. Claudius	C. Claudius	P. Clodius	Clodia Clodia Clodia
Claudius	Pulcher	Pulcher	Pulcher	Pulcher	
		cos. 54	praet. 56	trib. 58	

Claudius Russus...Italia...occupare temptauit: this second item has attracted some dispute, although most authorities now agree with Ihm in
restoring the name as Claudius Russus rather than Claudius Drusus (MSS).
Until the discovery in 1925 of Russus as the cognomen applied to Appius
Claudius (cos. 268 = *RE* s.v. Claudius no. 317) on the consular *fasti* of
Augustan date, only the Chronographer of AD 354 had preserved the name
correctly. Russus died in office in 268 BC. The accusation is that the character
in question attempted to seize some form of regal power over all Italy (the
traditional tyrannical vice of *regnum*). This he is supposed to have done by
setting up a diademed statue of himself at Forum Appi (on the Via Appia),
and through the use of his clients as a military force. Whoever is referred to
the date must be later than the building of the Via Appia (312 BC), as pointed
out by Wiseman (*Past Perspectives* [1986] 91). Russus is suitable chronologically for this list of hubristic Claudii, and would have inherited the
clientela from his father Appius Claudius Caecus. The diadem seems to be
an anachronism, inserted into the tradition by whichever authority started
the theme of Claudian pride. Wiseman does not believe that the diadem
reached Rome as a symbol of *regnum* until the final stages of the Republic
(ibid. 92). The idea of using clients for a military occupation of Italy surely
suggests that the whole basis of this attack on the Claudii originated in the
post-Gracchan era.

Claudius Pulcher...proelium nauale iniit: a reference to P. Claudius Pulcher's alleged treatment of the sacred chickens in 249 BC during his
consulship before engaging in battle at Drepana. In this battle he lost about
100 ships, and was recalled to Rome on a charge of treason. Ominous rainfall
interrupted the trial and he was fined 120,000 asses (Polyb. 1.49-52 [who
does not mention the chickens]; Schol. Cic. *Bob.* 90 St.; Livy *Per.* 19). See
RE s.v. Claudius no. 304, cols 2857-8; Broughton, *MRR* 1.214. The actual
words of Pulcher are also cited by Cic. *De Nat. Deorum* 2.7; cf. *De Div.*
1.29; 2.20; 71; Val. Max. 1.4.3; 8.1. 4. On the rhetorical origin of the story
about the chickens see Wiseman (1979) 91.

cum dictatorem dicere...iuberetur, Glycian uiatorem suum dixit: the
dictator was appointed by the consuls who had a right to name their preferred
candidate. Pulcher is portrayed as appointing a person of unsuitable status.
A *uiator* in the service of a magistrate was more lowly than a lictor, often a
freedman, and not necessarily a Roman citizen. See Du Four (1941) 60 n.
3. However, the Augustan Fasti Capitolini for the year 249 BC give his status
as *scriba: M. Claudius C. f. Glicia, qui scriba fuerat, dictator coact(us)*

abd(icauit) sine mag(istro) eq(uitum). In eius locum factus est A. Atilius A. f.
C. n. Caiatinus dict(ator) L. Caecilius L. f. C. n. Metellus mag(ister) eq(uitum)
[Inscr. Ital. 13.1.42ff.]. The *Periochae* of Livy (19) also emphasise his lowly
origin *(sortis ultimae hominem)*, appending the story to Pulcher's neglect of
the auspices and the subsequent naval calamity. It is interesting to note that
Glicia is another Claudian, whatever his origin. It seems unlikely that the
tradition of his lowly origin is acccurate, and the story appears to have been
manufactured to illustrate the *Claudiana superbia.* The suggestion of mockery
of public danger by Pulcher may be a Suetonian contribution to the theme
(uelut iterum inludens discrimini publico). For speculation on a more credible
version see J. Suolahti, *Arctos* 10 (1976) 97-103.

2.3

Extant et feminarum exempla diuersa: just as the hostile stories about
Claudian males were developed by opponents to exemplify the arrogance of
the family, so Claudian women became prominent in the war of words which
arose from aristocratic competition. The virtuous example concentrates on the
traditional feminine virtue of chastity *(pudicitia),* while the hostile example
returns to the theme of *superbia.* Interestingly Suetonius does not raise a single
example of sexual irregularity.

quae nauem...obhaerentem Tiberino uado extraxit: this was in 204 BC, and
is a proverbial story about the arrival of the sacred stone of the Idaean mother
goddess. Other sources name this paragon as Claudia Quinta, and she may be
a granddaughter of Ap. Claudius Caecus and daughter of P. Claudius Pulcher.
She is a much quoted model of antique virtue. For other sources on the story
see *RE* s.v. Claudius no. 435. In some versions there is an accretion by which
she becomes a Vestal Virgin. Another strand of the tradition has a Valeria
receiving the goddess (Diod. 34.33.2). This is believed to be the work of
Valerius Antias. See Wiseman (1979) 114-15.

2.4

P. Clodio...plebeio homini atque etiam natu minori in adoptionem se
dedit: legal rules covering adoptions specified that the adopter had to be at
least 60 years of age and older than the adoptee (Dig. 1.7.15 [Ulpian]).
Normally up to this time adoption involved social advancement rather than
as here political opportunism. Suetonius mentions the breaking of these
conventions to underline the political nature of the act. By his own time the
imperial family had thoroughly politicised adoption within their own ranks,
and it was not uncommon for the rules about age difference to be waived (e.g.
Caligula and Tiberius Gemellus). See M.-H. Prévost (1949) 35ff.

et quae...iudicium maiestatis...subiit, quod...optauerat, ut frater suus Pulcher reuiuisceret atque iterum classem amitteret: this story attached itself to a daughter of Appius Claudius Caecus, and consequently sister of P. Claudius Pulcher (*RE* s.v. Claudius no. 304: cos. 249 BC). The reference is to the loss of a fleet by her brother at Drepana, referred to above (*Tib.* 2.2). By the date of Claudia's misdemeanour, it is implicit that Pulcher is no longer alive. The story of this Claudia's punishment appears with variants in Valerius Maximus (8.1 damn. 4), the *Periochae* of Livy (19), and in Aulus Gellius, reporting Ateius Capito (*NA* 10.6.2), who dated the event to 246 BC. Wiseman places the event in 243 BC (Wiseman [1979] 90 with n. 102). Only Valerius Maximus proclaims Claudia innocent. All except Gellius link her story with her brother's disregard of the omens, and the very existence of the anecdote tells the tale of the power struggle against the Claudii mounted by the family's aristocratic competitors. For Claudia see *RE* s.v. Claudius no. 382; J. Suolahti, *Arctos* 11 (1977) 133-51, emphasising how Suetonius uses the story to prove the arrogant behaviour of Claudian ancestors of both sexes towards the plebs (139).

Suetonius claims that Claudia received a new form of punishment for treason (*iudicium maiestatis*), perhaps a deliberate colouring of the narrative by the biographer, intended to remind readers of the most characteristic charge of the last years of the reign of Tiberius. Tacitus in discussing treason claimed that in earlier times words had been immune from prosecution (Tac. *Ann.* 1.72.3: *facta arguebantur, dicta impune erant*). Under Tiberius and subsequently cases can be found where women were charged with both treasonable words and acts (Tac. *Ann.* 3.22.2; 12.22.1; 12.52.1; 16.30.2). The original version of why Claudia was fined has been obscured in the transformation of the anecdote. It is of some interest to note that Ateius Capito, a jurist in the age of Tiberius, who appears to have been hostile to the emperor, discussed Claudia's case in a commentary on *iudicia publica* (ap. Gell. *NA* 10.6.4; on Ateius see R.S. Rogers, *Synteleia V. Arangio-Ruiz* I (1964) 123-27). For prosecutions by the aediles see R. Bauman, *Latomus* 33 (1974) 245-64. Some of the problems with the anecdote are discussed by Wiseman (1979) 92-4.

adeo...contumaces, ut ne capitis...quisquam reus...mutare uestem... sustinuerit; nonnulli...tribunos plebi pulsauerint: the failure to wear mourning or supplicate at a capital trial and the beating of tribunes is ascribed only to Appius Claudius (cos. 471 BC) in extant sources (Dion. Hal. *Ant.* 9.48.2; 4; 54.2; Livy 2.61.5). However, generalisations of this type are a commonplace in Suetonius. See T.P. Wiseman (1979) 58. Beating a tribune is clearly a hubristic act since they were sacrosanct.

uirgo Vestalis fratrem iniussu populi triumphantem...prosecuta est: there is a legendary quality about this story, but regardless of this Suetonius is incorrect in saying that the Vestal was the sister of the triumphator. Other sources make it clear that she was his daughter (compare Cic. *Pro Cael.* 14.34; Val. Max. 5.4.6; Wiseman [1979] 58 n. 8 plausibly suggests a textual error in Suetonius, reading *patrem* for *fratrem*). The *triumphator* had triumphed over the Salassi as consul in 143 BC (Dio 22.74; Oros. 5.4.7; *CIL* 1^2 p. 26; Cic. *Pro Cael.* 14.34), and the Vestal is said to have mounted her father's chariot to enable him to celebrate what was perhaps an unauthorised triumph in the face of tribunician opposition (but for problems with this interpetation see Wiseman ibid.). He was an only child, but himself had 5 children of whom the Vestal must have been the eldest daughter. The other daughters married well, one to Tiberius Gracchus, the other to Q. Marcius Philippus. His two sons reached the consulship (C. Claudius Pulcher, cos. 92 BC; Ap. Claudius Pulcher, cos. 79 BC. See *RE* III cols 2665-6). This case is cited by S. Dixon (1988) 15 as an example of continuing family affection after emancipation. Vestals had no agnates, and thus no legal obligations to their family of origin, since they were liberated from the *patria potestas* (Gaius *Institutes* 1.145; Aul. Gell. *NA* 1.12). A triumph was normally a prerogative of the Senate, but their view could be overturned through direct appeal to the people (Livy 3.63.8; 7.17.9; 45.38.2). Here it is claimed that even that avenue was avoided (*iniussu populi*); the tribunes would normally have intervened in a case of violent seizure of the honour, but the presence of the Vestal made this impossible (Livy 10.37.9-12; Val. Max. 5.4.6; Cic. *Pro Cael.* 14.34). On the tradition see I. McDougall, *Hermes* 120 (1992) 452-60.

3.1

Tiberius Caesar genus trahit, et quidem utrumque: as if to underline these hereditary problems we learn that Tiberius inherited Claudian ancestry on both sides of his family, as also emphasised by Tac. *Ann.* 6.51. His mother's family had entered the Liuian *gens* through adoption (see Tac. *Ann.* 5.1). The Liuian family were plebeians and here too the background was somewhat chequered, with a strong pro-senatorial conservative streak emerging in the generation of the Gracchi. Suetonius seems to pick on this feature of the pedigree because of elements of Tiberius' career. It will be no surprise if his Tiberius respects the traditional role of the Senate.

paternum a Tiberio Nerone: see Stemma 2. On this man see *RE* s.v. Claudius no. 248.

maternum ab Appio Pulchro: this is a mistake since Liuia was in fact descended from P. Claudius Pulcher, consul in 249 BC (see Seager [1972] 7, and Stemma 1 above).

insertus est et Liuiorum familiae adoptato in eam materno auo: Tiberius' maternal grandfather was M. Liuius Drusus Claudianus (see Stemma 3). For discussion of the identity of the adoptive father see *RE* s.v. Liuius no. 19, col. 882 (Munzer) and compare Stemma 1.

quae familia...plebeia: see Livy 10.9.2; 35.10.3.

floruit octo consulatibus: only seven consulships are known from the *Fasti Consulares*. See *RE* s.v. Liuius, col. 810.

censuris duabus: See *CIL* 1^2 pp. 16-29; Livy 29.37.1.

triumphis tribus: as recorded by the *Acta Triumphalia*. See *CIL* 1^2 pp. 43-50.

dictatura: held by M. Liuius Salinator in 207 BC. See Livy 28.10.1.

magisterio equitum: a Drusus held the post under L. Papirius Cursor, who was dictator in 324 BC. See *CIL* 1^2 p. 130 (Fasti Hydatiani; Chron. Pasch.).

clara et insignis uiris ac maxime Salinatore Drusisque: see Stemma 3.

3.2
Salinator uniuersas tribus...notauit...quod...consulem iterum censoremque fecissent: Salinator had an outstanding career which included two consulships and two triumphs. See *RE* s.v. Liuius no. 33; Stemma 3. According to Livy (29.37.11-14) and Valerius Maximus (2.9.6), who also retail the Suetonian story, the Maecian tribe was excluded from the censure. Salinator deprived citizens in the the condemned tribes of their centuriate vote (Val. Max. 2.9.6). The charge against Salinator after his earlier consulship (219 BC) may have been failure to make a fair division of booty; it perhaps originated in a conflict with C. Claudius Nero, who became his fellow consul in 207 BC (Front. *Strat.* 4.1.45; cf. Val. Max. 4.2.2; Livy 27.34.3-4; Silius Italicus *Pun.* 15.596).

STEMMA 2: THE CLAUDII NERONES

Notes:

Numbers in bold type refer to *RE* s.v. Claudius. Names in bold type refer to individuals named by Suetonius.

1. There is insufficient evidence to complete the family tree for the second century BC (cf. *RE* s.v. Claudii Nerones, col. 2774).

2. The grandfather of the legate of 67 BC was definitely an Appius (see *RE* s.v. Claudius no. 253), but this cannot be the praetor of 195 BC.

3. A C. Claudius Nero, son of a Publius is known to have been governor of Asia in 80 BC after a praetorship (*RE* s.v. Claudius no. 247).

4. Three individuals with the name Ti. Claudius Nero can be identified in the second century as praetors in 189, 178 and 167 respectively (see *RE* s.v. Claudius nos 250-252). There is no way of identifying their interrelationship.

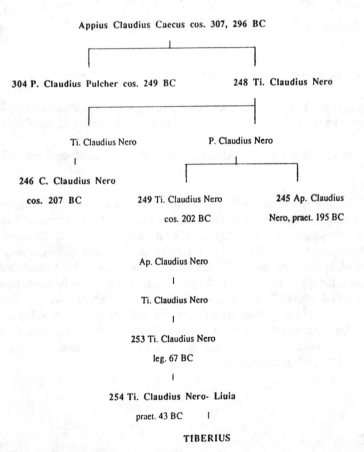

STEMMA 3: THE LIVIAN GENS

Notes:

Numbers in bold type refer to *RE* s.v. Liuius. Names in bold type refer to individuals mentioned by Suetonius.

Only the main line of relationship between Liuia and Liuius Salinator is traced here. Minor figures are omitted. For further details see *RE* s.v. Liuius col. 811-12.

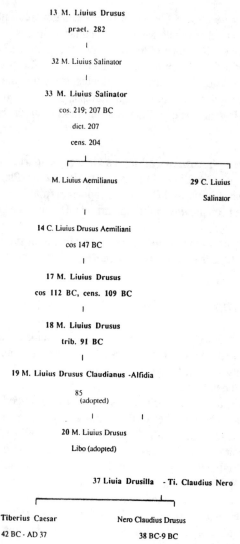

13 M. Liuius Drusus

praet. 282

32 M. Liuius Salinator

33 M. **Liuius Salinator**

cos. 219; 207 BC

dict. 207

cens. 204

M. Liuius Aemilianus   **29** C. Liuius Salinator

14 C. Liuius Drusus Aemiliani

cos 147 BC

17 M. **Liuius Drusus**

cos 112 BC, cens. 109 BC

18 M. **Liuius Drusus**

trib. **91 BC**

19 M. **Liuius Drusus Claudianus** -**Alfidia**

85
(adopted)

20 M. Liuius Drusus

Libo (adopted)

37 **Liuia Drusilla** - Ti. **Claudius Nero**

Tiberius Caesar   Nero Claudius Drusus

42 BC - AD 37   38 BC-9 BC

Drusus...sibi posterisque cognomen inuenit: for the importance of single combat as a means of attaining status in the Republic see W.V. Harris (1979) 38f.; S.P. Oakley, *CQ* 35 (1985) 392-410. Other *cognomina* are known to have been obtained by killing Gallic chieftains in single combat (Livy 7.10 [Torquatus]; Aulus Gellius *NA* 9.11 [Coruinus]). On the Celtic origin of the name Drusus see Du Four (1941) ad loc. For discussion of the present story, only found here in Suetonius, see *RE* s.v. Liuius nos 12 & 13, cols 853-5.

traditur...ex prouincia Gallia rettulisse aurum Senonibus...extortum a Camillo: this unlikely tale has some peculiar trappings. Gallia Narbonensis did not become a Roman province until 121 BC, yet the earliest known Drusus was praetor in 282 BC (= *RE* s.v. Liuius no. 13). The story is, however, of interest, and probably older than Suetonius, since it is intended to highlight an outstanding deed of a member of the *gens Liuia* in retrieving a shameful episode in Roman history. On the terms reached with the Gauls see Livy 5.48.8-9.

eius abnepos ob eximiam aduersus Gracchos operam patronus senatus dictus: this was M. Liuius Drusus, consul in 112 BC (Plut. *Gaius Gracchus* 38-42; *RE* s.v. Liuius no. 17). It will be apparent from Stemma 3 that this man cannot have been the *abnepos* of the original Drusus. See Du Four (1941) 17.

filium reliquit, quem...diuersa factio per fraudem interemit: a reference to the fate of the tribune of 91 BC. See *RE* s.v. Liuius no 18.

4.1 The Emperor's Father

Pater Tiberi, Nero: as in other biographies Suetonius uses the father's career as a pointer to the nature of the son, as well as merely for informatory purposes. Emphasis is on his links with the Republican past, as well as on his endurance and stubbornness.

It is known from Cicero's letters that Nero had hoped to marry Cicero's daughter Tullia in 50 BC, before the civil war broke out, when he joined Caesar (*Ad* Att. 6.6.1; *Ad Fam.* 13.64.2; see S. Treggiari [1991] 129). As quaestor to Julius Caesar during the Alexandrian war, Tiberius Nero is given credit by Suetonius for being instrumental in victory (see also [Caes.] *Bell.* Alex. 25.3; Dio 42.40.6). His career was suitably advanced by Caesar who employed him in a colonisation programme in the south of France (note later problems of his son with the people of Nemausus: 13.1). But he took a stubborn pro-Republican stand at the time of the assassination, even suggesting that rewards should be bestowed upon Brutus and Cassius. Despite this he became praetor and ended up in the camp of Lucius Antonius during the Perusine war. His resolution in being the last to capitulate is emphasised, as is his resourcefulness while on the run (cf. Vell. 2.74-5; Dio 48.15.3). His status was not sufficiently acknowledged by Sextus Pompey, and he soon joined Antony in Greece, and was captured in his train. The surrender of his wife Liuia to Augustus is treated summarily, but with no suggestion that Augustus used improper force. Nero is seen as yielding to the inevitable. For further details on Tiberius Claudius Nero see *RE* s.v. Claudius no. 254

ad deducendas in Galliam colonias, in quis Narbo et Arelate erant, missus est: it has been suggested that Suetonius only names here military colonies under Roman law, excluding others with the Latin right. See C. Goudineau, *Gallia* 44 (1986) 171-3. On the advance of Latin rights in the age of Caesar see A.N. Sherwin-White, *ANRW* 1.2 (1972) 40.

Caesare occiso...de praemiis tyrannicidarum referendum censuit: Appian mentions the proposal (*BC* 2.121). Through this detail Suetonius enhances the image of Tiberius Nero as a Republican traditionalist. On the assassination and the subsequent amnesty see Appian *BC* 2.118-35; Dio 45.11-15.

4.2
praetura deinde functus: Tiberius Nero was praetor in 42 BC, and propraetor in 41/40. He was also *pontifex* in 46-33 BC. See *MRR* 2.303; 359; 373; 381. Clearly Tiberius Nero had not been included on the proscription lists in 43 BC. Subsequently, however, he was placed on the list (Tac. *Ann.* 6.51; see F. Hinard [1985] no. 41, 451-53). It was not until late in 41 BC just before the Perusine war that dissensions between Octavian and Antony (mentioned here by Suetonius) became serious. Tiberius Nero was probably added to the list at that stage (Hinard, op.cit. 452). By 40 BC Velleius can describe him as *praetorius* (Vell. 2.75.1).

retentis ultra iustum tempus insignibus: a praetor was entitled to the *sella curulis* as well as lictors (2 in Rome, 6 while abroad) and the *toga praetexta*. See Mommsen, *StR* 1.384; 401-2; 418.

L. Antonium...ad Perusiam secutus: L. Antonius had a conspicuous level of support from senatorial quarters, as well as from Italy's middle class. See E. Gabba, *HSCPh* 75 (1971) 147. Tiberius Nero was thus a typical supporter of Antonius, sharing his role as protector of those who had lost their lands, at a time when Octauian was struggling for senatorial backing. For further comment see J.-M. Roddaz, *Historia* 37 (1988) 340ff.

solus...primus Praeneste, inde Neapolim euasit: this passage is important in demonstrating where regional support could be expected for the cause of Lucius Antonius, who claimed to be representing the interests of those dispossessed by Octauian. See also Vell. 2.75ff.; Tac. *Ann.* 5.1; Dio 48.15.3-4; Gabba, op.cit. 151. Fuluia had made Praeneste her headquarters just before the Perusine siege (Dio 48.10.3).

seruisque ad pilleum frustra uocatis: the *pilleus* was a small Phrygian cap employed as a symbol of liberty. The use of slaves on these terms was a sign of desperation. Velleius' grandfather committed suicide at this juncture (Vell. 2.76.1; see R. Syme [1939] 383; cf. Woodman [1983] ad loc.).

in Siciliam profugit: Sextus Pompey was at this time receiving refugees. Many of these were senatorial (Dio 48.15.1).

4.3
nec statim in conspectum Sexti Pompei admissum: see Dio 48.15.3.

breui reconciliata inter omnis pace: this was after the pact at Misenum in 39 BC. One term of that agreement was an amnesty for refugees. See Vell. 2.77.3; Tac. *Ann.* 5.1.

Liuiam Drusillam...petenti Augusto concessit: there seems no doubt that Nero voluntarily ceded his wife to the triumuir. Velleius - not infallible on such matters - describes the marriage as an event well-omened for the state (Vell. 2.79.2: *auspicatis reipublicae ominibus*). Liuia had been born on 30th January 58 BC (see *PIR*[2] L 301 for sources; an implausible variant on her age at death would mean that she was born in 54 BC: Plin. *NH* 14.59). She would have reached marriageable age in 46 BC, and the marriage to Nero will thus have occurred between 46 BC and the early part of 42 BC. Tiberius, their eldest son, was born on 16 November 42 BC (see 5 below). Nero's role in the settling of veterans in Gaul in 46-5 BC (4.1 above) might suggest a date after his return (Treggiari [1991] 129). For the development of hostile propaganda about the marriage with Augustus see M.B. Flory, *TAPhA* 118 (1988) 343-59. That marriage was celebrated on 17 January 38 BC (*Fasti Verul.*, *Inscr. Ital.* 13.2.159, 397; 161, 401 = *EJ*[2] p. 46). Liuia is commonly assumed to have been about six months pregnant with Drusus at this time, and this gave rise to the jests about his paternity. For his birth see Suet. *Claud.* 1.1; Tac. *Ann.* 1.10.5;

5.1; Dio 48.44. Sumner suggested that Drusus was born in either March or April 38 BC (see G.V. Sumner, *Latomus* 26 (1967) 424 n. 1). Notice, however, a quite different tradition which is to be found elsewhere in Suetonius. In an edict Claudius is made to proclaim that there was all the more reason for celebrating the birthday of his father Drusus because it was also the birthday of his grandfather Antony (Suet. *Claud.* 11.3). Antony's birthday is dated by the *Fasti Verulani* to 14th January (i.e. three days <u>before</u> the wedding). See *Inscr. Ital.* 13.2.159, 397 = *EJ*² p. 46. Only one late source implies that the marriage took place after the birth of Drusus (Ps. Vict. 1.26), but could the whole story of the three month child be a fabrication? Seager (1972) 10 supports the early date.

nec multo post diem obiit: it seems likely that this was in 33-2 BC, and that Suetonius is vague here. See 6.4 below. Nero had entrusted the guardianship of his sons to Octauian. See Dio 48.44.5.

5 Birth of Tiberius

Tiberium quidam Fundis natum existimauerunt: this segment deals with the future emperor's date and place of birth. The place of birth was disputed by those who judged him born at the place of origin of his maternal grandmother, Fundi (cf. Suet. *Cal.* 23.2, a passage with some errors about her pedigree: see Lindsay [1993] ad loc.). The present passage is discussed in *PIR*² C 941.

quod materna eius auia Fundana fuerit: Liuia's mother was an Alfidia (statues are known from Tucci in Baetica [*CIL* II 1667], Marruuium amongst the Marsi [IX 3661] and Samos [*IGR* IV 983]). Suetonius' error in thinking that she was called Aufidia (Suet. *Cal.* 23.2) does not inspire confidence in his material, but it should nevertheless be accepted that she came from Fundi. Alfidii do occur at Fundi (*CIL* X 6248). See T.P. Wiseman, *Historia* 14 (1965) 333-4.

quod mox simulacrum Felictatis ex s.c. publicatum ibi sit: this shows that Fundi is to be added to the list of towns where Alfidia and her husband M. Liuius Drusus Claudianus were honoured by the erection of statues. The statues appear to represent a celebration of Alfidia's relationship to Liuia. *Felicitas* had a special significance in imperial ideology, and the award can be presumed to be in honour of the *mater Augustae*. See J. Linderski, *Historia* 23 (1974) 463-80, esp. 465 n. 10.

On the development of *felicitas* as an imperial attribute under Tiberius see H. Erkell (1952) 112f.; M. Grant (1950a) 76f. Velleius alludes to his *felicitas* in Germany (2.106.3, with Woodman [1977] ad loc., who points out the military ancestry of the virtue), and it was symbolically commemorated (through the appearance of the *caduceus*) on coins of AD 34 which celebrated Tiberius' twentieth anniversary in office. See M. Grant (1950b) 45.

natus est Romae...sic enim in fastos actaque in publica relatum est: although he is not specific about his source (*ut plures certioresque tradunt*) Suetonius believed that Tiberius was born on the Palatine hill. The year and date, on the other hand, were attested from traditional Suetonian sources (the *acta* and the Calendar) as 16th November 42 BC (for the day see *Fer. Cum.* [*ILS* 108], *Fasti Ant., Act. Aru.* = EJ^2 p. 54; Dio 57.18.2). His insistence that some writers still made errors on this count shows how slowly the notion of using archival materials was grasped at Rome. Suetonius had reason to promote the value of this approach in view of his personal involvement in the secretariat, and his role as *a bybliothecis* (perhaps at the time of the opening of the Bibliotheca Ulpia in AD 112-13). Notice that elsewhere in this life Suetonius says that Tiberius refused to allow the month of September to be named after him. This may have been one source of ancient confusion (cf. 26.2). Lepidus and Plancus are confirmed to have been consuls in 42 BC by several sources. See EJ^2 p. 33. On the various types of *acta* see introduction **26-32** and Lindsay (1993) on Suet. Cal. 8.4. The *acta publica* were also known as the *acta diurna* and had first been published by Julius Caesar (Suet. *Iul.* 20.1). This daily record of events in the city included a record of births (Juv. 9.84). For further details see B. Baldwin, *Chiron* 9 (1979) 189-203.

6-7 Childhood and youth

6.1

Infantiam pueritiamque habuit laboriosam et exercitam: Suetonius provdes anecdotal material about Tiberius' experiences during the civil wars in flight with his parents. The emphasis on the instability of the circumstances of his upbringing is surely intended as a partial explanation of his later development. For some textual variants on the readings *laboriosam* and *exercitam* see discussion in Du Four (1941) 27 n. 2.

comes...parentum fugae: compare Tac. *Ann.* 6.51.2; Dio 48.15.4.

6.2

per Siciliam quoque et per Achaiam circumductus ac Lacedaemoniis publice...demandatus: for the flight to Sicily see Vell. 2.75.3. Dio confirms that the Spartans provided refuge for Liuia and her child during the Perusine war (Dio 54.7.2). It emerges from the present passage that the Claudii were patrons of the Lacedaemonians. On this see E. Rawson, *Historia* 22 (1973) 219-39, especially 227; 229, identifying the original patron as Appius Claudius Pulcher , cos. 185 BC. For an account of Spartan loyalties during the Civil war period see R. Baladié (1980) pp. 291ff. Despite his links with Sparta Tiberius kept absolute impartiality when in AD 22 a dispute over control of a temple was brought to the Senate by Messene and Sparta, allowing victory to the Messenians (Tac. *Ann.* 4.43.1ff.).

The story about Liuia's escape from Sparta underlines her pluckiness and individuality, points which are to emerge again later in the narrative. For the presence of Tiberius along with his parents in flight see also Tac. *Ann.* 6.51.

6.3

munera...durant ostendunturque adhuc Bais: Suetonius shows quite an interest in items of imperial *memorabilia* (cf. Suet. *Aug.* 5-6; *Dom.* 1.1). Baiae was the location of imperial villas as well as less reputable diversions. See J. D'Arms (1970), esp. 109-11. The gifts from Pompeia may have had political significance since it is known that Nero was piqued at the treatment he received from Sextus Pompey (see 4.1).

a M. Gallio senatore testamento adoptatus hereditate adita: included here is an inheritance received by Tiberius from the senatorial Marcus Gallius, which took the form of a testamentary adoption. While the inheritance was accepted, the name was a political embarrassment and soon dropped because he had been a political opponent of Augustus. M. Gallius had been a *praetorius* under Antony at Mutina (Cic. *Phil.* 13.26; App. *BC* 3.95), and he is believed to have been a brother of the praetor Q. Gallius whom Augustus had executed after a suspected assassination attempt in 43 BC (Suet. *Aug.* 27.4). Perhaps he was a relative of Gallia Polla who had estates in Egypt which later fell into imperial hands (see *PIR*^{2} G 46). The arrangement may have been made for Tiberius by his father on behalf of the childless Gallius. Although adoption normally included the *condicio nominis ferendi*, it seems to have been optional with testamentary adoptions, which are thought not to have been governed by the same strict rules: indeed testamentary adoption is not legally recognised at all by the jurists, and it seems uncertain whether the person adopted did enter the family of the testator. It is often assumed that such adoptions conferred no further rights at all apart from permission to use the name of the testator, but in this case an inheritance is specifically mentioned - surely not an unusual situation. There was an important difference with the testamentary adoption of Octauian in that he had the adoption confirmed by *lex curiata*. This underlined the political importance of the move. It is noticeable that Suetonius ignores other aspects of the early life of Tiberius. His education is of no interest (cf. Vell. 2.94.2; Hor. *Odes* 4.4.25-8): only the politically important phases are stressed. On testamentary adoptions see W. Schmitthenner (1973) 39-64; R. Syme, *Tituli* 4 (1982 [1984]) 397-410 = *Roman Papers* IV (1988) 159-73.

6.4 Tiberius' Introduction to Public Life

Nouem natus annos defunctum patrem pro rostris laudauit: Tiberius was 9 when he delivered his father's funeral *laudatio* (i.e. in 33-2 BC). Was his father recently dead at this time or had he died soon after the marriage in 38 BC, as suggested by 4.3 above? The former approach seems more likely, and has been taken by modern authorities (Seager [1972] 11; Levick [1976] 13). Levick points out the political sensitivity of Tiberius Nero's career at this time on the eve of Actium, and suggests that the *laudatio* would have concentrated on ancestry and the naval achievements of the future emperor's father. Conflicts of interest may, however, be exaggerated, and the conventional nature of the genre can be presumed to have assisted in a bland presentation. Tiberius Nero was sufficiently reconciled to consign his sons to the tutorship of Octauian (Dio 48.44.5).

Actiaco triumpho currum Augusti comitatus est: his participation in Augustus' triple triumph in 29 BC shows his inferior status in relation to Marcellus. Marcellus had a closer blood relationship to Augustus. He was the son C. Claudius Marcellus and Octauia, sister of Augustus. For the triumph see *Fasti Triumphales Barberini* = *EJ*[2] p. 35; *Fasti Antiates* = *EJ*[2] p. 50; Dio 51.21.5ff. At this time Tiberius was aged 12. The triumph was held over three days, August 13-15.

praesedit et asticis ludis: these were originally games celebrated at Athens in honour of Dionysus; cf. Suet. *Cal.* 20; *CIL* VI 32323 1.156f. It is not known when the *ludi astici* were transported to Rome. Suetonius had a special interest in the games, reflected here. His work on the area has not survived but an idea of its scope can be gained from Tertullian *De Spectaculis* (cf. Wallace-Hadrill [1983] 127-8).

Troiam circensibus...ductor turmae: this was an event for equestrian youths, normally below the age for the adoption of the *toga uirilis*. Boys were divided into two *turmae* of *maiores* and *minores*, but details are uncertain. For Tiberius' leadership of a *turma* in the Troy game in 29 BC see also Dio 51.22.4. For a literary description of this entertainment see Verg. *Aen.* 5.547-603, and on its significance within the equestrian order see L.R. Taylor, *JRS* 14 (1924) 158-71; K.W. Weeber, *Ancient Society* 5 (1974) 171-96. The Troy game appears elsewhere in Suetonius, and will have been a feature of his separate work on the games (cf. Suet. *Aug.* 43.2; *Cal.* 18.3).

7.1
Virili toga sumpta: the assumption of the *toga uirilis* is dated by the *Fasti Praenestini* to April 24th, 27 BC (*Inscr. Ital.* 13.2.130f.). At this time Tiberius would have been 14. On variations over the age at which the toga might be adopted see *D & S* s.v. toga; *RE* s.v. tirocinium fori.

munus gladiatorium in memoriam patris et alterum in aui Drusi dedit...primum in foro secundum in amphitheatro: originally gladiatorial games seem to have formed an active part in funeral ritual, possibly brought to Rome from either Campania or Etruria. The earliest known exhibition at Rome took place in 264 BC. However, we can note that in the early imperial age they have become purely commemorative, and often occurred several years after the death of the person honoured (G. Ville [1982] 117). In Republican times it was usual to hold these contests in the forum (either the *Forum Boarium* or the *Forum Romanum*), but there was a move to the use of amphitheatres under the Caesars. On some of the hazards and features of displays in the forum see A. Scobie, *Nikephoros* 1 (1988) 191-243, esp. 197-200.

The date of the gladiatorial contest in honour of Tiberius' father Nero is uncertain. Nero had died between 33 and 32 BC (see 4.3; 6.4 above). The memorial games were probably not celebrated immediately. The display in honour of his grandfather Drusus, who had died in 42 BC, was held in the amphitheatre: the reference is to the stone amphitheatre of Statilius Taurus, which was completed in 30 BC (Dio 51.23.1; Suet. *Aug.* 29.5). This provides a *terminus post quem* for the date of this display. But Suetonius is probably giving a chronological account of Tiberius' career here. The date for both memorial contests should then be later than his assumption of the *toga uirilis* in 27 BC and before his first marriage (20 or 19 BC, exact date uncertain: 7.2 below). His grandfather's full name was M. Liuius Drusus Claudianus (hence Drusus) (see above 3.1; Stemma 1). The dates of the contests are discussed by G. Ville (1982) 100-101.

rudiaris...reuocatis: a *rudiarius* was a gladiator who had been discharged, and thus had been given the equivalent of a fencing foil in place of a real weapon (a *rudis*; cf. Suet. *Cal.* 32.2). A *rudiarius* could be sought after for contests if he had something of a reputation. Eventually under Marcus Aurelius a maximum price for the *auctoramentum* (pay) was set at 12000 HS, in the event that a *rudiarius* was called back into service. This figure was clearly quite low in comparison with the Augustan contest mentioned here. For discussion see A. Guarino, *Labeo* 29 (1983) 7-24.

dedit et ludos, sed absens: cuncta magnifice, impensa matris ac uitrici: the extravagance of these games is emphasised, but Tiberius does not get full credit: he demonstrated a lack of *ciuilitas* even at this early stage by his failure to attend, and the money was supplied by his mother and step-father. See RG 22.1 for the seven *munera* given by Augustus in the name of sons and grandsons, although Ville has doubts over whether the present shows are included in Augustus' tally (op.cit. 101). The emperor's aim in funding these contests appears to have been to promote the popular image of members of the imperial family, especially potential successors.

7.2

Agrippinam...neptem Caecili Attici equitis R...duxit uxorem: Agrippa had chosen to marry the daughter of Atticus, Caecilia Attica, rather than a match with a family of more ancient lineage (Nep. *Att.* 12.1). Their daughter, Vipsania Agrippina (= PIR^1 V 462), became the wife of Tiberius (Sen. *Ep.* 21.4). This was arranged by the emperor when Vipsania was barely a year old, while Atticus was still alive. That is, before 31st March 32 BC (Nep. *Att.* 19.4; 22.3). As Levick points out this meant that Agrippa was assured of Claudian grandchildren even before Actium (Levick [1976] 19). Seager also sees political importance in the marriage, but with a different focus. He imagines the marriage as important to Liuia because it cemented links between her offspring and the emperor's henchman (Seager [1972] 14). Tiberius' marriage to Vipsania did not take place until she was of marriageable age in about 20 or 19 BC. Because of uncertainties over when Caecilia married Agrippa (soon after 37 BC), an exact date for the birth of Vipsania cannot be attained. In any case she may not have been the only child of the union. Hence a lack of clarity over when she would have been nubile. See N. Horsfall (1989) 84; 104.

sublatoque ex ea filio Druso, quanquam bene conuenientem rursusque grauidam: see also Suet. *Aug.* 63.2; Dio 54.31.2 with similar emphases. For her role as mother of Drusus see *ILS* 165. Nothing is heard of the child with whom she was pregnant at the time of divorce, and it can be presumed to have died in infancy (see Seager [1972] 25). Vipsania subsequently married Asinius Gallus, and had at least a further three sons by him (see *PIR*[1] V 462). She died in AD 20 (Tac. *Ann.* 3.19).

Iuliam Augusti filiam confestim coactus est ducere: after the death of Agrippa in February of 12 BC (Dio 54.28), the imperial family had to wait the ten months prescribed by law before making Tiberius marry Julia. This legal rule was designed to prevent confusions over paternity (see P.E. Corbett [1930] 250ff.; S. Treggiari [1991] 493-4). In fact there is some exaggeration in Suetonius' claim that the marriage took place immediately. Tiberius had been sent to Illyricum on the death of Agrippa. For the betrothal in 12 BC see Dio 54.31.2. He returned to Rome after two campagn seasons, and it was only then in 11 BC that the marriage took place (Dio 54.35.4; Vell. 2.96.1), doubtless because at the time of betrothal she was still pregnant by her previous husband (see Treggiari [1991] 155). Tiberius' distaste for Iulia is said to have originated when she sought him while she was still married to Agrippa (see Plin. *NH* 7.46 on Agrippa's knowledge of Julia's behaviour). Julia may have had reservations about Tiberius, since she is said to have thought his lineage inferior, perhaps because of her mother's connections (Tac. *Ann.* 1.53.2; cf. 4.40.2; on her distinguished lineage through Scribonia see J. Scheid, *MEFRA* 87 [1975] 349-75). According to Macrobius, however, her scorn was a product of a sense of her own importance as a daughter of Augustus (*Sat.* 2.5.8; see S. Treggiari [1991] 90: this may, however, be Macrobius' own inference; as Treggiari points out, Julia's first husband Agrippa could have caused her even greater distress on this account [Tac. *Ann.* 1.3.1; cf. Suet. *Cal.* 23.1]). Moreover, Tiberius is supposed to have been resentful of Asinius Gallus, the man who took over his ex-wife Vipsania. Tacitus says this was because he had ambitions to be more than a citizen (Tac. *Ann.* 1.12.6). It need hardly be said that these sources reflect intense speculation over the motives and attitudes of key players at the imperial court, and must be taken with a grain of salt.

7.3
Agrippinam...post diuortium doluit: the tradition makes much of Tiberius' distress over the separation, as noted above.

cum Iulia primo concorditer et amore mutuo uixit: there has been some dispute over when the marriage broke down. At the time of Tiberius' ovation in 9 BC she is still publicly celebrating the event by entertaining senatorial wives to a banquet along with Liuia (Dio 55.2.4; on the importance of these banquets see N. Purcell, *PCPhS* 32 [1986] 78-105). Dio does not mention her part in triumphal celebrations in 7 BC (Dio 55.8.2). So Levick (1976) 37. But Carcopino thinks that this standard view of when the marriage broke down is unlikely since Tiberius was away at war for so much of this time, and he associates tensions with the advancement of Tiberius in 6 BC. See J. Carcopino, *Revue de Paris* 65 (February 1958) 66-80.

mox dissedit...ut perpetuo secubaret: for the importance of this passage as a reflection of Roman ideals of marriage see S. Treggiari (1991) 252; 415.

intercepto communis fili pignore: the idea that offspring represent a guarantee between husband and wife is again a reflection of ideals in family life (Treggiari [1991] 429).

Aquileiae natus infans extinctus est: Tiberius had been sent to Illyricum to continue the *Bellum Pannonicum* after the death of Agrippa. There had been revolts amongst the Pannonians at this time, and Augustus himself had been at Aquileia in 12 BC (Jos. *AJ* 16.91). Tiberius was helped in the restoration of order amongst the Pannonians by the Scordisci (Dio 54.31.3). See J.J. Wilkes (1969) 63ff; A. Mócsy (1974) 34.

Drusum fratrem in Germania amisit: in 9 BC he broke his thigh bone in a fall from a horse somewhere between the Rivers Saale and Rhine (Strabo 7.1.3 = C291; Dio 55.1.4). Tiberius joined him still alive at the summer camp after a marathon ride to reach his death-bed (Val. Max. 5.5.3; Plin. *NH* 7.84). When Drusus died, Tiberius accompanied his cortège on foot all the way back to Rome (Sen. *Cons. ad Marc.* 89ff.; 171ff.). Tiberius made the centurions and military tribunes carry the corpse for the first stage of the journey, and then entrusted the body to the foremost men of each ensuing city (Suet. *Claud.* 1.3; Dio 55.2.1). Lengthy cortèges became a feature of Roman imperial funerals, with Augustus carried from Nola to Rome, and Tiberius from Misenum to Rome (Suet. *Aug.* 100.2; *Tib.* 73.3; Dio 56.31.2).

8 The Early Civil Career of Tiberius

Ciuilium officiorum rudimentis: note the early age at which Tiberius' public duties began, soon after his assumption of the toga in 27 BC (7.1 above). Some of the examples given by Suetonius date before his earliest military experience (9.1), some of them will have occurred subsequently. Within the rubric he appears to operate chronologically, as usual. For Tiberius' training as an orator see Tac. *Ann*. 13.3.2.

regem Archelaum Trallianos et Thessalos...defendit: Tiberius is later supposed to have become very angry with Archelaus, because of his duplicity. He had grovelled to Tiberius to obtain his services as an advocate, yet slighted him at Rhodes, while acknowledging Gaius Caesar (Dio 57.17.3ff.). Implausibly Dio believed that this was why he was brought to trial before the Senate and charged with rebellion in AD 17, by which time he was suffering from several ailments including, apparently, insanity (Dio 57.17.4). He had remained king of Cappadocia, after his trial under Augustus, and now it was converted into a Roman province (Suet. *Tib*. 37.4; Dio 57.17.7). At that time he was accused by his subjects (Dio), and it is clear that a new trial was mounted. At some stage in his career (probably just before his deposition), he is supposed to have conspired with the governor of Cilicia (Philostratus 1.12). The Augustan trial took place in about 23 BC, and the charge is unclear. See G.W. Bowersock (1965) Appendix iii. B.M. Levick, *CQ* 21 (1971) 478-86, has argued for an earlier date, 26 BC. This might make some sense, since the pleading of cases on behalf of clients came to be part of the early training of the imperial princes (cf. Suet. *Nero* 7.2; E.R. Parker, *AJPh* 67 [1946] 29-50 at 34 [Tiberius]; 39 [Germanicus]; 46 [Nero]).

On Archelaus' rule in Cappadocia see W.E. Gwatkin, *University of Missouri Studies* 5 (1930) 1-66; R.D. Sullivan, *ANRW* 2.7.2 (1980) 1149-60. After his trial he appears to have returned to favour, and in about 20 BC he obtained some accretion to his territory (Dio 54.9.2; Strabo 12.3.29 = C555).

It is not known on what charges the Trallians and Thessalians were appearing in court, but in each case the imperial prince was to plead in the presence of the emperor (*Augusto cognoscente*). Tiberius' father had already had a close relationship with the people of Tralles, and this was clearly part of the hereditary *clientela* of Tiberius (see E. Rawson, *Historia* 22 [1973] 227). Badian points out that the Thessalian connections of the Claudii can probably be traced back to the campaigns of Quinctius Flamininus (*CR* 24 [1974] 186). If Suetonius is chronologically precise here, the prosecutions will have taken place after the defence of Archelaus. They cannot have been in 26 or 25 BC, because of the problem of the absence of both Augustus and Tiberius in Spain at this time (Suet. *Aug*. 26); a date closer to 23 BC seems inescapable (cf. Levick, *CQ* 21 [1971] 483-86).

pro Laodicenis Thyatirenis Chiis...senatum deprecatus est: Tiberius' intervention was in response to applications for relief from eastern cities after earthquakes at Laodicea, Thyatira and on Chios in 27 BC (discussed by

R.J.A. Talbert [1984] 417). Ambassadors were sent to Augustus in Spain to request help (Orosius 6.21.19; Agathias 2.17). Strabo refers to Tiberius' restoration of various cities including Sardes, following his father's example (Strabo 12.8.18 = C578). The reference to the Augustan restorations of Laodicea and Tralles must be to the earthquake of 27 BC, and Strabo's reference to Tiberian intervention will be to the earthquake of AD 17. It appears that the pleas from the Asian cities cannot have been heard until after Tiberius' return from Spain in late 25 or 24 BC (Levick, *CQ* 21 [1971] 478-81). Tiberius then introduced the embassies to the senate.

Fannium Caepionem...reum...fecit...et condemnauit: was Caepio already dead at this time? (Macr. *Sat.* 1.11.21). It seems fairly clear that Murena was (Strabo 14.5.4 = C670; Vell. 2.91.2: *quod ui facere uoluerant, iure passi sunt*; See Levick [1976] 233 n. 22). Fannius may have been a descendant of that C. Fannius who as consul in 122 BC was an opponent of Gaius Gracchus, and a defender of Senatorial prerogatives (for speculation on his antecedents see Levick [1976] 233 n. 19).

   The charges of *maiestas* were heard in the *quaestio de maiestate*, as were those against Primus and Murena (Dio 54.3 [dated to 22 BC, but usually attributed to 23 BC]). At this stage the Senate was not sitting regularly as a court. On the development of Senatorial jurisdiction over cases of this sort see R.J.A. Talbert (1984) 460ff. Whatever Tiberius said on the occasion he did not convince all his audience, since there were quite a few votes for acquittal (Dio 54.3.6). The whole case has been seen as politically crucial and closely related to the constitutional settlement of 23 BC. A select bibliography is appended:

D. Stockton, 'Primus and Murena' *Historia* 14 (1965) 18-40.

M. Swan, 'The consular *fasti* of 23 BC and the conspiracy of Varro Murena' *HSCPh* 70 (1966) 235-47.

S. Jameson, '22 or 23?' *Historia* 18 (1969) 204-29.

G.V. Sumner, 'Varrones Murenae' *HSCPh* 82 (1978) 187-95.

L.J. Daly, 'The report of Varro Murena's death (Dio 54.3.5)' *Klio* 65 (1983) 245-61.

L.J. Daly, 'Augustus and the murder of Varro Murena (cos. 23 BC)' *Klio* 66 (1984) 157-69.

J.S. Arkenberg, 'Licinii Murenae, Terentii Varrones, and Varrones Murenae' *Historia* 42 (1993) 327-51; 471-91.

curam administrauit, annonae: see also Vell. 2.94.3, who associates the *cura annonae* with his quaestorship in 23 BC (Dio 53.28); Levick thought Tiberius might have been *quaestor Ostiensis*, but more attractive is Badian's idea that he held the quaestorship attached to the consul, who at this time was Augustus. It may be that after Augustus put aside the consulship Tiberius became the first *quaestor Caesaris* (*Mnemosyne* 27 [1974] 160-72). It is clear that Tiberius was still under close imperial supervsion at this stage. The dearth of corn lasted into the next year and was so severe that the emperor had to intervene (Dio 54.1.3f.; cf. RG 5.2). Once Tiberius became emperor he continued to take an interest in the area, first documented in AD 19 (Tac. *Ann.* 2.87; cf. 3.54 [AD 22]). In AD 23 he set a fixed retail price for corn, agreeing to make up any shortfall to the dealers (Tac. *Ann.* 4.6; cf. Vell. 2.126.3: *quando annona moderatior?*) But there were later problems with expensive corn in AD 32 (Tac. *Ann.* 6.13).

repurgandorum tota Italia ergastulorum: these were a sort of prison farm in the country for rebellious slaves. Interestingly Suetonius notes the presence of deserters from the army as well as travellers who had been unlawfully detained. The investigation of the *ergastula* cannot be dated, but may have occurred late in 23 BC or in the following year. Elsewhere Suetonius gives the credit for reform to Augustus, who was undoubtedly behind it (Suet. *Aug.* 32.1).

9 Early military career

9.1

Stipendia prima expeditione Cantabrica: for the participation of Tiberius and Marcellus in the Spanish campaigns of Augustus in 26-5 BC see also Dio 53.26.1. They may have joined him late in the campaign. Tiberius was at some point during this campaign adopted as patron by Carthago Noua (*ILS* 144). For allegations of drunkenness during this campaign see 42 below.

On the campaign see D. Magie, *CPh* 15 (1920) 323-39; R. Syme, *AJPh* 55 (1934) 293-337; W. Schmitthenner, *Historia* 11 (1962) 29-85.

tribunus militum: the military tribuneship held by Tiberius became a standard position for young men of noble origin as part of their training during the *tirocinium* on the way to the quaestorship. These were *tribuni militi laticlaui* who received appointment directly from the emperor from a minimum age of 16 (Aul. Gell. *NA* 10.28.1). Under Augustus the military tribunate came to be preceded by the vigintivirate, apparently from 13 BC, and thus not relevant to Tiberius' career pattern (Dio 54.26.5ff.; see further in V. Maxfield [1981] 23-24). In any case Tiberius was a special case and we could expect his career to have been advanced in an unconventional way. Nevertheless, if he joined Augustus in Spain in 26 BC he would only have reached the age of 16 at the end of that year. It seems more likely that he joined the emperor in the following year.

dein...regnum Armeniae Tigrani restituit: his next role was as leader of an expedition to the East in which he restored the Armenian king to his throne. This was the result of an embassy to Augustus on Samos during 21 BC, when he was approached by the pro-Roman party in Armenia and asked to replace their present incumbent Artaxes with his brother Tigranes, who at this time was living in exile at Rome. According to Velleius Tiberius was given a comprehensive mission of organising and inspecting the Eastern provinces. Even before Tiberius had arrived, Artaxes was killed, and Tiberius crowned Tigranes, thus converting Armenia into a client kingdom (RG 27.2 ; Vell. 2.94.4 [on problems in this passage see Woodman (1977) ad loc.]; Jos. *AJ* 15.105; Tac. *Ann.* 2.3.4). It was during this episode that he also received the standards and captives seized by the Parthians from Crassus in 53 BC, and later from Antony in 40 BC. Perhaps Agrippa had previously negotiated this settlement when he was based at Mytilene between 23-21 BC. The Parthian return of the standards may have been prompted by fear of Augustan vengeance, as Dio suggests (Dio 54.8.1). As pointed out by Du Four this was a reasonable fear, but it was fear of Augustus, not of the relatively inexperienced Tiberius ([1941] 49). Tiberius was rewarded on return with praetorian ornaments (Dio 54.10.4).

recepit et signa, quae M. Crasso ademerant Parthi: the theme of the acceptance of a standard from a Parthian is the subject of the *Prima Porta* Augustus. Levick doubts whether it is Tiberius who is represented as receiving the standard (Levick [1976] 234 n. 38). Crassus had lost his standards along with some 20000 dead and 10000 prisoners to the Parthian cavalry in 53 BC. Most modern authorities have questioned Suetonius at this point, and doubt whether it was Tiberius who received the standards in person. Even Velleius fails to mention it, which may support the modern view (Vell. 2.91.1, with Woodman (1977) 98 n. 2; (1983) ad loc.), although Seager has championed the cause of Suetonius (*LCM* 2 (1977) 201-2).

post hoc Comatam Galliam anno fere rexit: this governorship of Gallia Comata has been dated to 19-18 BC on the assumption that Suetonius is chronologically precise, a view also followed here. See R. Syme, *JRS* 23

(1933) 15ff., following E. Ritterling, *RE* XII (1925) 1223. Others prefer 16-15 BC (see Levick [1976] 27).

9.2

Raetico atque Vindelico gentis Alpinas: Strabo writing in AD 18 refers to a single critical campaign in 15 BC when these tribes were pacified (Strabo 4.6.8 = C206). Although Suetonius and other sources do not mention Noricum, it appears to be at this juncture that it was added to the Roman empire (see 16.2 below; Vell. 2.39.3; G. Alföldy [1974] 52-62).

Pannonico Breucos et Dalmatas subegit: the *Bellum Pannonicum* lasted from 13-9 BC. For a full account see J.J. Wilkes (1969) 63-5; Tiberius had inherited his role in this war from Agrippa on his death in 12 BC. The Breuci were a Pannonian tribe occupying the Papuk mountains between the Save and the Drave. This area was strategically important to the Romans since it provided the link between Italy and Macedonia. Their leader Bato led the insurrection in ad 6 (Dio 55.29.3; see *RE* s.v. Bato no. 4). The *Dalmatae* appear to be the *Delmatae* who occupied the region around Salona. Tiberius broke most of their resistance in the campaign of 11 BC (Dio 54.34.3-4), although there were further outbreaks over the next two seasons (Dio 54.36.2; 55.2.4).

Germanico...milia dediticiorum traiecit in Galliam: this was a result of Tiberius' campaign in 8 BC. He had become responsible for the war in Germany on the death of Drusus in 9 BC (Vell. 2.87.4; Dio 55.6.5). The tribes moved were the Suebi and the Sigambri (Dio 55.6.1ff; cf. Suet. *Aug.* 21.1: *Germanosque ultra Albim fluuium summouit, ex quibus Suebos et Sigambros dedentis se traduxit in Galliam atque in proximis Rheno agris conlocauit*; Tac. *Ann.* 12.39.4). On the resettlement of large ethnic groups as a method used by Augustus to achieve stability in the empire see A. Mócsy (1974) 37ff; C.M. Wells (1972) 156. For his work in Germany Tiberius was rewarded with the title of *imperator* and celebrated an ovation on January 1st, 7 BC (Vell. 2.97.4; Dio 55.8.2).

quas ob res et ouans et curru urbem ingressus est: his first entry into the city in ovation was in celebration of his victory over the Pannonians and Dalmatians, and occurred on 16th Jan. 9 BC (Vell. 2.96.3; Dio 55.2.4). See *EJ*[2] p. 45: *Ti. Caesar ex Pan[nonia ouans urbem intr]auit*, which was first restored and identified as this occasion by L.R. Taylor, *AJPh* 58 (1937) 186. There has been some controversy over whether Tiberius had already celebrated an *ouatio* in 11 BC (based on Dio 54.34.3), summarised by

Woodman (1977) 109-10.

prius...triumphalibus ornamentis honoratus: as Suetonius says he was previously honoured with the triumphal ornaments. All campaigns under the empire were conducted under imperial auspices, and thus only the emperor could properly gain credit for a victory (see T.D. Barnes, *JRS* 64 (1974) 21-6). This resulted in the replacement of the true triumph with triumphal ornaments, under which the recipient obtained the rank and distinctions of a *triumphalis*, together with the right to a laureate statue. The last senator to obtain a triumph was Balbus in 19 BC. In 12 BC Tiberius was the first general to obtain the new award (Dio 54.31.4), closely followed by Drusus the next year (Dio 54.33.5). For the nature of the award and its antecedents see A.A. Boyce, *CPh* 37 (1942) 130-41. Agrippa had shown the way by being content with a decoration, the *corona muralis*, in place of a triumph (Dio 54.24.7-8).

9.3
Magistratus et maturius incohauit: in 24 BC amongst privileges granted to Augustus was the right for Tiberius and Marcellus to stand for office five years before the normal age (Dio 53.28.3).

quaesturam: see 8 above. Tiberius became quaestor and Marcellus was made aedile for 23 BC (Dio 53.28.3-4). Normally the quaestorship could not be held by a man less than 25 years old, whereas in Tiberius' case he was only 19 in 23 BC. Velleius places the emphasis on Tiberius' election to the quaestorship in 24 BC. He took up office in December of that year (Vell. 2.94.3; cf. Dio 53.28.3-4). See E. Badian, *Mnemosyne* 27 (1974) 160-72; Woodman (1977) 99.

praeturam: Dio records his tenure in 16 BC, although he says that he already had praetorian rank before becoming praetor (Dio 54.19.6).

consulatum: Tiberius' first consulate was in 13 BC at the age of 28 (Dio 54.25.1).

interpositoque tempore consul iterum: this was in 7 BC (*EJ²* p. 38).

tribuniciam potestatem in quinquennium accepit: the initial award of the tribunician power was in 6 BC and was for 5 years. His tenure probably began at the end of June, corresponding to the day when Augustus began his 18th year of tenure. Augustus had first taken the power on or about 26th June 23 BC (*PIR²* I 215). This date was later to be the day when Tiberius was adopted in AD 4. On the trib. pot. see further *Tib.* 11; Dio 55.9.4; Vell. 2.99.1; Tac. *Ann.*

3.56.3, discussed by B.M. Levick, *Latomus* 31 (1972) 779-813.

10-13 Retirement to Rhodes

10.1

integra aetate ac ualitudine statuit repente secedere: for the sudden retirement in 6 BC Suetonius outlines the following possible motives:

1. Dislike of Julia and her immorality.

Dio also has this strand of the tradition (Dio 55.9.7). Suetonius claims that Tiberius did not dare to divorce her, and while this is credible it is unlikely to have been a sufficient reason for his departure. Tacitus alone cites Julia's contempt for his inferior birth, something not noted elsewhere and barely credible, especially coming from the ex-wife of Agrippa (Tac. *Ann.* 1.53.2: *[Iulia] fuerat in matrimonio Tiberii florentibus Caio et Lucio Caesaribus spreueratque ut imparem; nec alia tam intima Tiberio causa cur Rhodum abscederet*). See, however, 7.2 above.

2. Avoiding boring the Romans

3. Improving reputation by absence

Both of these points are most implausible. Tiberius had at this stage thoroughly proved his worth, and had all the trappings of the heir apparent. Dio centres on his anger at not being actually designated as successor, but by this stage this was hardly a novelty for him (55.9.7).

4. Voluntary departure to make way for Gaius and Lucius.

Velleius relates the retirement of Tiberius to his modesty in not wishing to crush the beginnings of the careers of Gaius and Lucius Caesar (Vell. 2.99.2: *cum Gaius sumpsisset iam togam uirilem, Lucius item maturus esset uiribus, ne fulgor suus orientium iuuenum obstaret initiis, dissimulata causa consilii sui, commeatum ab socero atque eidem uitrico adquiescendi a continuatione laborum petiit*). Suetonius relates this as the official motive given by Tiberius himself after his return, and that the process was a copy of the behaviour of Agrippa when Marcellus entered public life. Dio quotes an unbelievable rumour that he was expelled from Rome because he was plotting against Gaius and Lucius (Dio 55.9.7-8). He could not have been allowed to depart with impunity under such circumstances. It would not be incredible if Tiberius did depart in order to leave the way open for the beginnings of these youthful careers.

Nevertheless Suetonius clearly does not believe this most positive version since he cites the pleas of Liuia and the complaints of Augustus to the senate. An anecdote about Tiberius' hunger strike is appended to add verisimilitude, and his resolution is confirmed by his hasty and reclusive departure. The whole section is structured in such a way as to suggest that Tiberius had a stubborn and self-centered approach.

See Levick, *Latomus* 31 (1972) 779-813; [1976] 37ff. J.A. Weller, *Phoenix* 12 (1958) 31-5 shows some of the problems surrounding Tacitus' account of the reasons for retirement to Rhodes.

adultis iam Augusti liberis: Gaius and Lucius were born in 20 BC and 17 BC respectively (Dio 54.8.5; 54.18.1). Thus in 6 BC they were 14 and 11. Gaius was elected consul in 6 BC, but to hold office 5 years thence (RG 14.1). The adoption of these children in 17 BC signalled their favoured status (Tac. *Ann.* 1.3.2; Dio 54.18.1).

exemplo M. Agrippae, qui...Mytilenas abierit: Agrippa's retirement at Mytilene is first alluded to by Velleius who suggests tensions between Agrippa and Marcellus (2.93.2 [*ut fama loquitur*: see Woodman (1983) ad loc.]; cf. Tac. *Ann.* 14.53.3; Suet. *Aug.* 66.3; Dio 53.32.1). When Suetonius handles the episode in the life of Augustus, he sees the behaviour of Agrippa as a reaction to a conflict with Augustus over the advancement of Marcellus (*Aug.* 66.3). This appears to be a different approach from the present passage, which implies a voluntary departure by Agrippa. Other sources as early as the elder Pliny also thought that Augustus had caused Agrippa's withdrawal (Plin. *NH* 7.149: *pudenda Agrippae ablegatio*). Dio thought that Agrippa was sent to the East to ease conflict with Marcellus arising from the preferment of Agrippa (Dio 55.30.2; 53.32.1) Compare Jos. *AJ* 15.10.2-4, where Agrippa is merely sent to prepare for the emperor's imminent tour of the East - perhaps the official story to cover more clandestine activities. Syme rightly points out that someone who is politically suspect is not placed in command of armies. See Syme (1939) 342.

The above points show that speculation over tensions in the imperial family started early. It seems probable that comparisons between the situations of Agrippa and Tiberius fuelled ancient debate. For this reason little trust can be placed in the motives atrributed by any of these sources. Agrippa could have had a serious diplomatic role as a negotiator with the Parthian king, as suggested by Magie. See D. Magie, *CPh* 3 (1908) 145-52; M. Reinhold (1933) 78-83.

10.2

honorum satietatem ac requiem laborum praetendens commeatum petiit: see 21.7 below.

relictis Romae uxore et filio: it is interesting to note that Tiberius is seen as infringing normal Roman family values in abandoning them in this way.

paucosque admodum in digressu exosculatus: again the emphasis is on Tiberius' failure to observe the social graces.

11.1

imbecillitate Augusti nuntiata paulum substitit: a truly hostile interpretation of Tiberius' motives is adopted by Suetonius, but is far from plausible (cf. Seager [1972] 31). At this time (6 BC) Tiberius was clearly to be the emperor's successor. Gaius and Lucius needed him as guardian and regent because of their age.

salubritate...captus...ab Armenia rediens: this had been in 20 BC. On the reasons for the development of Rhodes into a major centre in the Hellenistic period see R. Berthold (1984) 38-58. On the attractions of the island see also H. von Gaertringen in *RE* Supp. V (1931) s.v. Rhodos.

sine lictore aut uiatore: as a result of the grant of tribunician power Tiberius was entitled to a number of lictors, perhaps five (see Dio 57.17.7). These would bear the *fasces*, symbols of a magistrate's power. A consul was entitled to twelve. It was an indication of *ciuilitas* for a magistrate to dispense with lictors, as Germanicus did on a visit to Athens. See Tac. *Ann.* 2.53.3; Suet. *Cal.* 3.2 and Lindsay (1993) ad loc.

The *uiator* was a subordinate for the lictors. He was an official assigned to magistrates without *imperium*, and was used for various petty official duties. See Du Four (1941) 60.

gymnasio interdum obambulans...cum Graeculis: for the sole gymnasium at Rhodes see Strabo 14.2.5 = C652. On Tiberius retinue in the East see J.C. Tarver (1902) 154ff; Hor. *Ep.* 1.3.15; 8.2; *Ep.* 2..2; Porph. *ad Hor. Ep.* 1.3.1. Roman contempt for Greek contemporaries is well known. See Juv. 3.86-108, and for some of the nuances A.E. Wardman (1976) 7-24.

11.2

aegri...per ualitudinum genera disponi: Levick suggests that the visit may have had as its object a scientific rather than humanitarian interest in the sick (Levick [1976] 122). Nevertheless Suetonius does seem to indicate a humane approach on the part of Tiberius. Velleius makes great claims for his consideration towards soldiers on campaign (Vell. 2.114.1-3). As Woodman (ad loc.) points out it was a conventional attribute of the ideal general to look after the health of his soldiers when they were ill.

11.3

neque...exeruisse ius tribuniciae potestatis uisus sit: this had been awarded to him in 6 BC. See 9 above. The single example of the exercise of his tribunician power given here is interpreted by Levick as an exercise of his *imperium maius* over the eastern provinces because of the presence of lictors and the tribunal, as well as the exercise of *uocatio*. There are signs that he had this power in the account of Dio (55.9.4 [Armenia]; 55.9.6 [Paros]). See Levick, *Latomus* 31 (1972) 781f.

circa scholas et auditoria professorum assiduus: Tiberius was especially keen on Theodorus of Gadara. See 57.1.

cum apparitores prodiit: on *apparitores* see N. Purcell, *PBSR* 38 (1983) 125-73.

conuiciatorem rapi iussit in carcerem: magistrates had the power to incarcerate temporarily as a disciplinary measure. It is not clear from this account whether the charge here was one of *maiestas*. See Du Four (1941) ad loc.

11.4

Comperit deinde Iuliam...damnatum repudiumque ei suo nomine ex auctoritate Augusti remissum: this was in 2 BC. See also Vell. 2.100.2-5; Sen. *Ben.* 6.32.1-2; Plin. *NH* 21.9; Tac. *Ann.* 1.53.4-5; Dio 55.10.14. For the legal issues see Levick, *Latomus* 31 (1972) 810 n. 2. For another instance of a *repudium* sent in the name of the husband see Suet. *Cal.* 36.2 with Lindsay (1993) ad loc. In the early empire the husband had unilateral powers of divorce. See S. Treggiari (1991) 436-7; 446-58 (on procedure). Levick suggests that this had the effect of severing Tiberius' link with the imperial family, especially since the careers of Gaius and Lucius continued to advance (*ILS* 137 [dedication of a temple to Gaius and Lucius at Acerrae]; Aulus Gellius *NA* 15.7.3 [letter of Augustus to Gaius on 23rd September AD 1]). The powers granted to Tiberius in 6 BC were due to expire the following year, and he would then be in an exposed position (Levick [1976] 44; cf. Seager [1972] 33). Ovid was already hailing Gaius Caesar as a future *princeps* (Ovid *Ars Amatoria* 1.177ff.).

On the relationship of Tiberius and Julia see also P. Sattler, *Studien aus dem Gebiet der alten Geschichte* (1962) 1-36, with further bibliography.

exorare filiae patrem...quidquid umquam dono dedisset, concedere: contrast this initial generosity during his insecure exile on Rhodes with his later alleged harshness to Julia once entrenched in power (Suet. *Tib.* 50.1; cf. Linderski, *ZPE* 72 [1988] 194). Gifts between husband and wife were closely regulated under Roman law, and could be revoked by the husband at point of divorce (Ulp. 6.9; see Treggiari [1991] 449-50).

11.5

transacto autem tribuniciae potestatis tempore: the tribunician power was due to expire in 1 BC. It is at this point that Tiberius is supposed to have made the claim that he retired to avoid standing in the way of Gaius and Lucius (cf. 10.1).

petit ut...permitteretur reuisere necessitudines: here Suetonius attributes to Tiberius a concern for his close relatives, perhaps a reference to Liuia and Drusus. Compare 51 and 52 below. The alleged refusal of permission to return may be an invention of Suetonius. No other source mentions it.

12.1

remansit igitur Rhodi contra uoluntatem...quasi legatus Augusto abesset: Suetonius emphasises his continued presence on Rhodes as being against his will, and his status as that of *legatus Augusti*, a title bestowed to prevent rumours of *infamia*. This however does nothing to clarify his status, and Du Four suggests that he held a *legatio libera* which enabled a senator to travel with the status of an envoy employed on state business (Du Four [1941] 68). The story that this status was only secured through maternal intervention is a suspect trapping.

12.2

abditus uitansque praeternauigantium officia: Suetonius puts an unfavourable slant on the visitations Tiberius received from senators who visited him on the way to the east, and appears to employ the common Suetonian habit of generalising. Tiberius is portrayed as cowering in embarrassment. This is in sharp contrast with Velleius' handling of the issue, who sees in Tiberius a dignified model of *ciuilitas*. See Vell. 2.99.4: *illud etiam in hoc transcursu dicendum est, ita septem annos Rhodum moratum, ut omnes, qui pro consulibus legatique in transmarinas sunt profecti prouincias, uisendi eius gratia + Rhodum deuerterint atque eum + conuenientes semper priuato, si illa maiestas priuata umquam fuit, fasces suos summiserint fassique sint otium eius honoratius imperio suo.* Woodman notes the frequency with which editors have emended this passage in the light of Suet. *Tib.* 12.2. For his full discussion of the problem see Woodman (1977) 119.

Gaium Orienti praepositum, cum uisendi gratia traiecisset Samum: Gaius had been sent to the East with an extraordinary command and duties that appear not to have been clearly defined (Tac. *Ann.* 2.42.3; Dio 55.10.19; Oros. 7.3). Among other themes mentioned we have his attempt to make an arrangement with the Armenians and Parthians (Vell. 2.100.1; 101.1ff.; Plin. *NH* 2.168; 6.41; Dio 55.10.18), as well as a projected trip to Arabia to assist with the opening of new trade routes to the East (Plin. *NH* 12.55-6). He had proconsular power and the title of imperator (Dio 55.10a.7), but was probably not campaigning under his own auspices. Dio says that the meeting took place on Chios (55.10.19), and more substantial variations in the story are to be found in Velleius, who goes so far as to suggest that Tiberius got a favourable reception from Gaius, and was treated by him as a superior (2.101.1; cf. Seager [1972] 34).

On Gaius' activities in the East see also J.E.G. Zetzel, *GRBS* 11 (1970) 259-66; F.E. Romer, *TAPhA* 108 (1978) 187-202; *TAPhA* 109 (1979) 199-214; G.W. Bowersock (1983) 56-58.

ex criminationibus M. Lolli comitis et rectoris eius: Augustus is said to have raised the issue of Lollius' mischievous intervention in his address to the Senate about a public funeral for Quirinius (Tac. *Ann.* 3.48; see further 13.2 below). Quirinius had become *rector* to Gaius after the death of Lollius in AD 2. Lollius had a longstanding hatred of Tiberius, derived from the aftermath of the *clades Lolliana* of 17 BC. Tiberius as praetor in 16 BC appears to have been sent to deal with the problems created by that reverse, and Lollius was supplanted (Dio 54.19.6; Syme [1939] 429). Nevertheless, Augustus himself still sufficiently trusted Lollius to send him to the East as Gaius' *comes*, as the present passage reveals (cf. Vell. 2.102.1, with Woodman [1977] ad loc.). For details of Lollius' career see *PIR*² L 311.

12.3
uenit...in suspicionem per quosdam beneficii sui centuriones: Suetonius says that Tiberius came under suspicion with the emperor because centurions who owed their positions to a *beneficium* of Tiberius had returned from Rhodes in a rebellious frame of mind. One can presume that these centurions returned to the camp of Lollius and Gaius, and this might raise the presumption that it was Lollius who created this mischief for Tiberius (if indeed it is historical).

de qua suspicione certior ab Augusto factus: this story of alleged Tiberian pique suggests that even Suetonius cannot find evidence that Tiberius came under imperial suspicion.

13.1

Equi quoque et armorum solitas exercitationes omisit: notice his attendance at the gymnasium on Rhodes, although there is no sign that he himself performed gymnastic exercises (11.1). Despite this Tiberius did send teams to compete in the chariot races at Olympia (SIG^3 782 = EJ^2 78) and Thespiae (*AE* 1960, 307).

redegitque se deposito patrio habitu ad pallium et crepidas: the emphasis is on criticism of his abandonment of Roman dress in favour of its Greek equivalent. On the fashion for criticising imperial dress see A. Alföldy, *MDAI (R)* 49 (1934) 1-118; 50 (1935) 1-171.

imagines eius et statuas Nemausenses subuerterint: Suetonius directly equates this with the unpopularity of the Rhodian exile. Notice that his father had been responsible for setting up colonies in Narbonensis (Suet. *Tib*. 4.1). The city had received its walls and gates from Augustus in 16 BC, and Agrippa had continued the imperial connection by building the Maison Carreve (*CIL* XII 3153f.; *AE* 1920, 43 = EJ^2 75). Levick sees the unpopularity of Tiberius at this point as part of the tussle with Gaius, who was also a patron of the town (*CIL* XII 3155; Levick [1976] 45). It can also be noted that Lucius spent time in Gaul, eventually dying there, and he could have had an impact on local opinion. Subsequently Tiberius' reputation in Gaul seems to have improved, although we can hardly take the comments of his panegyricist Velleius on the subject seriously (Vell. 2.104.3). In any case, Velleius' focus is on the army's response to Tiberius. His arrival in Gaul is recorded on an inscription set up by a Roman citizen, perhaps a businessman of Italian origin, and to be dated to about AD 4. See *CIL* XIII 3570, discussed by J. Heurgon, *AC* 17 (1948) 323-30. On Tiberius' reception in Gaul see W. Orth (1970) 14-15.

conuiuio...exstiterit qui Gaio...Rhodum nauigaturum caputque exsulis... relaturum: the story is surely apocryphal; it must have been clear to the imperial family that Tiberius had not suffered any of the indignities associated with a true exile.

13.2

tam suis quam matris inpensissimis precibus reditum expostulare...nihil...nisi ex uoluntate maioris fili statuere: Suetonius appears to be fleshing out speculation over how Tiberius came to return to Rome. It seems unlikely that details of the process were ever made public. There is emphasis again on the machinations of Liuia on behalf of Tiberius.

is forte tunc M. Lollio offensior: the cause of the split between Gaius and Lollius was the Parthian revelation in AD 2 that he was in the pay of Eastern client kings. Lollius died soon after under mysterious circumstances (Vell. 2.102.1 [for some discussion of the tradition about Lollius and the tone of Horace *Odes* 4.9 of 13 BC see Woodman (1977) ad loc.]; Plin. *NH* 9.118: *infamatus regum muneribus in toto oriente interdicta amicitia a C. Caesare Augusti filio uenenum biberet*; Tac. *Ann.* 3.48.3).

permittente ergo Gaio reuocatus est: as Suetonius makes clear the return in AD 2 was only on condition that he take no part in public life (cf. Dio 55.10a.10). Suetonius seems certain that the condition was imposed by Gaius, but may be based on Tiberius' lack of immediate participation rather than any harder evidence.

14-15 Return from Rhodes and adoption

14.1
Rediit...magna nec incerta spe futurorum: Tiberius believed even while on Rhodes in a golden future, according to Suetonius, because of a range of omens and prophecies. This type of lore tends to appeal to Suetonius, and he sees it as hubristic for his subject to ignore it. There is no such problem with Tiberius. Moreover his mother Liuia even before his birth is depicted as subscribing to belief, as the story of the broody hen shows. The omens of his grand future are then treated chronologically. While Tiberius was a child the astrologer Scribonius predicted his future accession to a crownless kingship. Similarly when he first commanded an army a miraculous sign portended his future status. Heading for Illyricum at an oracle near Padua he was advised to thow dice and attained the highest possible score. Prodigies are also associated with his eventual departure from Rhodes, which was foreshadowed by the arrival of an eagle, which perched on the roof of his house. A story that his tunic shone forth on the eve of the news is followed by a cliffside stroll with Thrasyllus, who was now saved from the wrath of Tiberius by the fulfilment of his prophecies. At the critical moment they catch sight of the ship bringing news of his reinstatement. The structure of this section has been carefully analysed by H. Gugel (1977) 47.

All these prodigies show that the imperial family was working hard at ensuring the divine status of its members. Although Tiberius failed to be deified, it is clear that much of the groundwork had been carried through carefully. Perhaps the signs first began to be observed after Tiberius replaced

Agrippa on the Balkan front in 12 BC, although the sources date some episodes earlier (Dio 54.31.2; A. Bernecker [1981] 138).

14.2

Praegnans eo Liuia...ouum incubanti gallinae subductum...fouit: this omen has a legendary quality about it, but it suggests that Liuia was thought to be a diligent observer of the omens.

Scribonius mathematicus...spopondit...regnaturum...ignota...adhuc Caesarum potestate: Suetonius reveals his implicit belief in the miraculous revelations of astrology. At the time of Tiberius' birth in 42 BC nobody could have been certain that the imperial system would emerge. The astrologer Scribonius is otherwise unknown.

14.3

ingresso primam expeditionem...per Macedoniam...in Syriam: the Armenian expedition of 20 BC is alluded to here. This was not strictly Tiberius' first expedition, but it was his first time in command.

accidit ut apud Philippos sacratae...arae...conlucerent: this was of course the scene of Antony's greatest victory, one in which Tiberius' father had played a distinguished part. The omen is mentioned again by Dio (54.9.6), who also dates it to the time of Tiberius' Armenian expedition (20 BC). For the miraculous occurence compare Verg. *Ecl.* 8.105-7; Suet. *Aug.* 94.5; Paus. 1.16.1 (Alexander); 5.27.6; App. *Bell. Syr.* 11.9.56. Omens of this sort are intended to show that Tiberius was especially favoured by the gods.

Illyricum petens iuxta Patauium adisset Geryonis oraculum: seventeen oracular responses engraved on bronze have been discovered near Patauium, and may belong to this oracle (*CIL* I^2 pp. 267-70). The oracle of Geryon had given advance notice of Caesar's victory at Pharsalus (Plut. *Caes.* 47). Geryon was a legendary king of Spain whose cattle had been led away by Hercules, according to an often recorded story.

qua...in Aponi fontem...summum numerum iacti ab eo ostenderent: this fountain consisted of mineral springs, some six miles southwest of Patauium, known to Pliny as *aquae Patauinae* (*NH* 2.227; 31.61; cf. Mart. 6.42.4). See Du Four (1941) 77. *Tali* were knucklebones of sheep; here the shape was imitated in the precious metal. They were not cubical like *tesserae*, but irregular in shape. They had four faces marked one (*canis*), three (*ternio*), four (*quaternio*), and six (*senio*). The highest score was the *iactus Veneris*, when each of the four *tali* revealed a different side. For the rarity of this throw see Plaut. *Asin*. 905; Mart. 14.14; Prop. 5.8.45; Suet. *Aug*. 71.2-3.

hodieque sub aqua uisuntur hi tali: Suetonius' claim that these were still visible in his own day is a sign of the biographer's obsession with such matters, and may reveal his knowledge of Northern Italy.

14.4

ante...quam reuocaretur...aquila...in culmine domus eius assedit: cf. Plin. *NH* 10.77: *Rhodos aquilam non habet*. The eagle was the bird of Zeus, and would bring promises of power to mortals on his behalf. See Du Four (1941) ad loc.

pridie...tunica ardere uisa est: on miracles involving fire see 14.3 above.

Thrasyllum quoque mathematicum, quem ut sapientiae professorem contubernio admouerat: Tacitus also highlights that the interest in astrology started on Rhodes (Tac. *Ann*. 6.20.3). Thrasyllus was, however, originally employed as a teacher of philosophy, as the present passage makes clear. Notice the length of this acquaintance which the present passage shows dated from at least AD 2. He was also known to the emperor Augustus (Suet. *Aug*. 98). Thrasyllus was a notable Platonic scholar who also had interests in Pythagoreanism. There had been other Pythagoreans in the Claudian *gens*. On the background of Thrasyllus see W. Gundel, *RE* VI A 583f.; A. Bernecker (1981) 117ff.; H. Tarrant (1993) 7-17.

15.1

Romam reuersus: Tiberius returned to the city in AD 2. According to Velleius he arrived before the death of Gaius or Lucius, but Dio says his return coincided with the death of Lucius (Vell. 2.103.1; Dio 55.10a.10). The exact time of Tiberius' return in AD 2 is thus not certain, perhaps August (cf. Woodman [1977] 130-131).

deducto in forum filio Druso: an exact birth date for Drusus eludes us, but we know that he was younger than Germanicus (Tac. *Ann*. 2.43). Germanicus was born on 24th May 15 BC (see Lindsay [1993] 53-4).The *feriale Cumanum* shows that Drusus was born on 7th October of a proximate year (*CIL* X 8375; 1^2 p. 331). Introduction to public life usually took place at about the age of 15. Perhaps therefore Drusus was born in 13 BC.

e Carinis ac Pompeiana domo Esquilias in hortos Maecenatianos trans-migrauit: *Carinae* was a well-known residential district on the western slope of Mons Oppius (Seru. *Ad* Aen. 8.361; area of the modern Via delle Carine). Here near the temple of Tellus several Republican dignitaries had had their homes. It remained an important residential area into late antiquity, and it is known that Gordian eventually occupied the house referred to in the present context (HA *Gord.* 2.3). The *Pompeiana domus* had been in Antony's hands (Vell. 2.77.1; App. *BC* 2.525), and probably became the home of Antonia (Jos. *AJ* 18. 143; Levick [1976] 239 n. 72, implying that Drusus was educated there during the absence of Tiberius on Rhodes).

The Esquiline only a few years earlier had had a bad reputation, since the area beyond the *agger* of Seruius had been used as a cemetery. Maecenas had reclaimed the terrain by filling it in and laying out gardens (Hor. *Sat.* 1.8.8-20). See P. Grimal (1969) 143-45. The gardens of Maecenas became imperial property on his death in 8 BC (Dio 55.7.6). Later Nero was to connect the *Domus Aurea* with the *Horti Maecenatiani* (Tac. *Ann.* 15.39.1), but it is not known what imperial residence Tiberius was occupying at this stage. The move represents an attempt to remove himself from the spotlight, giving him a standing befitting the ambiguities of his situation.

priuata modo officia obiens: on the scope of these see Plin. *Ep.* 1.9.2: *officio togae uirilis interfui; sponsalia aut nuptias frequentaui; ille me ad signandum testamentum, ille in aduocationem, ille in consilium rogauit* (cf. Du Four [1941] 81).

15.2

Gaio et Lucio intra triennium defunctis: Lucius died on 20th August AD 2 at Massilia (*CIL* 1^2 p. 326 = EJ^2 p. 51), while Gaius died on 21st February ad 4 at Limyra in Lycia (*CIL* XIV 2801; IX 5290 = EJ^2 p. 47; Tac. *Ann.* 1.3.3). Suetonius elsewhere says that they died within eighteen months of one another (Suet. *Aug.* 65.1). These statements can be reconciled with the dates of death by allowing for some imprecision in the use of inclusive reckoning. See also Vell. 2.102.3; Dio 55.10a.9. Tacitus and Dio predictably suggest that Liuia was responsible for their deaths.

adoptatur...coactus prius ipse Germanicum fratris sui filium adoptare: this was on 26th June ad 4 (*CIL* 1^2 p. 320). Velleius wrongly dates it to 27th June, perhaps a scribal error (Vell. 2.103.3). Included in the arrangement was Agrippa Postumus, son of Agrippa and Julia, but Velleius specifies that the adoption of Tiberius was specifically for reasons of state (2.104.1: *hoc, inquit, rei publicae causa facio*). The *Fasti Amiternini* of AD 20, as might be expected, do not include the adoption of Postumus (*EJ*² p.49).

The fact that Tiberius was compelled to adopt Germanicus to ensure his own adoption is discussed by Seager (1972) 37ff. As Levick points out it was a legal impossibility for Tiberius to adopt anybody once he himself had been adopted by the emperor (Levick [1976] 240 n.7). The subject is treated in some detail by H.U. Instinsky, *Hermes* 94 (1966) 324-43. Notice that it was through the adoption of Germanicus that Tiberius acquired slaves callled *Germaniciani*, not as a result of Germanicus' death. See Boulvert (1974) 22.

neque donauit neque manumisit, ne hereditatem...percepit: all these points show how seriously Tiberius was taking his new obligations to his 'father'. An adoptive son's property fell under control of the new father, and was handed back to him for enjoyment as a *peculium*. A *filiusfamilias* was not legally entitled in his own right to perform any formal acts under the *ius ciuile*, particularly those of the type mentioned by Suetonius. He could not make gifts or free slaves without permission from his father. See discussion by J. Linderski, *ZPE* 72 (1988) 185-6. Linderski questions whether Suetonius exaggerates the extent to which Tiberius kept within the letter of the law, but notes that there is no certain evidence for manumissions by Tiberius when he was a *priuatus*. Suetonius is using this aspect of his behaviour to forward the characterisation, since the theme here and in ensuing sections is the severity of the duteous Tiberius, but this is little help in ascertaining the authenticity of the Suetonian claims.

nihil...praetermissum..ad maiestatem eius augendam: cf. Tac. *Ann.* 1.3.3.

Agrippa abdicato atque seposito: initially Agrippa was kept at Surrentum, but in AD 7 he was removed to Planasia under guard, an arrangement confirmed by Senatorial decree (Tac. *Ann.* 11.3; Suet. *Aug.* 65.1; Dio 55.22.4;32.1ff.; Vell. 2.112.7). On his character as a factor in his exclusion from the succession see A.E. Pappano, *CPh* 36 (1941) 30-45. When Agrippa was adopted by Augustus, his property passed to the emperor, and when he was exiled this property was transferred to the *aerarium militare* (Dio 55.32.2).

16-20 Military campaigns in Germany

16.1

data rursus potestas tribunicia in quinquennium: this seems to be in error, also to be found at Suet. *Aug.* 27.5, since Dio and the epigraphical record show that he received the trib. pot. for 10 years on the second occasion. As we have seen (9; 11), the first award had been in 6 BC for 5 years. A ten year award may have been intended to quell once and for all speculation over the succession. This clearly differentiated Tiberius from all other contenders, and would have helped to crush any suggestion that Tiberius was only a stop-gap solution. On Tiberius' reluctance to take up office see Vell. 2.103.2-3. For this award in AD 4 see also Tac. *Ann.* 1.3.3; 1.10.7; Dio 55.13.1a-2; *CIL* 1^2 p. 29.

delegatus pacandae Germaniae status: this and the next item about the reception of Parthian ambassadors suggest that Tiberius was granted *maius imperium* over all the provinces at this time (see also Dio 55.13.2). For the campaigns in Germany in the period after AD 4 see Vell. 2.104.3ff. Tiberius was expanding Roman interests in Germany until the outbreak of the Pannonian revolt.

Parthorum legati...eum quoque adire in prouincia iussi: this was doubtless because of the extensive diplomatic experience that Tiberius had gained in the East as a result of his campaigns in 20 BC, but also indicated his political importance in the period after AD 4 (cf. Levick [1976] 145).

nuntiata Illyrici defectione...grauissimum omnium externorum bellorum post Punica: the Pannonian revolt, which broke out in AD 6 as Tiberius was setting off for a major campaign against Maroboduus of the Marcomanni, represented a serious threat. The enemy were at one point within ten days march of Rome (Vell. 2.110.6; cf. Dio 55.30.1. See Syme *CAH* 10 369ff.; Wells (1972) 237f.). Velleius himself had a critical role as quaestor in AD 7 and his evidence is of particular value on this phase of Tiberius' career. See Woodman (1977) 153. It appears that the cause of the revolt in AD 6 was a mass levy of the Pannonian tribes conducted by the governor of Illyricum, Valerius Messalla. Until this time Pannonians had not been enlisted in the Roman army (Vell. 2.110ff; Dio 55.28ff; 56.1;11-17). The course of the revolt is discussed by J.J. Wilkes (1969) 69-76; A. Mócsy (1974) 37-9.

Further bibliography: R. Rau, *Klio* 19 (1925) 313-46; E. Koestermann, *Hermes* 81 (1953) 345-78; J.J. Wilkes, *University of Birmingham Historical Journal* 10 (1965-6) 1-27.

16.2

et quamquam saepius reuocaretur: Tiberius may have been in the habit of returning to Rome for the winters. Dio says that he returned as often as he could (Dio 55.27.5). See Vell. 2.113.3 and Woodman (1977) ad loc.

toto Illyrico...perdomito et in dicionem redacto: his persistent and thorough methods are highlighted here. Compare Vell. 2.114.1ff. This passage shows that Suetonius believed that Tiberius had annexed Noricum at some stage, probably in 15 BC. See 9.2 above.

17.1

Quintilius Varus cum tribus legionibus in Germania periit: news of the Varian disaster reached Rome as Tiberius put the finishing touches to terms with the Pannonians. Germanicus had been sent to clean up a rebel group who had retreated to a fort at Arduba. He then returned to Tiberius leaving Vibius Postumus in charge, and announced the victory at Rome. Within 5 days of his news reaching Rome, there followed news of the destruction of Varus and his 3 legions (Dio 56.15.3; 18.1; Vell. 2.117.1ff.).

The Varian disaster of AD 9 saw the destruction of legions XVII, XVIII, XIX (see Du Four [1941] ad loc.). On the career of Quintilius Varus see W. John, *RE* s.v Quinctilius col. 922f.. He had been consul in 13 BC and governor of Syria between 6-4 BC. He had a connection with the imperial family through his marriage to a Claudia Pulchra, a grandniece of Augustus. Her identity is explored by L. Koenen, *ZPE* 5 (1970) 257-68 - he concludes that she was the daughter of the union between Agrippa and Claudia Marcella Maior, and had married Varus perhaps in 21 BC. The *laudatio* for Agrippa shows that the marriage had not ended in 12 BC (see also M. Reinhold, *CPh* 67 [1972] 119-21 for a different reconstruction).

nemine dubitante quin uictores Germani iuncturi se Pannoniis: Suetonius generalises and claims to know about morale in the city.

multi<que> et magni honores: see Vell. 2.122.2; Dio 56.17.1.

17.2

censuerunt...ut Pannonicus...Inuictus...Pius cognominaretur: as Suetonius notes, all these were rejected on Tiberius' behalf by Augustus. The coins at the time of the Pannonian triumph merely commemorated his imperatorial salutations and tenure of tribunician power (cf. Seager [1972] 47).

de cognomine intercessit Augustus: Augustus concentrated on handing down the *cognomen* Caesar to Tiberius. Intrusions commemorating virtues such as *pietas* were felt to be inappropriate. See Levick (1976) 62.

triumphum ipse distulit...nihilo minus urbem...intrauit: an entry into the city took place on 16 January of either AD 9 or 10 (for the day see *Fasti Praenestini*, *CIL* 1 p. 231 = *Inscr. Ital.* 13.2.114; for AD 9 see D.M. Pippidi, *REL* 10 (1933) 435; J. Schwartz, *Rev. Phil.* 19 (1945) 55; AD 10: G. Wissowa, *Hermes* 51 (1923) 377; see Levick (1976) 244 n. 53 for further references). Suetonius says that Tiberius postponed his triumph on account of the Varian disaster, but subsequently lists his return to Germany as an event of the year following the entry into the city mentioned here (the return to Germany was in AD 10; see 18.1). The triumph appears to have been celebrated in due course in AD 12 (20 below). According to Dio (56.17.1) the award of a triumph took place in AD 9 along with Tiberius' fifth salutation as imperator. The correspondence of the fifth salutation with the triumph is confirmed by coins (*RIC*^{2} Augustus nos. 238 [a & b]; *BMC* I 50 no. 271ff.), but Dio appears to have the year wrong. See Seager [1972] 44.

in Saeptis...medius inter duos consules...sedit: on the Saepta Iulia see Nash II (1961-62) 291-93. Agrippa had dedicated the structure in honour of Augustus (Dio 53.23.1-2). The position of the imperial pair was a clear dynastic statement.

18.1

Proximo anno repetita Germania: this was in AD 10. Tiberius dedicated the temple of Concordia on 16th January AD 10 before his departure (*EJ*^{2} p. 45). See 20 below for an error in Suetonius over the date of dedication. Du Four cites a coin struck in AD 10 and inscribed *Ti. Caesar Augusti f. imperat. (or imperator V) R pontifex Tribun. potestate XII* as one in honour of the campaign in Germany (Du Four [1941] 97; *RIC*^{2} Augustus no. 469).

Varianam cladem temeritate et neglegentia ducis accidisse: the Varian disaster was clearly caused by the incompetence of the general, but Suetonius here purports to know Tiberius' view of the situation. He is not alone in this. Velleius has several passages in which he talks both of the *segnitia* and *socordia* of Varus, and of Tiberius' recognition of this (Vell. 2.118.1; 2.118.2; 2.120.5; cf. Dio 56.19.1). *Segnitia* is a common charge in Roman historiography (cf. Woodman [1977] 196), but it is clear that the charge attached itself to the tradition about Varus at an early stage (cf. Sen. *Contr*. 1.3.10; Tac. *Ann*. 1.58.2).

cum compluribus de ratione belli communicauit: notice use of the general's *consilium* as a consultative body in this context. The comment is double-edged since Suetonius implies that his normal style was autocratic. What his motives may have been for sharing decision-making can only be guessed at. Du Four suggests that he was concerned to train men to succeed himself in the field so that he could return to assist the ageing Augustus at Rome (Du Four [1941] 99). Suetonius next gives an example of Tiberius' closer attention to detail under the circumstances. The avoidance of overburdening soldiers with equipment and careful scouting before crossing a river is commonsensical and in agreement with the testimony of Velleius (2.115.5). The simple way of life while on campaign is another feature of his behaviour noted by Velleius (2.114.3).

18.2

uitae ordinem tenuit, ut sedens in caespite nudo cibum caperet: he did not recline for his meals. This was a characteristic of the ideal general, (cf. Just. 32.4.10: *nec...cubantem cenasse* [on Hannibal]) as pointed by Woodman (1977) 176. Suetonius aims to show that Tiberius was presenting a strict example to his troops.

praecepta sequentis diei omnia...per libellos daret: use of written instuctions both for daily and emergency orders. The implication behind this point is that most generals would be content to issue verbal instructions. Perhaps this was an aspect in which he was following Augustan precedent (Suet. *Aug.* 84). Suetonius says that he too liked to be sure of the adequacy of communication.

addita monitione: on the *prudentia* of Tiberius see Levick (1976) 90; 254 n. 36.

19

disciplinam acerrime exegit: Suetonius has a considerable degree of harshness in the Tiberian prescription on matters of discipline. Velleius' verdict is more favourable, and we have to remember that he served under him. However, as a member of the officer class it is perhaps not unexpected that Velleius should see even quite tough treatment as moderate (Vell. 2.114.3: *non sequentibus disciplinam, quatenus exemplo non nocebatur, ignouit; admonito frequens, interdum et castigatio, uindicta tamen rarissima, agebatque medium plurima dissimulantis, aliqua inhibentis*).

lucubrante se...nullo propellente decideret lumen: as Tiberius was dying, embers from his evening fire at Misenum blazed up unexpectedly as a symptom of change (Suet. *Tib.* 74). This appears to relate to the present omen, where it is claimed that Tiberius and his ancestors were much encouraged in their tasks if the lamp by which they were working at night were to die down and go out of its own accord. The later omen is an inversion of this. See Krauss (1930) 91f.

Levick notes the concern of Tiberius to live up to ancestral models, which emerges once again from a speech attributed to Tiberius by Tacitus (*Ann.* 4.38.1; Levick [1976] 11). With his double Claudian ancestry he had plenty to choose from.

non multum afuit quin a Bructero quodam occideretur: the Bructeri had been subdued by Tiberius during the campaign of AD 6 (Vell. 2.105.1), but they remained an intermittent problem for Varus and Germanicus (Tac. *Ann.* 1.60.4; 1.51.4). They lived in northwestern Germany near the sources of the Ems and Lippe (Tac. *Germ.* 33).

tormentis expressa confessio est cogitati facinoris: for the use of torture on suspected assassins and others see P.D.A. Garnsey (1970) 143-4. In general free men were not subject to torture, but there are signs that this rule was not maintained under the reigns of Tiberius and Caligula. In this instance, since the man was not a Roman citizen, he might have been considered fair game. On evidence given under torture see P.A. Brunt, *ZRG* 97 (1980) 256-65.

20

a Germania in urbem post biennium regressus triumphum...egit: for the date of the triumph see also Vell 2.121.2: *in urbem reuersus iam pridem debitum, sed continuatione bellorum dilatum ex Pannoniis Delmatisque egit triumphum;* Dio 56.17.2. The date was 23rd October, in a year between AD 11-13, usually attributed to AD 12 (see Seager [1972] 45). See O. Marruchi, *Not. Scav.* 18 (1921) 277-83 = *AE* 1922, 96 = *EJ*[2] p. 54 = *Inscr. Ital.* 13.2.134 [*Fasti Praenestini*], who places the triumph in AD 11. The triumph had been deferred from AD 9/10 (17.2). Either immediately before or after the triumph all territorial limitation was removed from Tiberius' *imperium*. See below 21.1.

prosequentibus etiam legatis...ornamenta impetrarat: for the award of triumphal ornaments to his lieutenants see also Vell. 2.121.3. These are known by name from Velleius Paterculus, Dio, and inscriptional evidence:

Germanicus	Dio 56.11; 15; 17.2; Vell. 2.116.1
M. Aemilius Lepidus	Vell. 2.114.5; 115.1-3; Dio 56.12.2
C. Vibius Postumus	Vell. 2.116.2
M. Plautius Siluanus	Dio 56.12.2; *CIL* XIV 3605-6
M. Valerius Messalinus	Vell. 2.112.2
C. Velleius Paterculus	Vell. 2.111.4

e curru...praesidenti patri ad genua summisit: the act of hommage to Augustus is mentioned doubtless because it was represented on official propaganda. It is known to us from the Vienna cameo. See Du Four (1941) 101.

Batonem Pannonium ducem ingentibus praemiis Rauennam transtulit: Velleius says that the rebellion crushed by Tiberius was led by Pinnes and the two Batos (Vell. 2.110.4). Pinnes was captured and Bato surrendered (Vell. 2.114.4; on Pinnes see *RE* s.v. Pinnes no. 2), but nothing is said of the other Bato. Dio fills out the picture. He says that the revolt broke out amongst the Dalmatians, under the leadership of Bato from the tribe of the *Desidiates* (= *RE* s.v. Bato no. 5), who refused to supply contingents to Valerius Messalinus, governor of Illyricum, when he was about to join Tiberius against Maroboduus. The Pannonian *Breuci* joined the revolt under the other Bato (= *RE* s.v. Bato no. 4), and marched against the Romans. The Dalmatian leader was wounded during an attack on Salonae, but he subsequently regrouped and defeated Messalinus. This Bato soon encountered a Roman ambush, and was defeated, after which he had mixed fortunes in the company of the Pannonian leader (Dio 55.29.2-30.6). In AD 7 A. Caecina Seuerus attacked them from Moesia, where he was legate. He brought with him Thracian allies and defeated the opposition (Dio 55.32.3-4). The next year the Pannonian leader betrayed Pinnes to guarantee his leadership over the *Breuci*, and this treacherous act was quickly followed by the murder of the Breucian Bato by the Dalmatian leader (Dio 55.34.4-5). Pannonian unrest forced the Dalmatian Bato to take refuge at Andetrium, where Tiberius cornered him and forced him to seek terms (Dio 55.34.6; 56.12.3-14.7). He sent his son to Tiberius as a hostage, and offered surrender in exchange for a personal pardon (Dio 56.16.1-3). On these campaigns see Wells (1972) 237; Mócsy (1974) 37-9.

Suetonius describes Bato as the Pannonian leader, but the above outline shows that he is mistaken. For an outline of the Pannonian and Dalmatian tribes see Strabo 7.5.3 = C314, who also seems to have difficulty in distinguishing between Pannonian and Dalmatian tribes. The political prisoner at Rauenna must be Bato of the *Desidiates*. Rauenna was used in the early imperial period for imprisoning foreign dignitaries under low security conditions. Both the son of Arminius and Maroboduus had been held there under like conditions (Tac. *Ann.* 1.58.9; 2.63.5). It is clearly not a strict arrangement since Bato is to be so honoured for his assistance.

prandium dehinc populo: Tiberius had feasted the people at the time of his ovation in 11 BC, which had been granted for victory over the Pannonians and Dalmatians (Dio 55.2.4).

congiarium trecenos nummos uiritim dedit: a *congiarium* was originally the name given to a vessel holding a liquid measure, but came to refer to a largesse of food of like volume to the people. In the imperial period money was commonly substituted, and the usual occasions for the distributions were triumphs or other imperial occasions. This is our only evidence for a *congiarium* in honour of Tiberius' triumph (see Van Berchem [1939] 144). It is comparable in scale to the *congiarium* donated under Tiberius' will. See 76 below.

dedicauit et Concordiae aedem: after his German triumph in 7 BC Tiberius is said to have taken on the task of repairing the temple of Concordia (Dio 55.8.2). On the conservative associations of this temple in the Republican era see Levick (1976) 36-7. Both in this case and that of the temple of Castor and Pollux he is said to have inscribed the finished product with his own name and that of Drusus. Dio dates this to AD 10, and calendars show that this was on 16th January (Dio 56.25.1; *Fasti Praenestini*, *CIL* 1^2 p. 231; *Verul. AE* 1937, 5 = EJ^2 p. 45; Ovid *Fasti* 1.639f.).By that stage the brothers were identified with the Dioscuri, apparently taking the place of Gaius and Lucius (see below). On the temple see T. Pekary, *MDAI* (R) 73/4 (1966-67) 105-33. Suetonius associates the rededication with the triumph in AD 12, and this may be a confusion caused by the fact that the temples were restored *de manubiis*.

item Pollucis et Castoris...de manubiis: on the restoration of the temple of Castor and Pollux in his own name and that of Drusus (i.e as the Dioscuri) see also Dio 55.27.4; Ovid *Fasti* 1.705-8, who equates Tiberius and Drusus with the Dioscuri. The actual wording of the dedicatory inscription has not survived intact. The rededication of the temple occurred on 27th January AD 6, quite soon after Tiberius had become heir designate, as is known from the *Fasti Praenestini* (Ovid *Fasti* 1.705ff.; Dio 55.27.3ff.; *Inscr. Ital.* 13.2.116f; 403f. = EJ^2 p. 46). His brother Drusus was by this time dead. It has been suggested that this idea of seeing the heirs designate as the Dioscuri had started with Gaius and Lucius, and was now transferred to Tiberius. If this is correct it is unlikely that Tiberius was already involved in the repairs of the temple of Castor and Pollux as early as 7 BC, and the dedication of both temples to Tiberius and Drusus as Dioscuri should be seen as a product of Tiberius' recent designation as heir. The use of the star, the symbol of the Dioscuri, had importance as a link with the Hellenistic past, and as the primary symbol of the imperial cult. See B. Poulsen, *Symbolae Osloenses* 66 (1991) 119-46, with further bibliography. For recent archaeological work see S. Sande and J. Zahle in *Kaiser Augustus und die verlorene Republik*

(1988) 213-24. Suetonius is placing the dedication after the Illyrian triumph of AD 12, apparently wrongly (Levick [1976] 243 n. 45).

Both these temples seem to have been restored out of booty from the Pannonian triumph of AD 6 (*de manubiis*), but there are some signs that the plan in relation to the temple of Concordia did go back to before his exile. During a stay on Paros on the way to Rhodes he is said to have wanted the famous statue of Hestia for the temple of Concordia (Dio 55.9.6).

21 The Illyrian campaign

21.1

ac non multo post lege per consules lata, ut prouincias...administraret: this was under a consular law of AD 13, which provided that they should conduct a census together using their consular *imperium*. See RG 8.4; Suet. *Aug.* 27.5; Vell. 2.121.1, which seems to suggest that the law preceded the triumph (cf. Brunt, *ZPE* 13 [1974] 171-3; Woodman [1977] 210-11, who suggests that the *imperium* was decreed for Tiberius before the triumph, but not actually received until subsequently); Dio 56.28.6. Since AD 4 Tiberius had had *imperium proconsulare*, but it appears to have been geographically limited until this juncture.

censum ageret, condito lustro: the *lustrum* was on May 11th, AD 14 (Suet. *Aug.* 97.1).

ex itinere reuocatus...fuitque una secreto per totum diem: the same version is found in Suet. *Aug.* 98.5; Vell. 2.123.2 also records this meeting, and even claims to know what was discussed. Compare Dio, who denies it (56.31.1). Tacitus is undecided (*Ann.* 1.5.5f.). Most modern scholars accept the meeting as historical. See Woodman (1977) 218. As Levick points out the idea that Liuia concealed the death of Augustus until the return of Tiberius seems to have emanated from a later hostile tradition which viewed Tiberius as a usurper (Levick [1976] 68).

21.2

uox Augusti per cubicularios...“miserum populum R., qui sub tam lentis maxillis erit!”: Du Four points out that Suetonius elsewhere characterises Tiberius as slow and deliberate. See *Tib.* 57.1; 68.3; Du Four (1941) 106. *Cubicularii* were slaves or freedmen in charge of the bed chamber. They came to have immense power in the early imperial period because of their constant access to the emperor (e.g. Helicon under Caligula).

Commentary

Augustum...morum eius diritatem...improbasse: for the tradition that
Tiberius was chosen by Augustus to improve his own posthumous reputation see also Tac. *A nn*. 1.10.7: *ne Tiberium quidem caritate aut rei publicae
cura successorem adscitum, sed quoniam adrogantiam saeuitiamque eius
introspexerit, comparatione deterrima sibi gloriam quaesiuisse*; Dio
56.45.3. Harshness has been noticed in Tiberius' reactions under provoca-
tion. See K. Scott, *AJPh* 53 (1932) 139-51. Suetonius here goes to some
length in his refutation of the approach found in Tacitus and Dio (who may
rely on Tacitus in this instance). Goodyear (1972) 167 has discussed the
possibility that Suetonius here reacts to Tacitus, but is cautious, and believes
that Suetonius could have found the approach elsewhere. He rightly dismisses any solution based on Suetonius' vague statement *ne illud quidem
ignoro aliquos tradidisse*. See introduction **33-34**.

sed expugnatum precibus uxoris adoptionem non abnuisse: this tradition
that Liuia forced Augustus' hand over the adoption of Tiberius is also to be
found in Tacitus (e.g. Tac. *Ann*. 1.3; 1.10.6). This has been influenced both
by Roman traditions about wicked stepmothers, as well as by elite criticism
of female influence at court. On stepmothers see now D. Noy, *Journal of
Family History* 16 (1991) 345-62.

21.3
rei p. causa adoptare se eum pro contione iurauerit: thus also Vell.
2.104.1: *'hoc', inquit, 'rei publicae causa facio'*, but compare Tac. *Ann*.
1.10.7: *ne Tiberium quidem...r.p. cura successorem adscitum*. As Woodman
(1977) 136 points out these words are surely a compliment to Tiberius.
Compare Seager (1972) 37-8.

**et epistulis aliquot ut peritissimum rei militaris utque unicum p. R.
praesidium prosequatur:** on the debate over whether Suetonius had special access to the imperial correspondence see introduction **23-32**. Both
Quintilian and Pliny also quote letters of Augustus (Quint. 1.7.22; Plin. *NH*
13.83; 18.139). On the letters see also E. Bourne, *TAPhA* 49 (1918) 53-66;
R.A. Birch, *CQ* 31 (1981) 155-61. For the text of all surviving literary
references to Augustan letters see H. Malcovati (1928). The emphasis in the
following extracts is on Augustus' absolute trust in Tiberius at a military
level. Velleius echoes Augustus in describing Tiberius as the *rei publicae
praesidium* (2.103.1; cf. 2.111.2).

21.4
Vale, iucundissime Tiberi: these extracts from the imperial correspondence

103

show a close relationship; for a similarly friendly exchange compare Suet. *Aug.* 51.3. In many ways Tiberius owed everything to Augustus, and whatever he felt about individual issues, he owed dynastic loyalty to his step-father and the Julian house. See Levick (1976) 82. For a different reconstruction of the first Greek phrase see R. Shaw-Smith, *Greece and Rome* 18 (1971) 213-14.

21.5
Ordinem aestiuorum tuorum...non potuisse quemquam prudentius gerere se quam tu gesseris: this letter is usually attributed to about AD 9 and associated with Tiberius' handling of the Pannonian revolt. It seems that there had been some dispute between Augustus and Tiberius over his methods, and the despondency mentioned by Augustus is confirmed by Dio (56.12.2). See discussion of the *prudentia* and *prouidentia* of Tiberius in Woodman (1977) 182.

unus homo nobis uigilando restituit rem: this is a quotation from Ennius *Ann.* 363 (ed. Skutsch) with *uigilando* substituted for *cunctando*. Compare Verg. *Aen.* 6.846. Clearly Augustus expected his correspondent to appreciate the allusion (G.R. Stanton, *Antichthon* 5 [1971] 49-56 at 53). An original context for the unadapted line on Fabius Maximus is elusive. See O. Skutsch (1985) 530-31.

21.6
succurritque uersus ille Homericus: see *Iliad* 10.246-7. The context is the Greek scheme to steal into the Trojan camp in the hope of overhearing Trojan plans. Diomedes expresses his faith in Odysseus. On the use of Homeric quotations in Suetonius see J.-F. Berthet, *REL* 56 (1978) 314-34.

21.7
Attenuatum te esse continuatione laborum: cf. 10.2 above; Vell. 2.99.2: *commeatum ...adquiescendi a continuatione laborum petiit.* These passages suggest that Tiberius habitually complained of his burdens, or at least had a reputation for doing so.

22-25 Death of Augustus and accession of Tiberius

22
Excessum Augusti non...palam fecit: notice the tradition of secrecy after the death of Augustus. Tacitus ascribes to Liuia precautions to prevent the death of Augustus becoming common knowledge until everything for the succession had

been organised. Tiberius had to be recalled from Illyricum (Tac. *A nn*. 5.5-6: *uixdum ingressus Illyricum Tiberius properis matris litteris accitur; neque satis compertum est, spirantem adhuc Augustum apud urbem Nolam an exanimem repperit. acribus namque custodiis domum et uias saepserat Liuia, laetique interdum nuntii uulgabantur, donec prouisis quae tempus monebat simul excessisse Augustum et rerum potiri Neronem fama eadem tulit*). Similarities have been noticed between the literary descriptions of this advent to the throne and that of Seruius Tullius through the agency of Tanaquil (Livy 1.41). The emphasis on female intervention is also a feature of the Tacitean picture of the accession of Nero (Tac. *Ann*. 12.68). Each of the imperial women is portrayed defending a position in which she has persuaded a reigning emperor to adopt a stepson as heir, the emperor has shown last minute remorse over his own flesh and blood (Agrippa Postumus, Britannicus), and the dastardly woman has taken steps to ensure the realisation of her scheme. In the event the emperor dies suddenly and news of his death is kept quiet until the stepson's accession has been made secure. Tanaquil is a less sinister figure than either of the imperial women - indeed she is a model of antique virtue - but Tacitus may have modelled his handling of these imperial episodes on the Liuian passage. If this is the case, we have here an instance of Suetonius operating under influence of the Tacitean treatment, since he too appears to assume Liuia's intervention, although it is not directly mentioned.

On the parallels between Liuia and Tanaquil see M.P. Charlesworth, *CR* 41 (1927) 55-7. On the general problem of the excessive role given to Liuia by the sources see also his article in *AJPh* 44 (1923) 145-57, esp. 156. On Liuia see now N. Purcell, *PCPhS* 32 (1986) 78-105.

Agrippa iuuene interempto: Suetonius openly states that the disposal of Agrippa Postumus was a priority for Tiberius. He does however reveal that the entire tradition about the incident was obscure from the beginning, and that there was debate over whether Augustus, Liuia or Tiberius had issued the order on which the military tribune who was guarding him had acted. The incident is for Suetonius discreditable to Tiberius, since he is said on the one hand to have denied responsibility for the order but on the other quickly to have buried the incident (cf. Woodman [1977] 170 on Vell. 2.112.7). This approach has affinities with the Tacitean approach with its infamous *primum facinus noui principatus* (Tac. *Ann*. 1.6; see Goodyear [1972] 128f.), and assists with the development of the picture of a duplicitous Tiberius. There is no doubt that Tacitus held Liuia and Tiberius jointly responsible for the death, and this Suetonian discussion reflects his emphases. Dio Cassius is the third source to discuss the incident, and agrees with these main emphases: (1) Agrippa was killed immediately after the death of Augustus. (2) Tiberius denied resposibility for the order to kill him, and threatened to bring the tribune to account for the death. (3) Tiberius subsequently dropped the entire matter (Dio 57.3.5-6).

Seager follows Hohl in pointing out that Augustus must have made the decision, since Agrippa was not named in the emperor's will. Under Roman law had he been expected to be alive, it would have been necessary expressly to disinherit him. Augustus therefore cannot have intended Agrippa to be alive to take under the will, when he drew it up on 3rd April AD 13 (Suet. *Aug.* 101.1; Seager [1972] 49). This assumes that we know all details of the terms of the will, and may not be decisive.

Bibliography:

E. Hohl, 'Primum facinus noui principatus', *Hermes* 70 (1935) 350-55.

A.E. Pappano, 'Agrippa Postumus', *CPh* 36 (1941) 30-45.

W. Allen, 'The death of Agrippa Postumus', *TAPhA* 78 (1947) 131-9.

R. Detweiler, 'Historical perspectives on the death of Agrippa Postumus', *CJ* 65 (1969-70) 289-95.

B.M. Levick, 'Abdication and Agrippa Postumus', *Historia* 21 (1972) 674-97,

S. Jameson, 'Augustus and Agrippa Postumus', *Historia* 24 (1975) 287-314.

J.D. Lewis, 'Primum facinus noui principatus', *Auckland Classical Essays in honour of E.M. Blaicklock* (1970) 165-84.

hunc tribunus militum custos appositus occidit: although other sources agree that a military tribune brought the news of the execution, it appears that Suetonius is wrong in assigning the killing to the same man. It is otherwise attributed to the centurion who was in charge of Agrippa (Tac. *Ann.* 1.6.1; Dio 57.3.6). Du Four points out that centurions were generally employed to execute condemned persons (Du Four [1941] 110; see Tac. *Ann.* 16.15.1; 16.9.3).

renuntianti tribuno factum esse quod imperasset: this is very close to the wording of Tacitus (*Ann.* 1.6.5: *nuntianti centurioni, ut mos militiae, factum esse quod imperasset;* cf. Suet. *Claud.* 29.2: *renuntiante centurione factum esse quod imperasset negaret quicquam se imperasse*). See Furneaux ad loc; Goodyear (1972) 135-36. It has been usual to ascribe similarities of this sort to a common source, but the possibility that Suetonius knows Tacitus directly is worth considering. See introduction 33-34.

23

iure autem tribuniciae potestatis coacto senatu: that Tiberius convoked the Senate by virtue of his *tribunicia potestas* is also stated by both Tacitus and Dio (Tac. *Ann.* 1.7.5; Dio 56.28.1). The *ius senatus consulendi* was a prerogative of the holder of tribunician power (Aul. Gall. *NA* 14.7.4). On his deliberate avoidance of the use of consular power see Levick (1976) 63.

uelut impar dolori congemuit...perlegendum librum Druso filio tradidit: Suetonius presents the scene of him in the Senate claiming affliction with grief and handing over the reading of a prepared speech to his son Drusus. When this is taken together with the subsequent section and talk of the *impudentissimus mimus* (24.1), it is clear that a hostile view not dissimilar to that of Tacitus is being taken.

The employment of Germanicus by Augustus provided precedent for the use of an imperial prince to read communications to the Senate (Dio 56.26.2). According to Ulpian the *quaestores Augusti* took on this role, although some emperors made different arrangements (Dig. 1.13.1.2; cf. Suet. *Nero* 15.2 [the consuls]; Suet. *Tit.* 6.1 [his son]).

inlatum deinde Augusti testamentum: the details of the will are given by Suetonius in the life of Augustus (*Aug.* 101; cf. Tac. *Ann.* 1.8.1-3; Dio 56.32-33). Tacitus also notes it as the principal business in the senate at the first meeting after the death of Augustus.

A Roman will would be witnessed by seven men, although some uncertainties subsist over the formality of the occasion. See E. Champlin (1992) 75-81. The reference to the use of Senatorial signatories for the will appears to be intended as a contrast with Tiberius' own alleged exclusive use of lowly signatories (Suet. *Tib.* 76), but we can note that non-senatorial signatories were also used in this instance, and required to acknowledge their seals from outside the house (cf. Dio 56.32.1a = Zonaras 10.38). The will was read out by a freedman, but outsiders were not to be admitted. Suetonius seems to be making a point about Tiberian exclusivity here. According to Dio the freedman was Polybius, and he was employed because it was inappropriate for a senator to read a document of this sort (Dio [Xiph.] 56.32.1). Presumably only a member of the *familia* was considered fit.

quoniam atrox fortuna Gaium et Lucium filios mihi eripuit: Suetonius interprets the impact of *atrox fortuna* as forcing an unwilling Augustus to make Tiberius his heir, although he expresses this as the view of others. The terminology cited here also appears in Res Gestae 14 : *filios meos, quos iuuenes mihi eripuit fortuna.* Levick has shown some reasons for doubting whether the interpretation hostile to Tiberius is correct, above all on the legal ground that under Roman private law a testator had to either name his sons as heirs or explicitly disinherit them. See B. Levick, *CR* 22 (1972) 309-11.

ex parte dimidia et sextante heres esto: Tiberius was to receive two thirds of the estate once the legacies had been executed. The remaining third went to his widow Liuia.

24.1

Principatum...diu tamen recusauit: Suetonius aims to prove the hypocrisy of his subject by contrasting his immediate seizure of the *indicia* of power while at the same time mouthing uncertainties over whether he wanted the role. This interpretation has many parallels with that of Tacitus (*Ann.* 1.7.7-8; 1.11ff.; cf. Dio 57 2.1-3), and it may be suspected that he has been influenced by the consular historian (see introduction 33-34). The structure is as follows:

> 1. Tiberius immediately demanded a praetorian bodyguard. This has sinister overtones, since the presence of a bodyguard had been associated with tyranny since the age of Pisistratus.
> 2. He was encouraged by friends, who were scolded for their exhortations.
> 3. The Senate was kept guessing through evasive answers which elicited taunts.
> 4. Eventually he accepted amidst a show of reluctance and complaints. According to Tacitus he gradually moved to a position where he stopped denying his power, though he would not openly admit it (Tac. *Ann.* 1.13.6: *fessusque clamore omnium, expostulatione singulorum flexit paulatim, non ut fateretur suscipi a se imperium, sed ut negare et rogari desineret*). The more friendly Velleius separates the acceptance of the principate from the mutinies, but nevertheless suggests that final acceptance was forced on Tiberius by circumstances (Vell. 2.124.2: *tandem magis ratione quam honore uictus est, cum quicquid tuendum non suscepisset, periturum uideret*).

On the much discussed chronological problems see G. Kampff, *Phoenix* 17 (1963) 25-58; K. Wellesley, *JRS* 57 (1967) 23-30; M.M. Sage, *Ancient Society* 13/14 (1982/83) 293-321, which incorporates a full bibliography.

impudentissimo mimo: this well-known phrase is not in fact well attested. It was a conjecture from the pen of Gronouius, based on some parallels in other Suetonian lives (Suet. *Cal.* 45.2: *in hoc quoque mimo praeter modum intemperans; Otho* 3.2). Manuscripts read *animo*. Whichever is correct, a similarly sceptical view of the accession can be found in Tacitus (Tac. *Ann.* 1.46.1: *trepida ciuitas incusare Tiberium quod, dum patres et plebem, inualida et inermia, cunctatione ficta ludificetur, dissideat interim miles*).

adhortantis amicos increpans ut *ignaros, quanta belua esset imperium*: perhaps Asinius Gallus was one of those who pressed the emperor. Levick suggests that his official reaction was a response to the impracticality of the Tiberian approach to his powers (Levick [1976] 248 n. 22). Gallus' emphasis was on the indivisibility of power; this may have been an inheritance from Augustan propaganda. See Tac. *Ann.* 1.9.5: *non aliud discordantis patriae remedium quam ut ab uno regeretur* (cf. 1.11.1: *solam diui Aug. mentem tantae molis capacem...in ciuitate tot inlustribus uiris subnixa non ad unum omnia deferrent* [alleged to be the response of Tiberius]); Strabo 6.4.2 = C288: χαλεπὸν δὲ ἄλλως διοικεῖν τὴν τηλικαύτην ἡγεμονίαν ἢ ἑνὶ ἐπιτρέψαντας ὡς πατρί. In Tacitus there is more emphasis on the ambiguity of Tiberian behaviour at this juncture than the reluctance depicted here by Suetonius (Tac. *Ann.* 1.11.2).

nunc precantem senatum et procumbentem sibi ad genua: cf. Tac. *Ann.* 1.11; Vell. 2.124.2.

aut agat aut desistat: for interpretation of this loss of patience see Levick (1976) 76. The passage provides important evidence on the subject of interjections in the Senate. See R.J.A. Talbert (1984) 265. On the possibility that Suetonius obtained the quotation from the *acta senatus* see ibid. 324.

24.2

tandem quasi coactus...recepit imperium: cf. Vell. 2.124.2; Tac. *Ann.* 1.13.6; Dio 57.7.1. Suetonius then purports to give his actual words of acceptance. These are couched in terms intended to be suggestive of the Senate's power over imperial *imperium*. This implies that the emperor kept up throughout the facade that he was only to receive what the Senate insisted on conferring upon him. It may be that this was carried through to the extent that Tiberius' initial grant in AD 14 was for a ten year period only. There are some traces in Dio of renewals in AD 24 and 34 (Dio 57.24.1; 58.24.1; see Seager [1972] 56).

nec tamen aliter, quam ut depositurum se quandoque spem faceret: after the death of his son Drusus, Tiberius is said to have made what Tacitus saw as empty professions of this sort, picking up earlier observations about Tiberian hypocrisy (Tac. *Ann.* 4.9.1; cf. 1.11.2).

25.1

Cunctandi causa erat metus undique: Suetonius produces a somewhat implausible list of reasons for Tiberian hesitation. Modern scholarship has investigated closely the chronology of the acceptance as well as the reasons for the delay. What seems beyond question is that there was a delay, although there is divergence over whether it was feigned or not. Contemporary sources, Ovid and Velleius, both favourable to Tiberius, confirm it as historical (Ov. *Ex Pont.* 4.13.27-8: *qui frena rogatus saepe recusati ceperit imperii;* Vell. 2.124.2: *solique huic contigit paene diutius recusare principatum quam, ut occuparent eum, alii armis pugnauerant*). Tacitus believed it was a fraud (Tac. *Ann.* 1.46.1: *cunctatio ficta*), and this tradition has been followed either directly or indirectly by both Suetonius and Dio (Suet. *Tib.* 24.1: *impudentissimo mimo*; Dio 57.2.3).

Suetonius has the *duplex seditio* in Germany and Pannonia as a major cause for the hesitation, after mentioning other aspects of the military situation which he alleges were in confusion already at the time of accession. These were the activities of M. Scribonius Libo (wrongly given the *praenomen* L., a confusion with his brother who was consul in AD 16: see *PIR¹* S 214; *RE* s.v. Scribonius no. 23; E.J. Weinrib, *HSCPh* 72 [1967] 247-78), and of Clemens, who is supposed to have attempted the rescue of Agrippa Postumus. This seems to be a classic interpretation from after the event, and has been influenced by Suetonius' biographical interest in linking the theme of fear to the actual behaviour of the emperor. See M.M. Sage, *Ancient Society* 12/13 (1982/3) 293-321 at 299 (also Goodyear [1981] 271). The actual trial of Libo did not take place until AD 16, and although the affair may have had its beginning in the previous year (Suet. *Tib.* 3: *secundo demum anno*), it cannot have been a factor in the *cunctatio*. Similarly it appears impossible to accept that Tiberius already knew of the activities of Clemens at the moment of accession.

Dio also combines the idea that Tiberius' character influenced his behaviour with his fear of the Rhine and Pannonian legions, but is more dogmatic in his view that they influenced his delay (Dio 57.3.1ff). This has no independent value, but serves to confirm that the tradition was uncertain over the emperor's motives, and speculation had become entrenched in the Julio-Claudian tradition at an early stage.

A *recusatio* need not imply either hypocrisy or fear. It would fit with Tiberian handling of the Senate in the early debates described by Tacitus if

Tiberius was hoping for a formal offer of the principate from the Senate. Much of the tradition could be explained if this was never forthcoming, and Tiberius was forced to slip into the role of emperor as inconspicuously as he could. We would then have Tiberius attempting to follow the Augustan precedent of being offered powers in 27 BC, but failing. This would help to explain tensions with the Senate, especially in the first years of his reign. Perhaps the Senate wanted an open admission of his power, as is implied by the famous question 'What part of the state do you wish to have intrusted to you?' (Tac. *Ann.* 1.12).

saepe *lupum se auribus tenere* **diceret:** the phrase has been discussed recently by J.B. Campbell (1984) 417ff., who emphasises the ambiguities in Tiberius' position created by his close relationship with his troops. The comparison was proverbial (Terence *Phormio* 506: *immo, id quod aiunt, auribus teneo lupum \ nam neque quo pacto a me amittam neque uti retineam scio*).

seruus Agrippae Clemens nomine: for the other sources see Tac. *Ann.* 2.39-40; Dio 57.16.3-4 (repeating the Tacitean anecdote). He is said to have made an unsuccessful attempt to rescue Agrippa Postumus from Planasia in AD 14 before the episode mentioned here (Tac. *Ann.* 2.39). Mogenet is sceptical about the earlier event (*AC* 23 [1954] 321). See also Levick (1976) 150-51. All three sources emphasise a substantial following for Clemens. For a slave of Agrippa's who apparently did not pass into imperial hands at the time of Postumus' elimination from the succession see *CIL* V 3257: *Sex. Vipsanius M. f. Clemens*.

25.2

Germaniciani...ui Germanicum...ad capessendam rem p. urgebant: cf. Suet. *Cal.* 1.1; Tac. *Ann.* 1.34.1;35.4ff; Vell. 2.125.2; Dio 57.5.1ff.; 6.2;18.8. Despite this tradition that Germanicus had the opportunity of power there is no sign of anything but mutual loyalty (see Levick [1976] 148). Even Velleius who seems cool towards Germanicus concedes a tribute to his refusal of the opportunity for disloyalty (2.125.2: *defuitque qui contra rem publicam duceret, non qui sequerentur*; cf. 2.125.4 and Woodman [1977] 229-31). These sources are however in agreement over the political nature of the mutiny.

quem maxime casum timens: on Tiberius' fear and distrust of Germanicus see also Tac. *Ann.* 1.52; 2.5; Dio 57.6.2f. See also 52.1 below. This is an entrenched element of the tradition, but there have been some dissenters.

See Seager [1972] 64 n.4.

25.3
Libonem...secundo demum anno in senatu coarguit: on this conspiracy see Vell. 2.129.2; 130.3; Tac. *Ann.* 2.27-32; Dio 57.15.4f., discussed by R.S. Rogers (1935) 12ff. On the stupidity of Libo in following the promptings of Firmius Catus for him to seize the principate see Sen. *Ep.* 70.10. Catus is then said to have used an intermediary, Vescularius Flaccus, to betray Libo's intentions (Tac. *Ann.* 2.28; cf. 6.10; the notion that Catus deliberately plotted Libo's ruin is, however, dismissed by Rogers as Scribonian propaganda [op.cit. 13]). As for the date of the conspiracy, in Tacitus' account Tiberius was already emperor before Firmius made contact with Vescularius. Thus late in AD 14. Libo was still allowed to hold the praetorship in AD 15. See Seager (1972) 89-93. Libo was very well connected, and represented a serious threat. He was related to Scribonia, and a great-grandson of Pompey. On the prosopographics see J. Scheid, *MEFRA* 87 (1975) 349-75.

inter pontifices sacrificanti: Levick suggests that Libo was praetor in AD 15 (not AD 16), and could thus have been one of Velleius' colleagues (see Vell. 2.124.4: *nobilissimis ac sacerdotalibus uiris*), although Velleius later describes Libo as an ingrate (2.129.2: *ingratum*). In any case there is no surprise in a man of Libo's pedigree being a *pontifex*. The whole story of the incident with the lead knife is probably an accretion covering the long delay between the information against Libo and his eventual trial. Suetonius highlights a certain level of (possibly jocular) paranoia on the part of Tiberius. The *secespita* appears to have been an ornamental trapping of the office of *pontifex* at this period (cf. Festus s.v. *secespita*). See R. Gordon in M. Beard & J. North (eds) *Pagan Priests* (1990) 206.

26-40 Rule of Tiberius: up to retirement to Capri
26-32 Initial pretence of *moderatio*

26.1
ciuilem admodum inter initia...priuatum egit: honours are used to illustrate the *ciuilitas* of Tiberius and thus Suetonius begins a series of sections aimed at showing his insistence on freedom of speech. This is not aimed at showing a positive side of his character, but rather as a further proof of his hypocrisy, since he eventually abrogates virtually every freedom that he champions. Tacitus also has this initial good period. Various catalysts are suggested by both authors for a decline in the quality of the principate, with special

Commentary

emphasis on the impact of deaths within the imperial family. Either the death of Germanicus or that of Drusus is raised at different points in the narrative (Tac. *Ann.* 6.51.5; 4.1.1; 4.6.1; 4.7.1; Cf. Suet. *Tib.* 39; *Cal.* 6.2). Rietra points out that Suetonius' vocabulary shows Tiberius merely as an actor in this context (ad loc.).

natalem suum...uix unius bigae adiectione honorari passus est: Tiberius' birthday was 16th November. See 5 above. For his refusal of honours relating to his birthday see also Dio 58.12.8. Since the age of Augustus there had been games from 4th-17th November. These were *ludi scaenici* from 4th-11th, *ludi circenses* from 13th-17th. See *CIL* 1^2 p. 249.

templa, flamines, sacerdotes decerni sibi prohibuit: see also Dio 57.9.1f; for a list of instances not in accord with the spirit of this see Seager (1972) 144ff. Ancient sources misunderstood the purpose of Tiberian refusals of honours. It was important for the entrenchment of the imperial cult that honours should not be cheapened. On the imperial cult see:

M.P. Charlesworth, 'The refusal of divine honours: an Augustan formula' *PBSR* 15 (1939) 1-10.
D. Fishwick, *The imperial cult in the Latin West: studies in the ruler cult of the western provinces of the Roman Empire*, 3 vols (1987).
O. Montevecchi, 'Osservazioni sulla lettera di Tiberio ai Giteati' *Epigraphica* 7 (1945) 104-108.
S.R.F. Price, 'Between man and god: sacrifice in the Roman imperial cult' *JRS* 70 (1980) 28-43.
——*Rituals and Power: The Roman imperial cult in Asia Minor* (Cambridge, 1984).
——'Gods and emperors: the Greek language of the Roman imperial cult' *JHS* 104 (1984) 79-95.
L.R. Taylor, 'Tiberius' refusals of divine honours' *TAPhA* 60 (1929) 87-101.
——*The Divinity of the Roman Emperor* (**1931**).

etiam statuas atque imagines nisi permittente se poni: see Dio 57.9.1. For the relevance of this to the small number of surviving portraits of Tiberius see 68.1. The attitude of Pontius Pilate in Judaea appears discrepant. See Jos. *AJ* 18.55-59. Most emperors in the early Roman empire expressly forbade their images to be created in precious metals. Tiberius was even more moderate. See K. Scott, *TAPhA* 63 (1931) 101-23.

26.2

intercessit et quo minus in acta sua iuraretur: see also Tac. *Ann.* 1.72.2; Dio 57.8.4 for the refusal of the oath early in the reign. In AD 32 when the Senate was anxious to ingratiate itself with Tiberius individual oaths of allegiance were sworn. Dio tells us that these had been untraditional during the reign of Tiberius. Eventually one member of the Senate had been permitted to swear allegiance, and the remainder to assent (Dio 58.17.2-3; cf. 59.13.1). On oaths of allegiance to the emperor see P. Hermann (1968).

et ne mensis September Tiberius, October Liuius uocarentur: according to Dio the month of November was called Tiberius (Dio 57.18.2). This was perhaps in AD 17-18. Tiberius is supposed to have quipped: 'What will you do, then, if there are thirteen Caesars?' November was the month of the *princeps'* birthday (5 above). Scott suggests that the proposal mentioned here by Suetonius should be dated earlier in Tiberius' reign, soon after the death of Augustus, when extravagant honours were proposed for Liuia (K. Scott *YCS* 2 [1931] 227-8). According to Dio some of the proposed honours were not sanctioned by the emperor, and Suetonius may be correct in noting an imperial refusal at that stage (Dio 57.12.4-5; cf. Tac. *Ann.* 1.14.3). This accords with his policy of moderation over the imperial cult.

In Egypt attempts to curb honorific months were largely ineffectual, and in general Tiberius appears to have allowed some latitude in the Eastern provinces. The title applied to Tiberius in Egypt was Νέος Σεβαστός. This honorific name was applied to the month of Tiberius' birth. See Scott, *YCS* 2 (1931) 243-4.

On the island of Cyprus a calendar of about 15 BC shows honorific months for various members of the imperial family including Liuia. Liuia's month begins on the second day of December, not October as suggested here. See G. Grether, *AJPh* 67 (1946) 232.

On the naming of months after emperors and their relatives compare Suet. *Iul.* 76.1; *Aug.* 31.2; *Aug.* 100.3; *Cal.* 15.2; *Nero* 55; *Dom.* 13.3. The Suetonian interest in the area will have been a product of the work he had written on the Roman year (Suda s.v. Τράγκυλλος). See Wallace-Hadrill (1983) 43; 48; 132, who reminds us that the later works on the subject by Censorinus and Macrobius drew heavily on the antiquarian work of Suetonius.

For a full treatment of honorific months see K. Scott, *YCS* 2 (1931) 201-78.

praenomen imperatoris: cf. Dio 57.2.1; 57.8.1. Perhaps Tiberius refused to use the title Caesar Augustus at the beginning of his reign as much because it was identified with the person of Augustus as for reasons of *ciuilitas*. The *cognomen* Augustus was, however, later applied to all the emperors, which can explain why Suetonius mentions Tiberian caution. In the oath to Tiberius from Palaipaphos space is on two occasions left for the later insertion of the title. See T.B. Mitford, *JRS* 50 (1960) 75-79. For unofficial usage and provincial errors see list in Seager (1972) 142 n. 2. On the title *imperator* see R. Syme, *Historia* 7 (1958) 172-185.

cognomenque patris patriae et ciuicam in uestibulo coronam recusauit: see Tac. *Ann.* 1.72.1: *nomen patris patriae Tiberius, a populo saepius ingestum, repudiauit;* 2.87.2 (AD 19): *neque tamen ob ea parentis patriae delatum et antea uocabulum adsumsit.* See also Dio 57.8.1; 58.12.8 (AD 31); 58.22.1. On restraint over accepting the honour in the early empire see also Plin. *Pan.* 21.

Suetonius gives a fuller explanation of his attitude to the honour at 67.2, where details of the form of the *recusatio* are recorded. In fact the title is very rarely found on Tiberian inscriptions or coins. It is ascribed to him on the Gytheum decree of AD 15, apparently in error (*AE* 1929, 99 = *EJ*^{2} 102). Augustus had first formally taken the title in 2 BC, but there exists evidence that it was used before this (Dio 55.10.10; *ILS* 96 [6-5 BC]; 6755; *CIL* II 2107; 1^2 p. 309). See E.S. Shuckburgh (1896) 117f.

ne Augusti quidem nomen...addidit: see also Dio 57.2.1; 8.1f. On the falseness of this claim see K. Scott *CPh* 27 (1932) 43-50; Seager (1972) 143; Levick (1976) 247 n.11. On official letters see introduction **28**.

ciuicam in uestibulo coronam recusauit: but it is found on coins as early as AD 15, and can also be seen on busts. See *RIC*^{2} Tiberius no. 70; 94. The *corona ciuica* was originally granted for saving the life of a Roman citizen in battle under defined circumstances. It had been traditional since at least the time of Polybius to display *dona militaria* in the *uestibulum* (Polyb. 6.39). See *RE* s.v. *corona civica*; V. Maxfield (1981) 170-74. Augustus had taken up an idea started by Caesar (RG 34.2; Weinstock [1971] 203).

nullis nisi ad reges ac dynastas epistulis addidit: cf. Tac. *Ann.* 1.7.6; Dio 57.2.1; 57.8.1.

nec amplius quam mox tres consulatus unum paucis diebus: Tiberius was consul altogether on five occasions, three of them when he was emperor. Suetonius refers to the instances as emperor.

The first tenure as emperor was in AD 18. A suffect consul took his place early in the year, perhaps already by the ides of January. There is epigraphic evidence of the presence of a suffect on 19th April (*ILS* 3335).

alterum tribus mensibus: this was in AD 21 when he joined Drusus as consul. This was Drusus' second consulship and Tiberius' fourth. Two suffect consuls are known to be in office by 30th May. See A. Degrassi (1952) 8; *EJ*^{2} p. 41. Drusus probably gave up office at the same time as his father (Seager [1972] 120 n. 2).

tertium absens usque in Idus Maias: this consulship with Seianus in AD 31 came to an end on 8th May (*ILS* 6124; cf. Dio 58.4.4). There is probably a corruption in the text of Suetonius at this point, if it is not merely an error. This was actually Tiberius' 5th consulship (Suet. *Tib.* 65.1), but it was his third during his own principate. On consulates in absence see Syme, *JRS* 48 (1958) 1-9.

27

Adulationem...auersatus est: many examples of his hatred of flattery can be adduced from Tacitus. See Tac. *Ann.* 2.87.2; 3.18; 3.69; 3.70; 4.6.2; Dio 57.11.3-4; 57.17.8.

consularem...per genua orare conantem: this appears to be a reference to the episode involving Haterius Agrippa as related by Tac. *Ann.* 1.13. He is supposed to have come to apologise to Tiberius for his forthright behaviour during the succession debate, and barely escaped with his life after accidentally knocking over the emperor. On Haterius see *PIR*^{2} H 24.

dominus appellatus a quodam denuntiauit...alium dicentem sacras eius occupationes: cf. Tac. *Ann.* 2.87.2: *acerbe increpuit eos, qui diuinas occupationes ipsumque dominum dixerant*; Dio 57.8.2. Suetonius seems to personalise what is seen by Tacitus as a general trend. The title *dominus* had also met with hostility from Augustus. See Suet. *Aug.* 53.1; Dio 55.12.2. On the association between the title *dominus* and notions of autocracy and servitude see T.R. Stevenson, *CQ* 42 (1992) 421-36 at 421-2.

pro auctore suasorem: this is apparently because of its implication of *auctoritas*, clearly seen as having autocratic overtones.

28

aduersus conuicia...famosa de se ac suis carmina: for some samples see 59 below. Tacitus claims to quote Tiberius' refusal to prosecute on his own account on grounds of treasonous words under AD 17 (Tac. *Ann.* 2.50.2: *in se iacta nolle ad cognitionem uocari*; cf. Dio 52.31.5-8 [the advice of Maecenas to follow this procedure]). The first cases concerning prosecution relating to violation of the divinity of Augustus are found under AD 15 - those of the *equites* Falanius and Rubrius (Tac. *Ann.* 1.73); these were quickly dismissed. But as early as AD 17 the crime of profane utterance against the divinised Augustus was placed in a separate category from insults to the reigning emperor (Tac. *Ann.* 2.50.2; cf. Dio 57.9.2). On the crime of *maiestas* under Tiberius see:

R. Bauman, *Impietas in Principem* (1974).

C.W. Chilton, 'The Roman law of treason under the early principate' *JRS* 45 (1955) 73-81.

E. Koestermann, 'Die Majestatsprozesse unter Tiberius' *Historia* 4 (1955) 72-106.

B. Levick, 'Poena legis maiestatis' *Historia* 28 (1979) 358-79.

R.S. Rogers, *Criminal Trials and Criminal Legislation under Tiberius* (1935).

——'Treason in the early empire' *JRS* 49 (1959) 90-94.

in ciuitate libera linguam mentemque liberas esse debere: on his approach to freedom of speech compare Dio 57.9.2; 57.19.1 and see Levick (1976) 192, who notes his anxiety to avoid convictions for slander of the emperor. On the freedom of his approach to the Senate see 30 below.

omnium inimicitiae...ad uos deferentur: Levick sees in this statement the increasing cynicism and apapthy of an ageing emperor (Levick [1976] 195).

extat et sermo eius perciuilis: Suetonius quotes verbatim here and in the preceding examples, and it is highly probable that his source is the *acta senatus*. See R.J.A. Talbert (1984) 324; cf. Goodyear (1981) 185, discussing Tac. *Ann.* 1.81.1, who thinks it possible that there was a collection of speeches, perhaps that perused by Domitian (Suet. *Dom.* 20). See further comment in introduction **26-32**.

29 Relationship With The Senate

ipse in appellandis...prope excesserat humanitatis modum: see Suet. *Reliquiae* (Reiff.) 88: (*Passienus*) *Crispus tiricinio suo in senatu ita coepit: 'patres conscripti et tu Caesar', propter quod simulata oratione a Tiberio* *conlaudatus est.* Other examples at Dio 57.11.1; 57.7.4.

dissentiens in curia a Q. Haterio: see Tac. *Ann.* 1.13. For details of his career see *PIR*[2] H 24.

ignoscas...siquid..liberius sicut senator dixero: for analysis see Levick (1976) 77-8.

bonum et salutarem principem: for the conservative Republican origins of the notion of a *salutaris princeps* see Val. Max. 2.9.6; 8.13 praef; Levick (1976) 86. After the fall of Seianus in AD 32 *Salus Perpetua Augusta* appears on an inscription from Interamna (*ILS* 157 = *EJ*[2] 51).

The whole quotation is a clear statement of the emperor's view of his ideal relationship with the Senate, namely that his considerable powers were to be seen as a product of Senatorial gift, and that his own obligation was to act as their servant. This view had some precedents in the Republic, but too much can be made of his desire to follow any specific model (cf. Levick [1976] 33). Tiberius never attained his ideal relationship with the senate and he is later supposed to have described them as men ready for slavery (Tac. *Ann.* 3.65: *homines ad seruitutem paratos*; cf. Talbert [1984] 184).

30

Quin etiam speciem libertatis quandam induxit...neque tam paruum quicquam...de quo non ad patres conscriptos referretur: Tacitus talks in very similar terms of Tiberius' early relationship with the Senate and the magistrates. See Tac. *Ann.* 4.6.2: *iam primum publica negotia et priuatorum maxima apud patres tractabantur, dabaturque primoribus disserere et in adulationem lapsos cohibebat ipse; mandabatque honores, nobilitatem maiorum, claritudinem militiae, inlustres domi artes spectando, ut satis constaret non alios potiores fuisse. sua consulibus, sua praetoribus species; minorum quoque magistatuum exercita potestas*; 4.15.2; Dio 57.7.2ff.; 57.11.3. Even the language of Suetonius has echoes of Tacitus, with whom he shares the view that the liberty so bestowed was a mere sham. See Tac. *Ann.* 1.77.3: *silente Tiberio, qui ea simulacra libertatis senatui praebebat.* Each author shows a Tiberius who is attempting to recreate a Republican-style role for the Senate. Rietra cites Tiberian coins which emphasise the status of the Senate [(1941) 24]. This emerges clearly from the well-known transfer of praetorian elections to the Senate in ad 14 (Tac. *Ann.* 1.15.1; Vell. 2.124.3). Velleius says that Tiberius restored the *maiestas* of the Senate (2.126.2). See also Goodyear (1972) 322 on Tac. *Ann.* 1.52.2.

de uectigalibus ac monopoliis: this is of interest since it shows Tiberius trying to retain the Senate's traditional financial involvement. In so doing Tiberius was following an Augustan precedent. Pliny tells us that monopolies were a frequent subject of *senatus consulta*, and that every emperor up to his time had received complaints from the provinces relating to monopolies (Plin. *NH* 8.135; cf. 71 below). See R.J.A. Talbert (1984) 376; 415-6. Tacitus, however, says that it was the emperor himself who decided to reduce the *uectigal* from 1% to $^1/_2$% as a result of the revenues from the recently annexed Cappadocia (Tac. *Ann.* 2.42.6).

de extruendis reficiendisue operibus: thus M. Lepidus applied to the Senate when he wanted to restore the Basilica Aemilia in AD 22 (Tac. *Ann.* 3.72.3). On the other hand the emperor himself undertook to restore the theatre of Pompey on the grounds that no member of the family had sufficient resources (Tac. *Ann.* 3.72.4). What is clear is that major and conspicuous public benefactions were not permitted indiscriminately, and imperial interventions could be expected with major projects. However, despite the imperial intervention, the theatre of Pompey was allowed to keep its name. Augustus had appointed *curatores operum publicorum*, who provided a precedent for Senatorial involvement in this domain (Suet. *Aug.* 37). For the scope of their activities and an account of their antecedents see summary in J.M. Carter (1982) 148.

de legendo uel exauctorando milite ac legionum et auxiliorum discriptione: this might be a generalising reference to the extraordinary circumstances of the mutiny of AD 14 when Drusus promised to refer the mutineers claims to the Senate, as suggested by Levick [1976] 108. The mutineers disputed this mode of procedure (Tac. *Ann.* 1.26.5f.), but it appears that the emperor did at least confirm the arrangements made by both Germanicus and Drusus with the Senate (Tac. *Ann.* 1.52.2). When in AD 15 by edict he reversed the decisions made, it seems unlikely that Tiberius went through the consultative process (Tac. *Ann.* 1.78.2f.). For his sharp response to Gallio over a proposal relating to the praetorian guard see Tac. *Ann.* 6.3.1f. It also seems certain that the levying of troops remained firmly in imperial hands. See P.A. Brunt, *ZPE* 13 (1974) 161-85; R.J.A. Talbert (1984) 426-7.

Few significant changes in the disposition of the legions are known under Tiberius. In AD 20 legio IX Hispana was sent from Pannonia to Africa (Tac. *Ann.* 3.9.1; 4.5.4), but it was ordered back to Pannonia in AD 24 (Tac. *Ann.* 4.23.2; see E. Ritterling, *RE* s.v. legio col. 1242; 1666). Tacitus attributes the change to imperial initiative, and does not mention consultation with the Senate. This can, however, perhaps be assumed in view of the great care taken by the emperor to consult over this province. See Levick (1976) 110. Compare 31.2 below on the emperor insisting that reports from Africa be tabled in the Senate. On legion movements in the early empire see H.M.D. Parker (1928) 118-29.

denique quibus imperium prorogari aut extraordinaria bella mandari: for debate in the Senate over the merit of candidates we can turn to the discussion in AD 21 over the issue of whether to prorogue or appoint new candidates for the proconsulates of Asia and Africa. Tiberius eventually had the choice thrust back on him by the Senate, and is said to have chipped the Senators for their unwillingness to make a decision (Tac. *Ann.* 3.32-5). Suetonius may here generalise from that single instance, as suggested by Orth (1970) 41.

In AD 22 P. Dolabella proposed that the emperor should scrutinise the character of potential candidates, but this was met with a refusal (Tac. *Ann.* 3.69.1ff.). As time went on imperial intervention appears to have increased, to judge from the case of C. Galba in AD 36 (Tac. *Ann.* 6.40.3; Suet. *Galba* 3.4). He committed suicide after a letter from the emperor forbade him to be a candidate for a lucrative consular province. See Levick (1976) 109. Levick believes that Tiberius began to take more of the decisions independently after AD 28 (op.cit. 113).

For the emperor's right over war and peace see Strabo 17.3.25 = C840; *ILS* 244 (the *Lex de Imperio Vespasiani*, on which see P.A. Brunt, *JRS* 67 [1977] 95-116); Dio 53.17.5. As pointed out above Tacitus says nevertheless that Tiberius allowed the Senate a free choice over the most suitable soldier for the war with Tacfarinas (Tac. *Ann.* 3.32.1) - a sign of an unusually careful attitude to Senatorial prerogatives in Senatorial provinces.

quid et qua forma regum litteris rescribi placeret: this shows again that Tiberius was trying to include the Senate in its traditional sphere of foreign affairs (see Dio 57.17.9 for a statement of the policy). This is one reason why the trial of Archelaus in AD 17 is conducted before that body (8 above). Compare the activities of Caligula as discussed by A.A. Barrett, *CQ* 40 (1990) 284-86 and answered by D. Wardle, *CQ* 42 (1992) 437-43.

praefectum alae...in senatum dicere coegit: on the status of the *praefectus alae* see V. Maxfield (1981) 28-36. Tiberius appears to intend to compliment the Senate through an extension of its jurisdiction (cf. Dio 52.33.2 for Maecenas' advice on the area). Later emperors seem not to have followed his example. See P.D.A. Garnsey (1970) 31; 86. Compare the prosecution of Lucilius Capito, a procurator in Asia, and the Tacitean report of the emperor's motives (Tac. *Ann.* 4.15 [AD 23]).

numquam curiam nisi solus intrauit: this appears to have been the case in the earlier part of his principate despite Tac. *Ann.* 1.7.7: *miles in forum, miles in curiam comitabatur.* In AD 32, in the aftermath of the suppression of Seianus, Togonius Gallus proposed that the emperor should take a bodyguard (Tac. *Ann.* 6.2). In AD 33 the emperor himself requested permission for the praetorian prefect and some of the tribunes and centurions from the guard to accompany him to the Senate. Although this measure was passed without restriction, Dio says that in the following year a resolution was passed that the guard should be searched on entering. Tiberius never took advantage of the concession (Tac. *Ann.* 6.15.5-6; Dio 58.18.5-6). Caligula and Claudius entrenched the presence of a bodyguard (Dio 59.26.3; Suet. *Claud.* 12.1). See Barrett (1989) 159.

lectica quondam intro latus: cf. Dio 57.17.6 (Archelaus in a litter at his trial). Dio comments that even men (including Tiberius) would use a litter when ill. See also 60 below.

31.1
quaedam aduersus sententiam suam decerni ne questus quidem est: see Dio 57.7.5; 57.15.9. On the limits of imperial tolerance see Levick (1976) 112. An example of a senator testing his patience is Valerius Messalla Messallinus who proposed that the oath of allegiance should be repeated annually (Tac. *Ann.*1.8.5) Compare the attititude of Ateius Capito (*Ann.* 3.70.3), where the Senator's insistence on Senatorial prerogatives is interpreted by Tacitus as a mere sham.

Trebianis legatam in opus noui theatri pecuniam ad munitionem uiae transferre concederetur: this instance of the emperor conceding to Senatorial opinion may relate to a series of appeals by Italian towns, initiated after the *Curatores Aluei Tiberis* recommended diverting tributary waters upstream of Rome. See Tac. *Ann.* 1.79; 2.35.3 (AD 16). For the suggestion of this context see Levick [1976] 106. On embassies concerned with this type of request see R.J.A. Talbert (1984) 417.

cum senatus consultum per discessionem forte fieret: see also Tac. *Ann.* 3.53.2; Dio 57.7.3-4; 21.1 on Tiberius' moderate approach to interventions.

31.2
tanta consulum auctoritate...ipsum...assurgere et decedere uia: note that the emperor is said to have absented himself from Rome on 1st January to avoid overshadowing the consuls on their first day of office (Dio 57.8.5;

11.3). He would however send them injunctions (Dio 58. 21.3).

In this instance it appears that the embassy from Africa went to the consuls after failing to get satisfaction from the emperor (see R.J.A. Talbert [1984] 416). This is an unusual situation, since there is other evidence that under Tiberius the Senate was left to deal with matters in Senatorial provinces, and indeed was allowed greater freedom than we ever hear of under other Julio-Claudian emperors. As early as AD 15 the Senatorial provinces of Achaea and Macedonia were directing their appeals against their tax burden to the Senate. In the event it was resolved to transfer these provinces for the moment back into imperial jurisdiction, apparently on the grounds that this was less costly (Tac. *Ann.* 1.76.4 with Furneaux ad loc.; cf. Tac. *Ann.* 2.42.7-43 [AD 17], similar complaints from Syria and Judaea, perhaps also heard by the Senate). The Senate was allowed to sort out the issue of asylum in Greek cities (Tac. *Ann.* 3.60-63 [AD 22]). They were to handle further Greek embassies in the following year (Tac. *Ann.* 4.14). Notice the appeal of Baetica over imperial honours (Tac. *Ann.* 4.37.1). The earthquake in AD 17 shows some typical distribution of responsibility. The emperor was to provide largesse while the Senate was to send a man of praetorian rank to supervise its distribution (Tac. *Ann.* 2.47). Levick draws attention to the differences between the way Tiberius handled the episode, and the handling of the earthquake in 27 BC by Augustus, at which time direct imperial intervention was blatant. Senatorial involvement under Tiberius had relevance in determining the inclusion of the Senate in the imperial cult in Asia Minor (Tac. *Ann.* 4.15.4ff.; 37.4; 55f; Levick [1976] 107). It is possible that Tiberius even went so far as to acknowledge Senatorial interest in imperial provinces (Levick [1976] 107-8). On whole area see F. Millar, *JRS* 56 (1966) 156-66.

32.1

corripuit consulares...quod non de rebus gestis senatui scriberent: in the Republic letters to the Senate were a major element in the duties of provincial governors (Cic. *In Pis.* 16.38). Agrippa stopped the practice of sending them Dio 54.11.6 [19 BC]; 54.24.7 [14 BC]). Talbert notes the paucity of evidence of letters to the Senate in the early empire from governors of Senatorial provinces. See R.J.A. Talbert (1984) 230-31. The story of the rebuff for legates who sent their reports to the emperor instead of to the Senate is thus of special interest, but many uncertainties subsist over details of the division of labour between Senate and emperor in these provinces. See Talbert op.cit. Chapter 13. Suetonius includes this point to show the traditional standing Tiberius wanted for his Senate. On official letters see also introduction **28**.

de tribuendis quibusdam militaribus donis ad se referrent: this is a generalisation of the case of L. Apronius who made some awards in Africa, but was criticised for not using the full extent of the repertoire (Tac. *Ann.* 3.21.3f.; cf. Aul. Gell. *NA* 5.6.14). See also Seager (1972) 168. On the award of *dona militaria* see Maxfield (1981) 110-44.

quorundam illustrium exequias usque ad rogum frequentauit: Augustus had instituted a restriction on cremations within 15 stades of the city (Dio 48.43.3). However the imperial family itself had *ustrina* in the Campus Martius, a location where burial was only possible by vote of the Senate (Strabo 5.3.8 = C235; Dio 39.64; for a discussion of the *ustrina* see M. Boatwright, *AJA* 89 [1985] 485-97). Most people of rank would be buried outside the confines of the city. It is perhaps understandable that there is little evidence to support Suetonius' contention that Tiberius was in the habit of following funerary processions as far as the pyre. Dio records that Tiberius gave the funeral speech when one of his companions died; this may be a reference to the death of Lucilius Longus (cf. Tac. *Ann.* 4.15.3). The emperor's son Drusus is said to have assisted with carryinig out the body at a funeral after being left as heir to the man's estate (Dio 57.14.9).

32.2

Parem moderationem minoribus...exhibuit: Suetonius attributes this vir-tue to Augustus (*Aug.* 21.3), but it is Tiberius who made moderation his own. For the ubiquity of *moderatio* as a claim both by and for Tiberius see Levick, *The Ancient Historian and his Materials* (1975) 123-37; Levick (1976) 89; Rogers (1943) 60-88; Sutherland (1951) 97ff; *JRS* 28 (1938) 129-40. It also appears in Velleius as an imperial attribute (2.122.1). It fits in as the attribute to be sought by an emperor trying to make a display of his *ciuilitas*. Tacitus reports that the impact of his attitude to sumptuary legislation in AD 22 was to increase his reputation for *moderatio* (Tac. *Ann.* 3.54.5; cf. 3.56: *Tiberius, fama moderationis parta quod ingruentis accusatores represserat*). For its display on coinage see *RIC*^{2} Tiberius nos. 40-41; on official correspondence (*EJ*^{2} 102 [Gytheum]). The date of the *dupondii* commemorating the *moderatio* and *clementia* of Tiberius has been much discussed. See 53.2 for bibliography and discussion of the possibilities.

cum Rhodiorum magistratus...remisit: cf. Dio 57.11.1-2.

Diogenes grammaticus, disputare sabbatis Rhodi solitus...non admiserat: the anecdote that follows illustrates Tiberian *moderatio*. Dio repeats a similar story in a passage on Tiberius' customary *ciuilitas* (57.11.2). On Tiberius' philological interests see M. Billerbeck, *Greece and Rome* 37

(1990) 191-203, esp. 196. Diogenes is not otherwise known. See *RE* s.v. Diogenes no. 24. On Tiberius' handling of *Graeculi* see also 56.; 70.3.

praesidibus...rescripsit *boni pastoris esse tondere pecus, non deglubere*: 'a good shepherd shears his flock; he does not flay them'. Aemilius Rectus is said to have collected more than the stipulated tax while governor of Egypt, and in this way to have provoked the above response. See Dio 57.10.5. Rectus was apparently prefect of Egypt in about AD 15. See G. Bastianini, *ZPE* 17 (1975) 263-328 at 270; for some doubts see J. Schwartz, *ZPE* 48 (1982) 189-92, who wonders about the value of Dio's evidence in view of the certainty that an L. Aemilius Rectus held the post in the first year of Claudius. No documents have emerged for an early Tiberian Rectus, which gives some support for his approach. Levick sees the anecdote as attuned to other known aspects of the emperor's hierarchical attitude to the provinces, whether it is authentic or not (Levick [1976] 129; cf. Tac. *Ann.* 3.54.6ff.). Velleius also makes positive claims about Tiberius' provincial policy (2.126.4: *uindicatae ab iniuriis magistratuum prouinciae*), but modern authorities have been less convinced. See P.A. Brunt, *Historia* 10 (1961) 189-223; G. Alföldy, *Latomus* 24 (1965) 824-44; W. Orth (1970). On the official correspondence of the emperor see introduction **28**.

33-37 Increasing Imperial Control Leading To Autocracy

33

Paulatim principem exeruit...constitutiones senatus quasdam rescidit: this is an important interpretative statement for Suetonius' characterisation of Tiberius. The pretence of consultation and moderation has to be cast off to reveal the true tyrant. No instances of Tiberius actually rescinding senatorial *constitutiones* are known, although he undoubtedly had this power through the tribunician *intercessio*. See Mommsen, *StR* II.843; Rietra (1928) 31.

magistratibus pro tribunali cognoscentibus: Tacitus, who lists these appearances in the praetor's court under AD 15, believed that these interventions increased Senatorial servility (Tac. *Ann.* 1.75.1f.; Dio 57.7.6 [AD 14],discussed by Seager (1972) 151).

et si quem reorum elabi gratia rumor esset: on the role of *gratia* in favouring certain defendants during trials (usually because of their *potentia*) see P.D.A. Garnsey (1970) 209. Velleius suggests in general terms that Tiberius caused improvements in the administration of justice (Vell. 2.126.2-3).

34.1

ludorum ac munerum impensas corripuit: there were debates on sumptuary issues in the Senate in both AD 16 and 22, and Tiberius repeatedly refused to be the sole sponsor of measures of this type (Tac. *Ann.* 2.33; 3.52ff.). Suetonius implies that all these measures were a directive from the emperor, but this seems unlikely (cf. Dio 57.15.1). See Rogers (1935) 23-24. However, his list includes measures which had an impact on the plebeians, as well as the purely aristocratic concerns of Tacitus. For signs of moderation in the legislation at this time see Aulus Gellius *NA* 2.24.14. The attitude to gladiatorial shows is in marked contrast to that of Drusus (Tac. *Ann.* 1.76; cf. Dio 57.13.1). Suetonius appears to know of Tiberius' views through his official correspondence. See introduction **28**.

For various restrictive measures passed against actors see Tac. *Ann.* 1.77 and compare the SC from Larinum, discussed at 35.2 below.

Corinthiorum uasorum: on these see Plin. *NH* 34.7.

tresque mul<l>os triginta milibus nummum uenisse grauiter conquestus: Tiberius appears to have been very fond of this fish. See 60 below. His *triclinium* at Sperlonga was equipped with its own fish-farm. See G. Iacopi (1963) 22-24. Compare Plin. *NH* 9.167 on imperial fish-ponds.

adhibendum supellectili modum: in AD 16 the Senate passed restrictions on the use of precious vessels for serving food. See Tac. *Ann.* 2.33.1: *decretumque ne uasa auro solida ministrandis cibis fierent*; Dio 57.15.1.

annonamque macelli senatus arbitratu quotannis temperandam: as far as is known this proposal failed. See R.J.A. Talbert (1984) 287.

popinas ganeasque usque eo inhibendi, ut ne opera quidem pistoria proponi uenalia sinerent: see Seager (1972) 141. This is itemised by Suetonius as a sumptuary measure, but our other information suggests less direct imperial intervention in that area. A moral context may be more credible.

ut parsimoniam publicam...iuuaret...semesa obsonia apposuit dimidiatumque aprum: on his *parsimonia* see below 46.

34.2

Cotidiana oscula edicto prohibuit: although this is billed as an attempt to cut down on public entertainments of all types because of perceived meanness of disposition, Syme has suggested that its aim was to prevent the spread of the *mentagra* from Egypt, which was recognised as being transferred by kissing (Plin. *NH* 26.2-3). The disease was disfiguring, causing a scaly eruption, and the emperor may have suffered from it. See Syme, *Roman Papers* III (1984) 1376f. It is possible that the restriction merely applied to ceremonial kisses. See M. Benner (1975) 88.

strenarum commercium ne ultra Kal. Ian. exerceretur: Suetonius sees the aim as to restrict contact between the emperor and the people. The edict is also mentioned by Dio (57.17.1; cf. 71 below). For his handling of New Year's day see Dio 57.8.4-6.

35.1

matronas prostratae pudicitiae...ut propinqui...coercerent auctor fuit: for Tiberian enthusiasm for ancestral punishments as organised by the relatives compare Tac. *Ann.* 2.50.4: *liberauitque Appuleiam lege maiestatis: adulterii grauiorem poenam deprecatus, ut exemplo maiorum propinquis suis ultra ducentesimam lapidem remoueretur, suasit.* In this case the trial of Appuleia was before the Senate, and Tiberius asks that the penalties under the Julian law should not be imposed. However, according to Suetonius, this private castigation was intended as a supplement, and not as a substitute for public prosecutions. For other examples of family discipline see S. Treggiari (1991) 267. Note how this procedure complements the spirit of the SC from Larinum (see below).

eq(uiti) R(omano) iuris iurandi gratiam fecit, uxorem in stupro generi compertam: for the terminology cf. Suet. *Aug.* 17.2: *Bononiensibus...gratiam fecit coniurandi.* It appears that the emperor took over from the *pontifices* and *censores* of the Republic the ability to release a man from his oath (possibly in the emperor's capacity as *Pontifex Maximus?*).

35.2

feminae famosae...lenocinium profiteri coeperant: this was to avoid the provisions of the Julian law *De Adulteriis*. Penalties under that legislation included loss of half of the dowry and one third of other property, as well as *relegatio*. The legal situation is covered by P.E. Corbett (1930) 133ff. Suetonius appears to generalise from the notorious instance of Vistilia, recorded by Tacitus (Tac. *Ann.* 2.85: *Vistilia praetoria familia genita licentiam stupri apud aediles uulgauerat, more inter ueteres recepto, qui satis poenarum aduersum impudicas in ipsa professione flagitii credebant*). See full discussion in T.A.J. McGinn, *ZPE* 93 (1992) 280ff. Clearly Vistilia hoped to retain her property rights, but in the event was subjected to harsh penalties. It has been noticed that (unlike Tacitus) Suetonius allows an indication of status to take the place of a proper name, reflecting his interest in moral reputation rather than in immoral persons *per se*. See McGinn, *ZPE* 93 (1992) 273-95, esp. 288-9. Tiberius' overall motive seems to have been to preserve the traditional dignity of the upper orders. See Seager (1972) 140. Although we are dealing here with a senatorial decree, this legisaltion is attributed by Suetonius directly to the emperor.

ex iuuentute utriusque ordinis...quominus in opera scaenae harenaeque edenda senatus consulto teneretur: Augustus had in 38 BC prevented Senators from engaging in gladiatorial combat (Dio 48.43.3; Suet. *Aug.* 43.3). In 22 BC this ban was extended to their descendants, and the stage as well as the arena was ruled out (Dio 54.2.5). In this way the ban had been extended to certain equestrian families. In AD 11 the ban on equestrian performances was lifted, but perhaps only temporarily (Dio 56.25.7-8). Tiberius himself followed this Augustan precedent when in AD 15 he allowed equestrians to fight in the games given by his son Drusus and Germanicus (Dio 57.14.3). See summary in B. Levick, *JRS* 73 (1983) 105-108. The SC from Larinum (*AE* 1978 145) has shown that Tiberius subsequently took much interest in the area, and it appears to be this restrictive measure of AD 19 to which Suetonius refers. Initially it was thought that the SC covered both the areas (i.e. both women of rank who wished to register as prostitutes, and young men who wished to appear in the arena), but closer analysis has suggested that two separate measures are canvassed here. See B. Levick, *JRS* 73 (1983) 97-115; W. Lebek, *ZPE* 81 (1990) 37-96; W. Lebek, *ZPE* 85 (1991) 41-70; T.A.J. McGinn, *ZPE* 93 (1992) 273-95 (for a clear summary in English).

eos easque omnes...exilio adfecit: according to Tacitus Vistilia was exiled on Seriphos (*Ann.* 2.85.4). As Lebek notes Suetonius appears to make a careless generalisation here, and it seems unlikely that exile has any relevance to the subject matter of the SC from Larinum, although it may have been a potential penalty for those who infringed its terms. See W. Lebek, *ZPE* 85 (1991) 41-70, esp. 56-61.

senatori latum clauum ademit: i.e deprived him of his entitlement to senatorial rank. On the *latus clauus* see A. Chastagnol, *RHD* 53 (1975) 375-94.

sub Kal. Iul. demigrasse in hortos, quo uilius post diem aedes in urbe conduceret: this was because 1st July was the date from which tenancy agreements started to roll. See Cic *Ad Q.f.* 2.3.7; *ad diu.* 13.2; Petron. *Sat.* 38.10; Martial *Ep.* 12.32. See B.W. Frier (1980) 34; 39. Senatorial participation in the rental market appears to be no rarity. It is a reflection of Tiberius' view of Senatorial dignity that he would not allow a senator to be seen to economise in this manner. See R.J.A. Talbert (1984) 57. Notice that there had been considerable inflation in rents by the age of Tiberius as compared with the time of the augur M. Lepidus Porcina (125 BC). He had received the censorial *nota* for renting a house at more than HS 6000, while Velleius Paterculus (writing in AD 30) thought this too little for a man of senatorial status (Vell. 2.10.1).

alium e quaestura remouit, quod uxorem pridie...ductam...repudiasset: why does he need a wife before the *sortitio* and not afterwards? It appears to have been in order to comply with a requirement of the Lex Pappaea Poppaea. The passage shows that in the imperial period quaestors continued to draw lots on a particular day for the posts they were to hold during their year of office, perhaps on 2nd December. See R.J.A. Talbert (1984) 208.

36

Aegyptios Iudaicosque ritus compescuit: the abolition of foreign cults at Rome was in AD 19. See Jos. *AJ* 18.81-4; Tac. *Ann.* 2.85.5; Dio 57.18.5a; cf. Sen. *Ep.* 108.22. There is little sign that Tiberius was intolerant of the religion elsewhere in the empire, and the action should probably be connected with proselytism at Rome. On attitudes to Jews in the age of Tiberius see also Philo *In Flacc.* 1.1; *Legatio* 24, 159, who sees moves against Jews as starting with Seianus rather than Tiberius. See detailed note by Rietra (1928) ad loc. Moves against the cult of Isis show that this movement was on some scale already in the age of Tiberius. Tiberius at some stage also suppressed druidism (Plin. *NH* 30.13: see Seager [1972] 150).

coactis qui superstitione ea tenebantur religiosas uestes...comburere: perhaps not relevant to the Jewish community. Priests and members of the Isis cult wore white linen garments which appear to be the subject of this measure. See Ovid *Met.* 1.747; *Pont.* 1.1.51; Tibull. 1.3.30; Suet. *Otho* 12; Juv. *Sat.* 6.533; App.*BC* 4.47, 200; Apul.*Met.* 11.10; Plut. *De Is.* 3, and further in Rietra (1928) ad loc.

Iudaeorum iuuentutem...in prouincias grauioris caeli distribuit: 4000 freedmen of military age were sent to Sardinia to deal with brigandage there, and Tacitus claimed that the emperor thought it would be *uile damnum* (Tac. *Ann.* 2.85.5; cf. Jos. *AJ* 18.84) if they were to die from the rigours of the climate. The emperor's real motives have attracted much attention. The following is a selection from the extensive bibliography:

E.T. Merrill, 'The Expulsion of the Jews from Rome under Tiberius', *CPh* 14 (1919) 365-72.

W.A. Heidel, 'Why were the Jews banished from Italy in AD 19?, *AJPh* 41 (1920) 38-47.

E.M. Smallwood, 'Some notes on the Jews under Tiberius', *Latomus* 15 (1956) 314-29.

——*The Jews under Roman Rule* (Leiden, Brill, 1976) 201-10.

H.R. Moehring, 'The persecution of the Jews and the adherents of the Isis cult at Rome AD 19', *Novum Testamentum* 3 (1959) 293-304.

E. Abel, 'Were the Jews banished from Rome in AD 19?', *REJ* 127 (1968) 383-6

M.H. Williams, 'The Expulsion of the Jews from Rome in AD 19', *Latomus* 48 (1989) 765-84.

expulit et mathematicos: see also Tac. *Ann.* 2.32.5: *facta et de mathematicis Italia pellendis senatus consulta; quorum e numero L. Pituanius saxo deiectus est, in P. Marcium consules extra portum Esquilinam, cum classicum canere iussissent, more prisco aduertere* (discussed by Goodyear [1981] 284); Dio 57.15.8; Ulp. 15.2.1: *denique extat senatus consultum Pomponio et Rufo conss. (AD 17) factum, quo cauetur, ut mathematicis Chaldeis ariolis et ceteris qui simile inceptum fecerunt, aqua et igni interdicantur omniaque bona eorum publicentur, et si externarum gentium quis id fecerit, ut in eum animaduerteretur.* Suetonius talks in vague terms of specific exemption for those who recanted, while Dio under AD 16 mentions two decrees of increasing severity. Ulpian places a single decree in AD 17, but (if we believe Dio) it may have had a predecessor. See discussion in F.H. Cramer (1954) 102.

37.1

In primis tuendae pacis...curam habuit: we have already seen that Tiberius took special measures in Sardinia to curb brigandage (36 above). From Ilium there exists an inscription in honour of T. Valerius Proclus for his assistance in curbing brigandage at the Hellespont (*CIG* 3612). Several of the campaigns against Tacfarinas were justified as suppression of brigandage (Tac. *Ann.* 3.73-4; 4.23-6). Campaigns in Thrace by Rhescuporis against his brother Cotys also fell under this mantle (Tac. *Ann.* 2.64.2-68). For an idea of the official view of the *pax Augusta* and brigandage see Vell. 2.126.3 (note comments of Woodman [1977] 241-2).

stationes militum...frequentiores disposuit: cf. Suet. *Aug.* 32.1 and see Carter (1982) ad loc; Strabo 4.6.6 = C204; Appian *BC* 5.132. Tiberius had to continue and strengthen Augustan measures to suppress highway robbery.

castra...constituit, quibus praetorianae cohortes...continerentur: on the Augustan arrangement see Suet. *Aug.* 49.1: *neque tamen umquam plures quam tres cohortes in urbe passus est easque sine castris, reliquas in hiberna et aestiua circa finitima oppida dimettere assuerat.*

Tacitus credits Seianus with the intiative here, although other sources do not have this emphasis. See Tac. *Ann.* 4.2.1; Dio 57.19.6; Aur. Vict. *Caes.* 2.4. Suetonius situates the move in the context of a general tightening of policing both in Italy and in the provinces. The more sinster motive of intimidating the Senate is attributed to Tiberius by Dio (57.24.5). Tacitus has Seianus working on Tiberius with this idea (Tac. *Ann.* 4.2.2). But the move appears to have occurred in AD 20, which makes Seianus' direct involvement in the decision less plausible (Dio 57.19.5). For an introductory assessment of the guard see G. Powell, *History Today* 18 (1968) 858-66. On the praetorian camp see I.A. Richmond, *PBSR* 10 (1927) 12-22; E. Nash I (1961-2) 221-24.

37.2
Populares tumultus...coercuit: cf. Tac. *Ann.* 4.27.3 (an incipient slave revolt in AD 24).

caede in theatro...capita factionum et histriones...relegauit: see Tac. *Ann.* 1.54.3: *ludos Augustales tunc primus coeptos turbauit discordia ex certamine histrionum.* This was in AD 14. See also Suet. *Aug.* 45.4 and Dio 56.47.2, who says that the absence of a striking actor caused the disturbance in that year. It was followed in AD 15 by deaths. See Tac. *Ann.* 1.77.1: *at theatri licentia, proximo priore anno coepta, grauius tum erupit, occisis non modo e plebe sed militibus et centurione, uulnerato tribuno praetoriae cohortis, dum probra in magistratus et dissensionem uulgi prohibent.* According to Dio Drusus attracted blame (Dio 57.14.10).

Tacitus uses the incident to exemplify Tiberian behaviour in the Senate. After open debate was permitted measures were passed to regulate their pay, to check their factions, and in general to regulate their social conduct, and the relationship of equestrians and senators to them (Tac. *Ann.* 1.77.2, dating from AD 15). This was followed by other legislation over acting and its relationship to polite society, including the SC from Larinum of AD 19. See B. Levick, *JRS* 73 (1983) 97-115. Eventually in AD 23 the emperor himself was forced to intervene, and the players were banished from Italy (Vell. 2.126.2: *compressa theatralis seditio*; Tac. *Ann.* 4.14.4; Dio 57.21.3). Suetonius is more plausible than Tacitus and Dio in his statement that only the ringleaders were cast out. There was no shortage of actors under Caligula (Dio 59.2.5).

On Augustan measures, particularly in relation to seating arrangements, see E. Rawson, *PBSR* 55 (1987) 83-113; A. Scobie, *Nikephoros* 1 (1988) 191-243; C. Schnurr, *LCM* 17.10 (1992) 147-60.

37.3

Pollentina plebs funus cuiusdam primipilaris...extorta pecunia...ad gladiatorium munus, cohortem...in oppidum immisit: this example is again intended to illustrate his extreme reaction to popular demands for entertainment. The popular request for a *munus* is a reminder of the enormous pensions obtained by *primipili*, and thus the capacity of the heirs to provide largesse. On the location of Pollentia in Liguria see Plin. *NH* 3..49; Ptol. 3.1.41. On the site see *PECS* s.v. Pollentina.

According to this story, which is intended to exemplify Tiberius' strict control over public disturbances, one urban cohort was sent out to quell the trouble, as well as another from the kingdom in the Cottian Alps. M. Iulius Cottius was son of King Donnus and was granted a prefecture in the Cottian Alps with control over 14 cantons in the aftermath of his reception into *amicitia* by Augustus (*EJ*² 165; 166). This emerges from the inscription on the arch at Segusio, dated 9-8 BC (cf. Amm. Marc. 15.10.2). The kingly title was eventually restored by Claudius in AD 44 (Dio 60.24.4), but the Cottian Alps became an imperial province under Nero (Suet. *Nero* 18; Eutrop. 7.14.5; Aur. Vict. *Caes.* 5.2). Precise boundaries of the *regnum* elude detection.

The cohort to which reference is made may have been merely a military unit under imperial control stationed in Cottius' territory (cf. Strabo 4.6.4 =C203, the *ala Vocontiorum* in Gallia Narbonensis). See Rietra (1928) 52-53.

partem maiorem plebei ac decurionum in perpetua uincula coiecit: this is an example of an instance where imprisonment has become a punishment *per se*. Ulpian believed that prison should be a means of detaining men rather than punishing them (Dig. 48.19.8.9; P.D.A. Garnsey [1970] 149). Thus the example fits Suetonius' theme here that the emperor reacted harshly to a minor incident.

aboleuit et ius moremque asylorum quae usquam erat: this was in fact a task delegated to the Senate in AD 22, and with specific reference to the Eastern half of the empire. It was notorious that temples were filled with runaway slaves, debtors and criminals (Tac. *Ann.* 3.60-63). In AD 23 there were petitions from Samos and Cos to have their entitlements restored (Tac. *Ann.* 4.14). See Rietra (1928) 54-56; Seager (1972) 150.

Cyzicenis...libertatem ademit: in AD 25 Tacitus tells us that the people of Cyzicus were puinshed for failure to observe the imperial cult, and for acts of violence against Roman citizens. The city was stripped of its freedom, which had been awarded after they had assisted Lucullus in repulsing Mithridates, who had besieged their city (Tac. *Ann.* 4.36.2; Dio 57.24.6. Dio 54.7.6 claims that Augustus reduced the people of Cyzicus to slavery in 20 BC for the same offence, but this may be a doublet). For the details see Strabo 12.8.11 = C575-76. In his account Strabo says that it is still free in his own time, which has significance for the date at which the text of his Geography was finalised (i.e. before AD 25). The case of Cyzicus shows that once the imperial cult had been established it might actually be enforced. See Seager (1972) 144. On the history of Cyzicus see A.H.M. Jones (1971) 86-88.

37.4

Hostiles motus...per legatos compescuit: this foreshadows Suetonius' theme that Tiberius was lazy over adminstrative matters (41 below). The use of legates for this purpose was, however, no Tiberian innovation, although quite an extensive list of examples of insurrections crushed by Tiberian legates can be adduced. See Rietra (1928) 57.

Maroboduum Germanum: Maroboduus had first had contact with Rome in all likelihood as a hostage during his youth, and will have been a beneficiary of the education offered to the sons of client kings by Augustus (Strabo 7.1.3 = C290; Suet. *Aug.* 48; *De Gramm.* 17). As an adult he returned to Germany and eventually came to be recognised as both king and friend of the Roman people (Tac. *Ann.* 2.63). After the recall of Germanicus in AD 16 conflict arose between Arminius and Maroboduus, and Tiberius was forced to send his son Drusus to conclude a peace between the adversaries. Drusus is supposed to have had secret instructions to foster discord between these rivals so that the German tribes might be weakened (Vell. 2.129.3; Tac. *Ann.* 2.46; 62; 63). A young Germanic nobleman named Catualda was used by the Romans to break the power of Maroboduus, probably in AD 19, and to lure him into Roman territory, from which he was never to return. He was granted a safe conduct to Rome for further negotiations, but once he was safely within Italy Drusus was awarded an *ouatio* (Tac. *Ann*. 2.64; 3.11. This was not celebrated until 28th May AD 20 [*CIL* XIV 244 = 4534]), and Maroboduus was sent to live at Rauenna, a common arrangement for princelings of like status (Tac. *Ann*. 1.58; for Bato's residence here see Suet. *Tib*. 20 above. See J. Dobiás, *Klio* 38 (1960) 155-66.

Rhascuporim Thracem: there is some inconsistency over the spelling of this Thracian prince's name. See Woodman (1977) 265. On the death of Rhoemetalces in AD 12 Augustus had divided his kingdom between his son Cotys and his his brother Rhescuporis. Rhesuporis, who had received the less settled parts of the kingdom, soon began to interfere in his nephew's preserve. Tiberius did entice Rhescuporis to Rome, after initial attempts at a diplomatic solution. Rhescuporis had in the meantime murdered Cotys, and in AD 18 L. Pomponius Flaccus was sent out to Moesia, and succeeded in effecting the arrrest of Rhescuporis (Vell. 2.129.1; Tac. *Ann*. 2.64-7). On Flaccus see W. Eck in *RE* Suppl. XIV s.v. Pomponius no. 46a. For the episode see also R. Seager (1972) 163-5; R.D. Sullivan, *ANRW* 2.7.1 (1980) 186-211, esp. 200ff.

Archelaum Cappadocem: it is true that his kingdom became a province of the Roman empire under an equestrian procurator after his death in AD 17. Germanicus was delegated to organise this as part of his Eastern tour in AD 18 (Strabo 12.1.4 = C534; Vell. 2.39.3; Tac. *Ann*. 2.42.4; 56.4; Dio 57.17.7). See 8 above for Tiberius' role in the defence of Archelaus and for literature on his reign.

38-40 The Reclusiveness Of Tiberius

38

Biennio continuo post adeptum imperium pedem porta non extulit: on Tiberius' reasons for staying at Rome see Tac. *Ann*. 1.47 (AD 14), with excuses over the need for impartiality towards the armies in Pannonia and on the Rhine (cf. Tac. *Ann*. 2.35.1 and Goodyear [1981] 295). See also 3.47 (AD 21) on the indignity of emperors leaving the city merely because of a commotion in the provinces; Tac. *Ann*. 4.4.2 (AD 23): here Tacitus accuses the emperor of insincerity when he brought up the topic of an imperial progress through the provinces. Levick notes that Augustus also showed an unwillingness to leave Italy in his later years ([1976] 127). In the early stages of Tiberius' reign, both Drusus and Germanicus were available to satisfy the need for imperial presence in the provinces.

in propinqua oppida: Aulus Gellius refers to the conversion of Praeneste from a colony to a *municipium* because Tiberius had recovered from a dangerous illness in its vicinity (*NA* 16.13.5).

Antio: this was the birthplace of Caligula (Suet. *Cal.* 8); according to Dio it was also where Tiberius held the marriage festivities for Caligula (Dio 58.25.2). It had been a favorite spot for aristocratic villas since the late Republic, and Tiberius may have himself owned one here. See J. D'Arms (1970) 90.

quamuis prouincias...reuisurum se saepe pronuntiasset: there are three recorded occasions on which Tiberius mooted such a plan. (Tac. *Ann.* 1.47.5 [AD 14]; 3.47.3 [AD 21]; 4.4.4 [AD 23]). Suetonius appears to generalise when he talks of the frequency with which the theme recurred.

commeatibus...dispositis: Suetonius appears to exaggerate Tiberius' state of preparedness for rhetorical effect (cf. Suet. *Cal.* 43: *contracto omnis generis commeatu quanto numquam antea*).

ut uulgo iam per iocum Callip<p>ides uocaretur: apparently a comic actor, who simulated a marathon runner, but never advanced from the same spot. This proverbial example is also found in Cic. *Ad Att.* 13.12.3: *biennium praeteriit, cum ille* Καλλιππίδης *adsiduo cursu cubitum nullum processerat.* See Diehl in *RE* s.v. Καλλιππίδης no.3.

39

orbatus utroque filio...secessum Campaniae petit: Tacitus says that he concealed his real motive for retirement to Campania under the pretext of dedicating temples at Capua and Nola. He mentions a variety of motives which include the intervention of Seianus and a desire to conceal his viciousness, or an urge to escape the control of his mother. It emerges that Tacitus was uncertain (Tac. *Ann.* 4.57.1; cf. Dio 57.12.6; 58.1.1 [AD 26]). It seems to be Suetonius' own idea that there was a connection between the deaths of Germanicus and Drusus and the retirement of Tiberius. Chonology makes this unlikely, and Suetonius elsewhere emphasises Tiberius' lack of paternal feelings (52). Rietra suggests that he became increasingly misanthropic, strongly rejecting any suggestion that Capri was strategically superior (Rietra [1928] 65).

in praetorio...incenante: originally a *praetorium* was a general's tent, but it came to have a more informal meaning. See very full note in Rietra (1928) ad loc.; cf. Stewart, *JRS* 67 (1977) 83. Here the reference is to the quarters employed by an emperor on his travels. Excavators at Sperlonga have been uncertain whether the villa adjoining the grotto was an imperial possession. See literature cited below. The thematic content of the sculptures at Sperlonga is a good reason for suspecting that they were commissioned under imperial sponsorship, and hence Tiberius' ownership of the site. It has also been confirmed that a *triclinium* faces into the cave, and is the intended viewing point for the sculptural groups. This assists in completing the picture provided by Suetonius and Tacitus.

Speluncae...ingentia saxa...dilapsa sunt: for his lucky escape from death in AD 26 at this location near Tarracina see also Tac. *Ann.* 4.59.1-4. Tacitus sees this as the event opening the way for Seianus to attack Nero, and the praetorian prefect was said to have agents reporting every indiscretion to the emperor (*Ann.* 4.59ff.). A. Bernecker suggests that the episode was an assassination attempt on the *princeps*, orchestrated by Nero and Agrippina. This is not impossible, although it cannot be proved conclusively. See A. Bernecker (1981) 12-23.

For grottoes along this coastline see Strabo 5.3.6 = C233 ; Plut. *Luc.* 39; Appian *BC* 4.4.29; see Plin. *NH* 3.59 for the position (for the geography of the area see X. Lafon, *MEFRA* 91 [1979] 399-419). The grotto at Sperlonga was rediscovered in September 1957, and great debate has ensued over its contents and their date. A careful analysis of the great corpus of sculptures discovered there was provided by B. Conticello and B. Andreae, *Antike Plastik* 14 (1974). That they are of Tiberian date is argued forcefully by A.F. Stewart, *JRS* 67 (1977) 77, and (if accepted) this has important consequences for any examination of Tiberian interests and tastes. Stewart thinks it possible that the sculptures were commissioned by the emperor himself at some time between his first prolonged visit to Campania in AD 21, and the rock fall at Sperlonga in AD 26 (op.cit. 83). The common theme in each of the major groups of sculpture is provided by the person of Odysseus. Specifically they depict diverse aspects of Odysseus' activities, carrying the characterisation outside the realm of the Homeric treatment. The sculptures are either originals or copies of work by the famous Rhodian artists Hagasandros, Athanodoros and Polydoros, who were also responsible for the Laocoon group (Plin. *NH* 36.37).

40

Capuae Capitolium: see also Tac. *Ann.* 4.57.1; 67.1; Suet. *Cal.* 57.2. The

Capitolium was a temple of Jupiter, as at Rome. It was a commonplace that Rome and Capua had a shared Trojan origin (Verg. *Aen*. 10.145; Dion. Hal. *Ant*. 1.73; Stat. *Silu*. 3.5.77; Suet. *Iul*. 81.1). See Rietra (1928) *AD*. loc; *RE* s.v. Capua; *PECS* s.v. Capua. The temple of Jupiter Capitolinus at Capua was dedicated on the Ides of September. See G. Wissowa (1971) 126.

Nolae templum Augusti: Augustus had died in his father's house at Nola (Vell. 2.123; Suet. *Aug*. 98.5; 100.1; Tac. *Ann*. 1.5.5; 9.1; Dio 56.29.1), and this was immediately transformed into a temple of the imperial cult, with Liuia as his priestess (Dio 56.46.1-3). The temple may have been dedicated either on the day of Augustus' consecration (17th September) or on his birthday (23/24th September). See Wissowa, op.cit. 342f.; K. Latte (1960) 306f.; A. Bernecker (1981) 9. Little is known of the topography of Roman Nola. See *PECS* s.v. Nola.

Capreas se contulit: the island of Capri had become a private possession of the imperial family when Augustus bought it from the people of Naples in 29 BC in exchange for Ischia (Strabo 5.4.9 = C248; Suet. *Aug*. 92; Dio 52.43.2).

On Tiberius' preference for Capri see Tac. *Ann*. 4.67.1: *Capreas se in insulam abdidit, trium milium freto ab extremis Surrentini promunturii diiunctam. solitudinem eius placuisse maxime crediderim, quoniam importuosum circa mare et uix modicis nauigiis pauca subsidia; neque adpulerit quisquam nisi gnaro custode. caeli temperies hieme mitis, obiectu montis, quo saeua uentorum arcentur; aestas in fauonium obuersa et aperto circum pelago peramoena; prospectabatque pulcherrimum sinum, antequam Vesuuius mons ardescens faciem loci uerterat.*

For this part of Tiberius' reign see A. Bernecker (1981) 65ff.; G.W. Houston, *G & R* 32 (1985) 179-96.

apud Fidenas...amphitheatri ruina: see Tac. *Ann*. 4.62-63.3; Dio 58.1.1a; cf. Suet. *Cal*. 31; Oros. 7.4. This catastrophe at Fidenae was in AD 27, when a freedman by the name of Atilius had built a wooden structure to display gladiatorial contests which collapsed. According to Tacitus 50000 people were either crushed or maimed (Tac. *Ann*. 4.63.2). The Suetonian figure, which only encompasses the killed, puts the dead at 20000.

urbe egrediens ne quis se interpellaret edixerat ac...adeuntes submouerat: it is interesting to note that this edict was enforced by military force (see also Tac. *Ann*. 4.67; M. Benner [1975] 87). Caligula is said to have enforced an edict on mourning for Drusilla in a similar manner (Suet. *Cal*. 24.2).

41-67 Aspects of the Reign After Retirement to Capri

41-5 Tiberius On Capri

The various charges against Tiberian conduct on Capri are a classic in the history of rhetorical *uituperatio*. The material is uncheckable, but may be a result of speculation over his reclusive life, which is known to have been not totally without companionship. A court of a sort existed on Capri (discussed by G.W. Houston, *G & R* 32 [1985] 179-96). The process of ignoring traditional political processes caused annoyance in Senatorial circles, and some of the hostility may have been a product of the breakdown of the patronage network, and the difficulty of access to the emperor. Tacitus shares the approach of Suetonius and attributes Tiberius' unwillingness to show his face in Rome to shame over his debaucheries (*Ann.* 6.1).

41

Regressus in insulam...curam...abiecit: Suetonius claims that after retirement to Capri Tiberius allowed matters to slide, neither filling vacancies in the equestrian order, nor filling vacancies in senior military posts. Although Suetonius generalises the situation still further, other sources agree that he was slack over provincial affairs, and this tradition can be assumed to have gained currency at an early stage. Thus Josephus says that provincial commanders were only superceded if they actually died (Jos. *AJ* 18.170). Similar views emerge from Tacitus (Tac. *Ann.*1.80.1). Dio claims that lengthened tenures in the provinces became the norm because of a shortage of qualified personnel, which in turn was a result of his destruction of Senatorials. Thus those of praetorian rank were to hold office for three years, while consulars were to be retained for six (Dio 58.23.5). For the actual length of provincial tenures under Tiberius see Orth (1970) 71ff and table summarising conclusions on 131ff.

The big question is why Tiberius left commanders in place for so long. Much of the modern debate has centered on whether or not Tiberius was an innovator in provincial policy, with scholars in support of both positions. Tiberius is supposed to have said that governors were like gorged flies on a sore: it was better to leave them there rather than to drive them off and leave the wound open to fresh successors (Jos. *AJ* 18.171ff.; discussed by Levick [1976] 128). He was late in his reign also heard to complain about the shortage of capable men prepared to take provincial positions (Tac. *Ann.*

6.27.3), and this probably accounts for Dio's approach.

As far as review of the equestrian order is concerned, Suetonius gives Caligula credit for a major reversal of Tiberian slackness during the early stages of his reign. This careful attention to membership was one of the measures employed to gain popularity for the new emperor (Suet. *Cal.* 16.2). Dio confirms a change of emphasis under Caligula (Dio 59.9.5). For bibliography see Millar (1977) 279.

Hispaniam et Syriam per aliquot annos sine consularibus legatis habuerit: see 63.2 below for details.

Armeniam a Parthis occupari...Gallias a Germanis uastari neglexerit: this appears to be a calumny, and in one case we can actually see his very swift response to an external threat, even at a late stage in his reign. When there was a problem on the Eastern frontier he was not slow to appoint Lucius Vitellius as governor of Syria. Details of Vitellius' effectiveness are provided by Tacitus (*Ann.* 6.31-44).

42.1

cuncta simul uitia male diu dissimulata tandem profudit: a clear statement about the hypocrisy of Tiberius. See introduction 43-44, and compare the vices of Tiberius outlined by Artabanus at 66 below.

de quibus singillatim ab exordio referam: Suetonius starts with drunkenness, luxury, lust, and avarice. Stinginess soon turns to rapacity and murder (49-57). *Iganuia* has already been covered (41). See introductory analysis of the *species*.

in castris tiro...pro Tiberio Biberius, pro Claudio Caldius, pro Nerone Mero: cf. Dio 58 fr. 3, but notice that text has been adjusted in the light of the present passage. Tiberius is portrayed as a hardened drinker, and Levick reminds us that Drusus inherited his father's taste for wine (Levick [1976] 158). This probably started when Tiberius was on campaign in Spain in 26-5 BC. Suetonius here talks of him developing the habit as a *tiro*. Spanish wines had begun to be known at Rome at about this time (Plin. *NH* 14.71-72). According to the elder Pliny Tiberius became more moderate in his drinking habits as he grew older (*NH* 19.144). See Syme, *Athenaeum* 67 (1989) 268. He is said to have had strong views about *Surrentinum*, which he described as *generosum acetum* (Plin. *NH* 14.64); these stories in Pliny are a reflection of the interest in and criticism of imperial taste. See also Plin. *NH* 14.16.

princeps...cum Pomponio Flacco et L. Pisone noctem continuumque biduum epulando potandoque consumpsit: there are serious chronological objections to the story of the drinking bout once he had become *princeps*. After this he is supposed to have given Piso the prefecture of the city, and Pomponius Flaccus the province of Syria. Although the story of Piso's selection is also to be found in Pliny (*NH* 14.144-45), with the variant that the party was a *perpotatio* continuing for two days and nights, it has been deduced from Tacitus that he was appointed in AD 13 (Tac. *Ann.* 6.11.3; see Syme, *Athenaeum* 67 (1989) 267). Seager thought that Suetonius and Pliny were, however, right in seeing Piso as a Tiberian appointment ([1972] 229 n. 2). The appointment of Flaccus was considerably later. He went to Syria in AD 33 after the death of Aelius Lamia (Tac. *Ann.* 6.27.2). The story as a whole has been improved in transmission, and fits into the tradition of criticising imperial conduct at the table. See now on the tyrant at the table J. Goddard in J. Elsner & J. Masters (eds) (1994) 67-82.

Seneca admits to Piso's efficiency, although retailing the story of drunkenness. He refers not only to the friendship of Piso and Tiberius, but reminds his readers that Augustus had appointed him as governor of Thrace. The choice of Piso is used by Seneca to explain why Tiberius was later prepared to take on Cornelius Cossus as *praefectus urbi* (Sen. *Ep.* 83.14-15). Velleius unsurprisingly approves of Piso (2.98.3), and provides a minor panegyric on Flaccus (2.129.1). For fuller details of the careers of these men see *PIR*[1] P 538 (Flaccus); *PIR*[2] C 289 (Piso).

42.2

Cestio Gall[i]o...increpito cenam ea lege condixit, ne quid...demeret, utque nudis puellis...cenaretur: Suetonius moves on from the theme of drunkenness to that of lust. These are naturally tyrannical vices, and it is not surprising to find to find a tyrant lustful at the dinner table. There is some uncertainty over the name of this libidinous old man, who appears in the *codices* as Sestius Gallius (see *PIR*[1] S 435). If the name is correct, nothing is known of his career. The correction to Cestius Gallus was first made by Roth, and taken up by Ihm. But Groag has reservations, and doubts whether Suetonius refers to C. Cestius Gallus, consul in AD 35; see *PIR*[2] C 690. However, this man's involvement in a trial as an informer in AD 32 could certainly provide a credible reason why he might have been the subjected to the type of vituperation exhibited by Suetonius here (see Tac. *Ann.* 6.7).

ignotissimum...nobilissimis anteposuit: Suetonius says that he gave an unknown candidate for the quaestorship preference because of his prowess in wine drinking. He says the man drank an entire amphora. Pliny identifies the man as Nouellius Torquatus of Milan, and claims he drank two and a quarter gallons in one draught (Plin. *NH* 14.144). It happens that his career inscription has survived (*ILS* 950). Pliny dates the episode to Tiberius' old age, and Syme has suggested that it should be placed just before the retirement to Capri in AD 26 (R. Syme, *Athenaeum* 67 (1989) 268). See also *PIR*[2] N 141, which, however, does not make the link with the present passage.

Asellio Sabino sestertia ducenta donauit: Syme has noted the surprising omission from this biography of any account of Tiberius' eating habits. There is quite extensive comment on his preferences in the Pliny's *Naturalis Historia*. He had an idiosyncratic taste in pears and his preference for smoked grapes started a fashion (Plin. *NH* 15.53-4; 14.16). Various green vegetables featured on his table. He liked a type of broccoli favoured by Apicius, and was also partial to cucumbers and asparagus (Plin. *NH* 19.137; 19.64; 19.145). Parsnips (*siser*) are a further vegetarian element (Plin. *NH* 19.90). He may have turned vegetarian after his return from life in the army. Syme refuses to countenance a non-carnivorous diet until then (*Athenaeum* 67 [1989] 269). But the present passage may suggest a more general interest in exotic food. If he was a well known vegetarian the story of the presentation of the mullet related at Suet. *Tib.* 60 would make little sense! Asellius Sabinus was described by the elder Seneca as *uetustissimus inter rhetores scurra* (Sen. *Suas.* 2.12; *PIR*[2] A 1213).

officium instituit a uoluptatibus, praeposito equite R. T. Caesonio Prisco: the office of *procurator a uoluptatibus* established by Tiberius appears to be a purely domestic one. Suetonius reveals that its first incumbent was a knight, T. Caesonius Priscus (*PIR*[2] C 211). Suetonius deliberately leaves this vague, with suggestions of its relevance to his perversions, but it is more probable that he had a serious function as a director of imperial leisure. Suetonius is often critical of imperial taste. Under Priscus' control there will have been a variegated crowd of freedmen and slaves such as *musicarii*, *pantomimi*, *acroamenae*, and *pilarii*. For details see Boulvert (1970) 83. The tenure of the post by an equestrian (rather than a freedman) is significant. Tiberius had close links with the order (see Levick [1976] 116ff.).

43.1

secessu uero Caprensi etiam sellaria excogitauit: cf. Tac. *Ann.* 6..1: *tumque primum ignota ante uocabula reperta sunt sellariorum et spintriarum ex foeditate loci ac multiplici patientia.* On the etymology of *sellarius* see Carcopino (1944) 149 n. 5. Carcopino believed that Suetonius derives his scabrous account of these features of life on Capri from Tacitus (op.cit. 150).

For other possible parallels with Tacitus' narrative see introduction **33-34**.

monstrosique concubitus repertores, quos spintrias appellabat: on the *spintriae*, who were male prostitutes, see also Suet. *Cal*. 16.1; *Vit*. 3. Stories of sexual exploits of Tiberius on Capri are often dismissed as the product of rhetorical *uituperatio* (cf. Wallace-Hadrill [1983] 184). Coins depicting erotic scenes are known from the age of Tiberius (dated AD 22-37), and could have created speculation over the emperor's tastes. See T.V. Buttrey, NC 13 (1973) 52-63; C.L. Murison, *AHB* 1, 4 (1987) 97-99.

43.2

in siluis...Venerios locos commentus est prost[r]antisque per antra et cauas rupes ex utriusque sexus pube Paniscorum et Nympharum habitu: for the traditional trappings of grottoes such as that at Sperlonga see Stewart, *JRS* 67 (1977) 78-79. A fashion for grottoes reached Rome under Hellenistic influence by the end of the first century BC. What we have here is a hostile interpretation of the emperor's taste for this highly popular type of amenity.

uulgo nomine abutentes Caprineum dictitabant: for the possible appearance of this term in the περὶ βλασφημιῶν see A. Bernecker (1981) 72; 89. On that work see also J. Taillardat (1967).

44.1

pueros primae teneritudinis, quos pisciculos uocabat, institueret: the story of the *pisciculi* fits in with other aspects of the *uituperatio* against Tiberius. See 43.1 above.

44.2

Parrasi quoque tabulam, in qua Meleagro Atalanta ore morigeratur: Parrhasius was an Ephesian painter of the 5-4th century BC who later moved to Athens and wrote on painting as well as developing a reputation for subtlety of outline. He was well known in the early imperial period, and his gods and heroes were used as types by artists in the age of Pliny (see Lippold, *RE* s.v. Parrasios (1949) col 1874f.). On his style see Plin. *NH* 35.67. The elder Pliny says that Tiberius owned a picture of a High Priest of Cybele (*archigallus*) by Parrhasius valued at 6,000,000 HS, which he kept in his bedroom, but there are textual difficulties in the passage (Plin. *NH* 35.69: discussed by J. Carcopino [1944] 123ff., who argues that there was only one picture). Nevertheless it does not sound as though Pliny is talking of the same picture as emerges from the Suetonian anecdote.

The story of the picture of Atalanta engaged in *fellatio* (or possibly mutual stimulation: see J.P. Hallett, *AC* 47 [1978] 196-200) with Meleager is intended to bring discredit on Tiberius; he is portrayed as choosing a picture with a subject of this type when he had the choice of a cash inheritance instead (1,000,000 HS). Yet it may well be that Tiberius' interest in erotic art of one sort or another in conjunction with speculation over his activities on Capri combined to create the hostile tradition representing him as a sexual pervert.

The painting has created some modern controversy. I. Cazzaniga was troubled by the lack of other references to a sexual encounter between Atalanta and Meleager, but concludes that Atalanta's reputation had declined during the Hellenistic period (*ASNP* 4 [1974] 1301-6). Wilamowitz had earlier suggested that Suetonius made a mistake in alluding to Meleager rather than Milanion. Whether this approach is right or not, no authority has rejected the explicit nature of the scene depicted. The literature is briefly discussed by D.T. Benediktson, *CW* 86 (1993) 410.

The best evidence for Tiberian taste in art is provided by two sources: (1) The sculptures from Sperlonga. Their significance has been fully discussed by A.F. Stewart, *JRS* 67 (1977) 76-90. (2) The coins known as *spintriae*, which represent various erotic scenes, and have been surveyed by T.V. Buttrey, *NC* 1973 52-63. The Tiberian date of these coins is highly probable, but not conclusively proved.

45

feminarum...capitibus quanto opere solitus sit inludere, euidentissime apparuit Malloniae cuiusdam exitu: the theme here is Tiberius' capacity for sexual insults to women. Tiberius is depicted as a cruel tyrant who not only forces himself on the woman, but also pursues her in court on unspecified charges when she expressed disgust. As far as Mallonia is concerned, the *nomen* is not otherwise recorded, nor is she otherwise known in the Tiberian tradition. See *PIR*[1] M 87. Rogers suggests that the incident mentioned here may have occurred on Capri. See Rogers (1935) 170. It may, however, be suspected that it is unhistorical. Bernecker detects echoes of the story that he liked involvement in the handling of *quaestiones* (*Ann.* 1.75-6; Suet. *Tib.* 33), and therefore places the trial before the retreat to Capri (Bernecker [1981] 89).

in Atellanico exhodio...percrebruit, hircum uetulum capreis naturam ligurire: Atellan farces were notorious for their scabrous content. On the *Atellanae fabulae* see W. Beare (1950) 137-48; *D & S* s.v. atellana. There is other evidence to show that political themes were common in the Atellan farce (cf. Suet. *Cal.* 27.4; *Nero* 39.3).

46-48 Stinginess and *auaritia* of Tiberius

46

Pecuniae parcus ac tenax: cf. Tac. *Ann*. 3.52.2: *antiquae parsimoniae*. The same sort of point is made about his expenditures on private building (Tac. *Ann*. 6.45.1: *modicus priuatis aedificationibus*). Suetonius earlier notes his parsimony in serving up a half-eaten boar at dinner (34.1).

47

Princeps neque opera ulla magnifica fecit: this whole area is treated in similar manner by Tacitus (*Ann*. 6.45). *Liberalitas* enabled the emperor to display his interest in community concerns (see H. Kloft [1970] 115ff. on the importance of erecting public buildings) Tiberius is poorly rated by Suetonius for his failure to engage in major public works, and for his failure to provide public spectacles. Suetonius relates this to meanness about money. Another failure was his absence from public shows. This would give an emperor a chance to parade his *ciuilitas*. Here an example is given to show meanness of spirit. Because he had been asked to manumit a performer on a previous occasion, Tiberius is portrayed as unwilling to have anything further to do with public entertainments.

Tiberius did nevertheless repair buildings dilapidated by age or damaged by fire (Tac. *Ann*. 2.49; Dio 57.10). See Vell. 2.130.1 for a naively favourable view of Tiberian policy (cf. Woodman [1977] 270). A sceptical view of the value of ancient comments on imperial attitudes to building is taken by J. Elsner in J. Elsner & J, Masters (eds) (1994) 112-27. Reading between the lines, it would seem that Tiberius was attempting show a continuity between his own reign and that of Augustus (Elsner, op.cit. 114). It was less important from his perspective to be active in his own right. Notice that the so-called *Domus Tiberiana* appears to have been built largely by later emperors. See C. Krause (1985) 123 (and figures 131-32); 134 (for a brief summary of findings). On the buildings of Tiberius see also M.E. Blake (1959) 10-18.

Augusti templum restitutionemque Pompeiani theatri, imperfecta...reliquit: his two major public works acknowledged by Suetonius were the building of the temple of Augustus and the restoration of Pompey's theatre, both allegedly incomplete at the end of his reign. But Tacitus says that Tiberius completed the temple of Augustus (Tac. *Ann*. 6.45.2). It was dedicated by Caligula on his own birthday, 31st August AD 37, and it is therefore unlikely that Caligula had much to add to it (Suet. *Cal*. 21; Dio 59.7.1; *BMC* I 153 pl. 28: 6, 9; pl. 29: 14). Tiberius had adorned the temple with two paintings, one a favorite of the emperor Augustus (Plin. *NH* 35.28; 131). These were a Hyacinthus by Nicias, and a Danae. The Hyacinthus is described by Pausanias (3.19.4). Both pictures are included in the more complete review of the collection in the temple provided by the poet Martial (14.170-82; cf. K. Lehmann, *Hesperia* 14 [1945] 259-69). On Tiberius' taste for Hellenistic art see 44.2 above; 74 below. The temple has not been located with certainty by topographers. See Nash 1 (1961-2) 164; Castagnoli (1978) 77; cf. Platner/ Ashby (1929) 62-65. The theatre of Pompey had burnt down in AD 21, and Tiberius undertook its repair in the absence of any surviving family member (Vell. 2.130; Sen. *Cons. ad Marc.* 22.4; Tac. *Ann.* 3.72 [AD 22]). These repairs were also apparently completed within the reign of Tiberius (Tac. *Ann.* 6.45.2), although it was not rededicated until the first year of Claudius' reign (Suet. *Cal.* 21; *Claud.* 21; Dio 60.6.8). Velleius appears to allude to his *moderatio* in allowing the Pompeian monument to be restored (Vell. 2.130.1; cf. RG 20.1: *Pompeium theatrum...refeci sine ulla inscriptione nominis mei*; Woodman [1977] 271).

negauit se...subuenturum aliis...in quibus Hortalum: Suetonius, who at this point is trying to emphasise how mean the emperor is, discusses the unwillingness of the Tiberius to contribute to the upkeep of senatorial families, after making a small number of individual grants (see Tac. *Ann.* 1.75.3 on the case of Propertius Celer, who did get assistance from Tiberius, once he had ascertained that his poverty was inherited; Sen. *De Ben.* 2.7.2 on Marius Nepos who was grudgingly assisted, but later nevertheless excluded from the Senate). Sen. *De Ben.* 2.8.1 says that other cases were assisted after a careful review of their circumstances. In reality Tiberius seems only to have excluded assistance to those whose poverty was of their own making. The scrupulous were favoured with unattributed inheritances (M. Lepidus and M. Seruilius; see Tac. *Ann.* 2.48; cf. Suet. *Vit.* 2.2; Vell. 2.129.3; Dio 57.10.4). See discussion in Seager (1972) 134-6. Velleius appears anxious to defend Tiberius' behaviour on such matters, and emphasises his consultation of the Senate over grants (2.129.3).

Children were proverbially seen as a burden, and pleas of impoverishment seem to have been taken seriously (see S. Dixon [1988] 96). Suetonius alleges that others were deterred from asking for assistance through *modestia* and *pudor*, including Hortalus, the grandson of the orator Hortensius. The orator's immenses resources were well known, and his daughter was still extremely rich after Philippi (App. *BC* 4.32). The grandson Hortalus had incurred expenses as a result of dutiful adherence to the Augustan exhortation to procreate, which had left him with a family of four children. However, quite a different slant is put on the story by Tacitus, in the context of gifts to supplement senatorial capital in AD 16. (1) Hortalus had in fact already received a gift of a million sesterces from Augustus (2) Hortalus did make a direct appeal to the Senate, dragging along his family for display at the doors of the senate house. (3) The senate was favourable, but Tiberius resisted the plea as an importunity. (4) After muttered dissent amongst the senators Tiberius proposed to give each male child 200,000 sesterces. (5) The house of Hortensius did subsequently sink into obscurity. It seems probable that the disbursements were actually made and that Suetonius has it wrong. See Tac. *Ann.* 2.37-38; J. Geiger, *CQ* 20 (1970)132-4.

A recent discovery of a fragment of the *Acta Arvalium* has opened up a debate over the nomenclature and details of the career of Hortensius' grandson. The fragment reveals that a Marcius Hortalus was peregrine praetor in AD 25. It seems to be conceded by all scholars that this has the implication that the Tacitean passage does not supply the *praenomen*, but rather the *nomen* of the indigent senator. As Corbier has argued the *nomen* Hortensius appears to have been lost through the adoption of either the suppliant's father or the suppliant himself by a member of the family of the orator Hortensius' second wife. This Marcia was apparently the grand-mother of the suppliant, and it appears that the *nomen* entered the family through one of her relatives. But there is some dispute over whether the suppliant of AD 16, who must already at that time have quaestorian rank, would have had to wait until AD 25 before reaching the praetorship. Eck has pointed out how extraordinary this would have been. Despite his doubts, it is probable that the same man is alluded to, and not a brother or some other relative. His career may have been seriously hindered by the contretemps with Tiberius. See P. Arnaud, *MEFRA* 98 (1986) 403-6; M. Corbier, *MEFRA* 103 (1991) 655-701; J. Briscoe, *ZPE* 95 (1993) 249-50; W. Eck, *ZPE* 95 (1993) 251-60.

Soon after the case of Hortalus Tiberius did in fact force some senators to resign (Tac. *Ann.* 2.48.3 [five named victims]; cf. Suet. *Vit.* 2.2). Extravagance and consequent impoverishment were adduced as pretexts.

48.1
Publice munificentiam bis omnino exhibuit: liberality is of course one of the imperial virtues, and Suetonius suggests deficiencies in the area. Velleius can find no other occasion to praise apart from his generosity on the occasion of the fire on the Caelian hill in AD 27 (Tac. *Ann.* 4.64; Vell. 2.130.2). Tacitus talks of similar generosity after a fire on the Aventine (Tac. *Ann.* 6.45.1f. [AD 37]), naturally omitted by Velleius writing in AD 30.

proposito milies sestertium gratuito in trienni tempus: this loan of 100 million HS was because of the economic crisis in AD 33. See Tac. *Ann.* 6.16-17; Dio 58.21.5, who indicates that Tiberius made the sum over to the *aerarium* for the purpose of the loan. On Tiberius' old-fashioned economics see Levick (1976) 133; 257 n. 52. The nature of the financial crisis in AD 33 is best discussed by C. Rodewald (1976) 1-17, who points out serious fallacies in the earlier approach of Tenney Frank (*AJPh* 56 (1935) 336-41). Frank had argued that the volume of coinage put into circulation had undergone a continuing decline from about 10 BC, but there is little evidence to show that Tiberius ended the problem through a massive injection of currency into the system, as his argument might suggest.

rursus quibusdam dominis insularum, quae in monte Caelio deflagrarant: on the fires on the Caelian hill see Tac. *Ann.* 4.64-5.

48.2
militi post duplicata ex Augusti testamento legata nihil umquam largitus est: according to Tacitus at the height of the the mutiny on the Rhine in AD 14 Germanicus and his friends rashly promised to double these legacies under Augustus' will (Tac. *Ann.* 1.36.3). This evidence in Suetonius suggests that the promise was honoured. It is clear that Tiberius was very concerned about the cost of concessions to the mutineers in AD 14 (Tac. *Ann.* 1.52), and the claim that he was stingy to the soldiers may be based on the subsequent revocation of the settlement (Tac. *Ann.* 1.78). See J.B. Campbell (1984) 166; 172-73.

singula milia denariorum praetorianis, quod Seiano se non accommodassent: as we learn from Dio the praetorians were disgruntled at the thought that their loyalty had been called in question and went on the rampage against their former leader's adherents (Dio 58.12.1ff.; cf. Plin. *NH* 8.197). For the donative see also Dio 58.18.2. This was the beginning of a dramatic increase in imperial benevolence towards the army. See Campbell (1984) 166; 188.

quaedam munera Syriacis legionibus, quod solae nullam Seiani imaginem inter signa coluissent: moreover the governor of Syria, L. Aelius Lamia, was rewarded for his loyalty with the post of *praefectus urbi* after the death of Piso the Pontifex in AD 32 (Tac. *Ann.* 6.27.2; Dio 58.19.5; see *PIR*[2] A *200*). Lamia was one of those governors retained at Rome by the emperor (63.2 below). According to Tacitus the emperor had actually been compliant about the display of images of Seianus at legionary headquarters (Tac. *Ann.* 4.2.4).

ne prouincias...liberalitate...subleuauit, excepta Asia: disasters were an opportunity for the display of *liberalitas*; see Suet. *Cal.* 30. On the Asian earthquake in AD 17 see Tac. *Ann.* 2.47 (twelve cities destroyed); Plin. *NH* 2.200; Dio 57.17.7; Strabo 12.8.18 = C576; 13.3.5 = C621; 13.4.8 = C627; Vell. 2.126.4: *restitutae urbes A siae*; Sen. *NQ* 6.1.13; Phlegon 257 F36 xiiif. Gratitude: *BCH* 1887 89f. no.9 [AD 31]; Cibyra and Ephesus: *CIL* X 1624 = *ILS* 156 = *EJ*² 50 [AD 30]. Some damage also occurred in Sicily and the country around Rhegium. Sardis received 1,000,000 HS, and all towns were granted a five year remission of tribute. Other cities were helped in AD 23 (Cibyra, along with Aegium in Achaea), both granted a three year stay of tribute (Tac. *Ann.* 4.13.1), as well as Nysa (*SIG*³ 781 = *EJ*² 316). An ex-praetor, M. Ateius, was sent out on these occasions as inspector and supervisor of repairs (Tac. *Ann.* 4.13). Coins inscribed *ciuitatibus Asiae restitutis* are usually thought to reflect assistance following the quake in AD 17, but not by Grant (1950b) 65f. See *RIC*² Tiberius no. 48 (dated AD 21-2).

49-57 Stinginess turns to rapacity and widespread saeuitia

49.1

Procedente mox tempore etiam ad rapinas conuertit: this is a common complaint in Suetonius against those emperors who are perceived as tyrannical. Compare Suet. *Cal.* 38: *Exhaustus igitur... ad rapinas conuertit.* see Lindsay (1993) ad loc; Suet. *Nero* 32.1: *calumniis rapinisque intendit animum.* The standard theme is that stinginess led to rapacity.

Cn. Lentulum Augurem...ad fastidium uitae ab eo actum et ut ne quo nisi ipso herede moreretur: Suetonius claims that Tiberius forced Lentulus the Augur to name him as sole heir. There is some confirmation of this in Seneca, who specifies the size of his fortune as HS 400 million, equal to the largest known private fortune under the principate (*De Ben.* 2.27; see E. Champlin [1991] 152-3), but note Tac. *Ann.* 2.48 for Tiberius' general attitude to wills. Lentulus died in AD 25 (Tac. *Ann.* 4.44). For further details of the Augur's career see *PIR*² C 1379.

condemnatam et generosissimam feminam Lepidam in gratiam Quirini: she could count both Pompey and Sulla amongst her antecedents, and had been intended as the bride of Lucius Caesar. for details of the case see Tac. *Ann.* 3.22-3. It was unusual for a charge of *falsum* to be heard by the Senate, but the high rank of Lepida provides the reason (see R.J.A. Talbert [1984] 467). She was defended by her brother M. Lepidus. Quirinius was alleged to be gratified by execution of his ex-wife Aemilia Lepida. The emperor's motive was apparently thought to be that Quirinius was childless, and Tiberius expected to get his money (cf. Tac. *Ann*. 3.48). Her claim to have had a child by Quirinius, if true, would have damaged this expectation. It was answered by accusations of adultery, amongst other things. It is difficult to believe that Tiberius contrived Aemila's downfall as a favour to Quirinius, as Suetonius suggests. The emperor's real motive may have been to block this branch of the family from any thoughts of imperial ambition.

On the family tree see L. Hayne, *AC* 42 1973 497-507; for further details of the trial see G.B. Townend, *Latomus* 21 (1962) 484-93; D.C.A. Shotter, *Historia* 15 (1966) 312-17; Garnsey (1970) 29; Seager (1972) 155-7.

49.2
praeterea Galliarum et Hispaniarum Syriaeque et Graeciae principes confiscatos: the story of these confiscations from rich provincials are apparently a generalisation from some rare instances. See Tac. *Ann*. 4.20.1 [AD 24], on the conviction of Gaius Silius. Property of Seianus was transferred to the *fiscus* in AD 32 (Tac. *Ann*. 6.2.1). Tac. *Ann*. 6.19 [AD 33] discusses Sextus Marius from Spain, accused of incest and thrown from the Tarpeian rock (perhaps he was a friend of Seianus, if we believe any of the generalisation at Dio 58.16.7). His case is seen by Tacitus as an irregularity in that the *bona damnatorum* would normally go to the *aerarium*, whereas Tiberius apparently arrogated the moneys for his own *patrimonium*. Dio on the other hand says that Marius had first become rich through the emperor's favour (Dio 58.22.2). On this area see G.B. Townend, *Latomus* 21 (1962) 484ff.; Rogers [1935] 176f. The motive for the confiscation seems to have been to increase imperial control of mines, closely related to control over monetary supply and output. See O. Davies (1935) 97ff.; C.H.V. Sutherland (1976) 31-2. For discussion of a fragmentary bronze inscription which appears to refer to Sextus Marius see W. Eck - F. Fernández, *ZPE* 85 (1991) 217-22. See also *PIR*[2] M 195.

plurimis etiam ciuitatibus et priuatis ueteres immunitates et ius metallorum ac uectigalium adempta: here in the absence of the existence of the *fiscus* it seems that these taxes would now benefit the provincial *fisci* and the *aerarium*, and that the existence of an imperial *a rationibus* at this period had a purely private function. He was not employed to gather monies of this sort from the provinces as such, but as a domestic functionary with control over private monetary affairs of the emperor. See Boulvert (1970) 78. In imperial provinces the emperor would employ as his own private employees equestrian procurators who would have the control over the provincial *fisci*. These can be seen as tributaries of the *aerarium*. But Tiberius himself made it clear that his procurators in Senatorial provinces did not have responsibilities of this type. They were to be restricted to matters relating to his slaves and his property (Tac. *Ann.* 4.15 ; Dio 57.23.4- 5 [case of Lucilius Capito, a procurator in Asia]). As Boulvert ponts out this makes them comparable with the procurators who have control over territory under in personal ownership of the emperor such as the Thracian Chersonese and Jamnia in Palestine, an inheritance from Liuia.

Vononem regem...cum ingenti gaza...receperat. spoliatum perfidia et occisum: Suetonius fits the treatment of Vonones into his theme of imperial confiscations. However, there were serious political reasons why Vonones became unacceptable to both Rome and Parthia. After a request from a Parthian embassy (Suet. *Tib.* 16.1), the hostage Vonones returned to the Parthian throne (the date was perhaps c. AD 6; see N. Debevoise [1935] 151), but his unsuitability as a result of his Romanisation soon emerged. By the last years of Augustus he had been expelled and was reduced to seeking the vacant Armenian throne. He ended up as a prisoner of the Syrian governor, Creticus Silanus (Tac. *Ann.* 2.1-4; 58.3; 68.3; Jos. *AJ* 18.46ff.). Thus Suetonius appears to be unfair in claiming that Vonones' death was a product of the greed of Tiberius. See Goodyear (1981) 406. Further details in R.D. Sullivan, *ANRW* 2.7.2 (1980) 1160-61; M. Pani (1974) 155ff.

50-52 *Saeuitia* towards his immediate family

50.1
Odium...in Druso primum fratre detexit, prodita eius epistula...de cogendo ad restituendam libertatem Augusto: the whole section is concerned to underline Tiberius' bad relationship with his family. Levick, who dates the conflict with Drusus in about 10 BC, suggests that this letter may ultimately originate from the memoirs of the younger Agrippina (Levick [1976] 237 n. 8). But the whole story of Drusus' desire for a return to *libertas* and Tiberius' betrayal should surely be regarded as suspect. It could reflect the tradition that during the accession debate Tiberius hypocritically attempted to restore *libertas* to the Senate, and thus be a product of anti-Tiberian propaganda. Some speculation over preferable incumbents of the principate has entered the tradition, and Drusus has emerged with a reputation for *ciuilitas*. For other references to Drusus' hankering for the past see Suet. *Claud.* 1.4 and sensible comments of Mottershead ad loc.; Tac. *Ann.* 1.33.3; 2.82.3.

Suetonius' emphasis on the hatred held by Tiberius for family members appears particularly exaggerated in this case when we hear of the marathon ride undertaken by Tiberius to be at his brother's death-bed (Val. Max. 5.5.3; Plin. *NH* 7.84). After his death he accompanied the funeral cortège on foot all the way to Rome (Suet. *Tib.* 7.3; Sen. *Cons. ad Liu.* 89ff.; 171ff.).

Iuliae uxori tantum afuit ut...offici aut humanitatis aliquid impertiret: Suetonius portrays Tiberius as even more severe than Augustus at this juncture. After the scandal of 2 BC Julia had been kept in exile first on Pandateria, then at Regium, from AD 3 or 4. The move to Regium was a response to popular pressure, and may have been linked with the adoptions of AD 4 (Suet. *Aug.* 65.3; Dio [Xiph.] 55.13.1; J. Linderski, *ZPE* 72 [1988] 181-200 at 182-3). Suetonius claims that Tiberius on accession now deprived her of her allowance on the grounds that it had not been provided for in her father's will (see below). The circumstances of her death are obscure, but she was dead before the end of AD 14 either through despair or starvation (for a bibliography of modern views see Meise (1969) 34 n. 201). Her last son Agrippa had died some months earlier, and her former lover Sempronius Gracchus was executed by Tiberius at about this time (Tac. *Ann.* 1.53.1-2; Dio 57.18.1a). See discussion of R.S. Rogers, *TAPhA* 98 (1967) 387, who, however, imagines that Augustus was behind the death of Gracchus.

domo...egredi et commercio hominum frui uetuerit: Linderski is probably too extreme when he suggests that this means that Julia was now deprived by Tiberius not merely of male companionship but also of the company of her mother Scribonia (op.cit. 195-6).

peculio concesso...fraudauit, per speciem publici iuris: this passage provides interesting details of financial arrangements made for Julia by Augustus. She appears to have had harsher treatment initially on Pandateria (Suet. *Aug.* 65.3), but on return to Regium Augustus allowed her the use of *peculium* and a monetary allowance. As Linderski points out this reveals aspects of her legal situation. She must have been a *filiafamilias*, and not married to Tiberius *cum manu*. Otherwise on divorce she would have been *sui iuris*, and thus owned her own property (Linderski, op.cit. 185). As it was she was subject to paternal control while Augustus was alive. Once he had died she would have been *sui iuris*, although probably under the guardianship of Tiberius. Suetonius says that Tiberius' excuse for depriving her of the *peculium* and allowance was that Augustus had made no provision for it in his will (*quod nihil de his Augustus testamento cauisset*). Linderski plausibly suggests that Augustus made no specific mention of these items in his will, which meant that the *peculium* ceased to be her property and reverted to the patrimony of Augustus, and the mean-spirited Tiberius took advantage of the omission to have his revenge on Julia (Linderski, op.cit. 189-93). Notice the contrast with his considerate treatment of Julia at the time of her exile in 2 BC (Suet. *Tib.* 11.4). Not surprisingly, Suetonius interprets Tiberius' strict interpretation of the legal situation as malice.

50.2

matrem Liuiam grauatus uelut partes sibi aequas potentiae uindican-tem: Suetonius alleges that Liuia had political ambitions; this tradition is to be found in other sources (Tac. *Ann.* 3.64; Dio 57. 12.1ff.; 58.2), and is a reflection of her powerful lineage (see Dixon [1988] 77). Tacitus elsewhere talks of the inveterate *obsequium* of Tiberius towards his mother (*Ann.* 5.3.1). It is noteworthy that he punished her detractors on grounds of *maiestas* (Dio 57.19.1).

tulit etiam perindigne...ut titulis suis quasi Augusti, ita et Liuiae filius adiceretur: cf. Dio 57.12.4; on the allegation that he fumed at a senatorial decree which honoured him as son of Liuia and Augustus, note nevertheless honours granted to her even in old age, on recovery from illness. In addition there are coins inscribed SALVS AVGVSTA (*RIC*² Tiberius no. 47). This passage has been seen as a sign that Suetonius used the *acta senatus*. See introduction **26-27**.

50.3

quare non parentem patriae appellari, non ullum insignem honorem recipere publice passus est: Suetonius has perhaps made deductions here based on his own reading of the situation, although other sources also suggest that there were tensions over honours. Tacitus records that in AD 14 Tiberius responded with hostility to a suggestion that the month of October should be given the title Liuian (*Ann.* 1.14). However, in apparent contradiction of this position in AD 23 a temple in honour of Tiberius and his mother dedicated by the cities of Asia was accepted (*Ann.* 4.15). His diffidence over acceptance of honours either on his own account or for himself and his mother emerges clearly from the refusal of the temple for Hispania Ulterior in AD 25 and the Gytheum decree of AD 15 (Tac. *Ann.* 4.37-38; *EJ*² 102). What was in fact an official policy of moderation over honours was interpreted by hostile sources as friction between mother and son. On honours for Liuia see G. Grether, *AJPh* 67 (1946) 222-52; H.W. Ritter, *Chiron* 2 (1972) 313-38. See further 51.2 below.

maioribus...negotiis abstineret, praecipue ut animaduertit incendio

iuxta aedem Vestae...interuenisse: Dio also records assistance given by Liuia at the time of fires in AD 16 (Dio 57.16.2). For criticism of her role by the sources see below.

51.1

instanti saepius, ut ciuitate donatum in decurias adlegeret...extortum id sibi a matre: stories of a bad relationship are also found in Tacitus who may have influenced the Suetonian approach (cf. M.P. Charlesworth, *CR* 41 (1927) 55-7). Tensions certainly seem to be exaggerated, and the historiographical record has become polluted with material criticising her involvement in politics, which may reflect Senatorial distaste for the court structure as much as any complaints from Tiberius about his mother's interference. Examples of her supposed participation are listed by Levick (1976) 271-2 n. 32. For some less incredible examples see Tac. *Ann.* 5.2.1; Suet. *Claud.* 4.1ff.; Vell. 2.130.5. Levick suggests that Tiberius was often at odds with Liuia, as implied here. She points out that Tiberius had used his mother's name to justify the defence of Plancina at the trial of Piso in AD 20. We are left to understand that he did not approve of Plancina, who soon distanced herself from her husband (Tac. *Ann.* 3.15.1ff;17.2; Levick [1976] 210-11). Important but unfortunately incomplete new evidence on Plancina has now emerged from the *Senatus consultum de Cn. Pisone patre* from Irni (supplemented by other copies from elsewhere in Spain): there is reference to her *plurima et grauissima crimina* and the fact that she is reliant on the mercy of the *princeps* and the Senate (*se omnem spem in misericordiam principis nostri et senatus habere*). See W. Eck, *Cahiers du Centre G. Glotz* 4 (1993) 199, and 52.3 below.

The first example of conflict given here concerns her alleged attempt to get a man who had been granted citizenship put onto the juror list. Under the Republic there had been three *decuriae of iudices*. See A.H.M. Jones (1960) 41. A fourth group of lower census rating (200,000 HS) and subject to an entry age of 25 was added by Augustus in AD 4, after he held a census in that year (Suet. *Aug.* 32.3; see Carter [1982] ad loc.; Dio 55.13). Before this the minimum age was 30. Little else is known about the process of selection.

illa...Augusti codicillos de acerbitate et intolerantia morum eius...protulit: a frequent theme in the sources is that Augustus cast aspersions in private on Tiberius' character. Here we are told that Liuia possessed *codicilli* addressed to her by Augustus and that they were located in her *sacrarium*. Tiberius had an *a sacrario* who was a freedman of Liuia, but his exact function is unclear since he is only epigraphically attested (*CIL* VI 4027). The present passage casts doubt on the suggestion that private papers of the emperors were to be found in some central archive. See L. de Concinck, *ANRW* 2.33.5 (1991) 3682 and introduction 26-34.

ut quidam putent inter causas secessus hanc ei uel praecipuam fuisse:
on the causes of Tiberius leaving Rome see Tac. *Ann.* 4.57 (Seianus; hiding
cruelty and vices; ashamed of his appearance; Liuia). Only Dio follows
Suetonius in attributing the retirement solely to the influence of Liuia (Dio
57.12.6). Nevertheless there is little evidence of them working together after
AD 26. See A. Bernecker (1981) 10.

toto quidem triennio, quo...afuit, semel...paucissimis uidit horis: a picture of a lack of *pietas* on the part of Tiberius in final years is entrenched in
the tradition; see Tac. *Ann.* 5.1-2; Dio 58.2.1-6.

aduentus sui spem facit...corrupto demum et tabido corpore funeratam:
Suetonius spices up non-attendance at the funeral with this unlikely story
about maltreatment of the corpse. Tacitus provides a less coloured account
(*Ann.* 5.1-2).

prohibuit consecrari: Tiberius vetoed Liuia's deification, and seems to
have been unable to escape a reputation for meanness on this issue (Tac.
Ann. 5.2; Dio 58.2.1). Suetonius says that Tiberius put about the story that
she herself had forbidden the consecration (*quasi id ipsa mandasset*).
Claudius eventually granted Liuia the status of *diua* in AD 42, and also
granted her other posthumous honours (Suet. *Claud.* 11.2; Dio 60.5.2). This
may in part explain how Tiberius came to be seen as mean-spirited over
honours for Liuia.
 On honours curtailed compare 26.2; 50.2; Tac. *Ann.* 1.14.1ff.; 4.37f.;
Dio 57.12 [all during lifetime]; Tac. *Ann.* 5.1.4; 2.1; Dio 58..2.1-6; Suet.
Cal. 16.3; *Galba* 5.2 [after death]. Dio mentions an arch offered by the
Senate as an honour never previously conferred upon any woman (Dio
58.2.3). This is discussed by F.S. Kleiner, *Athenaeum* 68 (1990) 508-14. For
Tiberius' general conservatism about honours see Tac. *Ann.* 4.8ff; 4.15;
4.37-38, and the Gytheum decree (= *EJ*^{2} 102).

testamentum quoque eius pro irrito habuit: it was later used as political
ammunition by Caligula, who took care to carry through its terms (Tac. *Ann.*
5.1.6; Suet. *Cal.* 16.3; Dio 58.2.3a; 59.2.3-4; Suet. *Galba* 5, which gives an
example of Tiberius' alleged handling of the legacies. Galba was said to
have obtained the largest legacy under Liuia's will, which Tiberius reduced
on grounds of a technicality).

omnisque amicitias et familiaritates...afflixit: this appears to be a generalisation from rare instances. There is, however, some evidence to support the contention. See Tac. *Ann.* 6.10.1. For revenge on friends/confidants see Tac. *Ann.* 6.26 (Plancina); Tac. *Ann.* 6.10 (Vitia, the mother of Fufius Geminus); Tac. *Ann.* 5.2 (Fufius Geminus); his wife, Mutilia Prisca, was also a victim (Tac. *Ann.* 4.12.6; cf. Dio 58.4.5ff.). It is hard to ascertain from whom the charges originated. See Levick (1976) 177.

equestris ordinis uiro, et in antiliam condemnato: what Suetonius appears to object to here is not the penalty, but its imposition on a man of equestrian status. Two severe penalties which could accompany imprisonment were *metallum* and *opus publicum.* Caligula is also said to have inflicted what Suetonius clearly believed was an outrageous type of punishment for a man of this status (Suet. *Cal.* 27.3; P.D.A. Garnsey [1970] 134; 241).

52.1
Filiorum neque naturalem Drusum neque adoptiuum Germanicum...dilexit: stories of a bad relationship between Tiberius and Drusus abound. See Tac. *Ann.* 1.76.3f.; Dio 57.13.1f.; 22.3.

nam Drusus fluxioris remissiorisque uitae erat: this is Suetonius' own observation, and need not represent Tiberius' own view of the situation. On his temperament see also Tac. *Ann.* 1.29. He is said to have had a quarrel with Seianus, and Tiberius' lack of paternal feeling is related by the sources to his dissolute behaviour (Tac. *Ann.* 4.3; Dio 57.13.1ff.).

a funere ad negotiorum consuetudinem rediit iustitio longiore inhibito: on his lack of emotion after the death of Drusus see Tac. *Ann.* 4.8, where his continuation of Senatorial business is criticised; cf. Tac. *Ann.* 4. 13. Dio dismisses suggestions that Tiberius was in some way involved in the death of Drusus, and points out that the unemotional response was unremarkable in a Tiberius, placing emphasis on his attachment to Drusus (Dio 57.22.3).

A suspension of public business (*iustitium*) after the death of a member of the imperial family became normal in the empire (see *D & S s.v. iustitium*; *RE s.v. iustitium*). Did Tiberius in fact shorten the period of the *iustitium*? No other source mentions it, and the reference may merely be to his immediate return to Senatorial business. After the death of Liuia the Senate insisted on a full year of mourning for her on the part of the women, although approving an immediate return to public business (Dio 58.2.2). There is a notable contrast with the *iustitium* after the death of Drusilla which is said to have been enforced ferociously (Sen. *Cons. ad Polyb.* 17.4-5; Suet. *Cal.* 24.2; Dio 59.11.1ff.).

The *Tabula Siarensis*, an important inscription discovered near Seville in 1982, has revealed valuable details about mourning and honours for Germanicus. Some of these honours supplement the *Tabula Hebana*, and make it clear that at an official level Germanicus received substantial commemoration. However, official documents of this sort do little to resolve the justice of Suetonian claims about lack of genuine emotion from Tiberius in the aftermath of the death of family members. It is hard to estimate the extent to which the honours on this inscription were initiated by the Senate itself, as well as to understand why certain proposals appear in the SC, while others come into the *rogatio* (on the interrelationship between the *Tabula Siarensis* and the other known inscriptions concerned with funerary honours for Germanicus see J.S. Richardson, *Estudios sobre la tabula Siarensis* (1988) 35-41). The inscription has generated a massive amount of discussion of many aspects of the relationship between the Senate, Germanicus and Tiberius, and the following list can only represent some of the major contributions on this critical new piece of evidence:

A. Fraschetti, 'La *Tabula Hebana*, la *Tabula Siarensis* e il *iustitium* per la morte di Germanico' *MEFRA* 100 (1988) 867-89.

J. González and F. Fernandez, 'Tabula Siarensis' *Iura* 32 (1981) [1985] 1-36 [first full publication with photographs].

———'*Tabula Siarensis, Fortunales Siarenses et municipia civium Romanorum*' *ZPE* 55 (1984) 55-100 [with full text].

J. González and J. Arce (eds), *Estudios sobre la tabula Siarensis* (1988) [this is a valuable collection of essays on the inscription with contributions by international scholars].

W.D. Lebek, 'Schwierige Stellen der *Tabula Siarensis*' *ZPE* 66 (1986) 31-48.

———'Die drei Ehrenbogen für Germanicus: Tab. siar. frg. I 9-34; *CIL* VI 31199 a 2-17' *ZPE* 67 (1987) 129-48.

———'Kleinere Ergänzungsprobleme in der Tabula Siarensis' *ZPE* 70 (1987) 57-62.

———'*Consensus universorum civium*: Tab. Siar. frg. II col. b. 21-27' *ZPE* 72 (1988) 235-40.

———'Die circensischen Ehrungen für Germanicus und das Referat des Tacitus im Lichte von Tab. Siar. frg. II col. C 2-11' *ZPE* 73 (1988) 249-74.

———'Tab. siar. frg. I 25-28; frg. II col. A 7-8 und éinige Liviusstellen' *ZPE* 73 (1988) 281-84.

———'Augustalspiele und Landestrauer (Tab. Siar. frg. II col. A 11-14)' *ZPE* 75 (1988) 59-70.

———'Sub edicto suo proponere: Tab. siar. frg. II col. B 12 und Suet. *Aug.*

89.2' *ZPE* 77 (1989) 39-41.

——'Die Mainzer Ehrungen für Germanicus, den alteren Drusus und Domitian (Tab. Siar. frg. I 26-34; Suet. *Claud.* 1,3)' *ZPE* 78 (1989) 45-82.

——'Der proconsulat des Germanicus und die auctoritas des Senats: Tab. Siar. frg. I 22-24' *ZPE* 87 (1991) 103-24.

C. Nicolet, 'La Tabula Siarensis, la lex de imperio Vespasiani, et le jus relationis de l'empereur au sénat' *MEFRA* 100 (1988) 827-66.

D.S. Potter, 'The *Tabula Siarensis*, Tiberius, the senate and the Eastern boundary of the Roman empire' *ZPE* 64 (1987) 269-76.

52.2

Iliensium legatis...consolantibus...respondit...dolere, quod egregium ciuem Hectorem amisissent: this story is part of the larger theme of his hard-heartedness in the face of the death of relatives. It may be a product of the picture of Tiberius as tyrant. As a story it assists in Suetonius' picture of a haughty Tiberius.

Germanico...gloriosissimas uictorias ceu damnosas rei p. increparet: Suetonius follows the tradition in its strong support for the deeds of Germanicus, but appears to exaggerate tensions. Tacitus only reports that Tiberius had recommended that Germanicus should leave some scope for Drusus to attain military glory (Tac. *Ann.* 2.26). Note however that Goodyear thought that Suetonius might reflect the actual attitude of Tiberius to Germanicus. See Goodyear (1981) 258.

quod uero Alexandream...adisset, questus est in senatu: a letter of complaint about invasion of imperial domain was addressed to the Senate when Germanicus went to Alexandria ostensibly ɔ relieve a disastrous famine. Tacitus takes a hostile view, and claims soliciiude was merely a pretext for a visit to learn about the history of Egypt. He also explains why Tiberius had placed a ban on senators and knights visiting Egypt (Tac. *Ann.* 2.59). Goodyear (1981) 378 thought that Tacitus was probably relying on the *acta senatus* at this point, since he seems to know details of the imperial rebuke (cf. Seager [1972] 104; Levick [1976] 272 n.38). Suetonius in his reflection of the more favourable tradition to the effect that Germanicus acted to deal with a genuine crisis may reflect the position taken by his family and friends (Goodyear [1981] 372-73). Some further details may be gleaned from *P. Oxy.* 2435. This document tends to confirm the Tacitean view that Germanicus was in Egypt to see Alexandria and other Egyptian antiquities. Details of his activites and their purpose are discussed by D. Weingartner (1969), esp. 1-28.

52.3

causa mortis...per Cn. Pisonem...creditur: the story that he arranged for Piso to poison Germanicus suits argument here, but is still only recorded as a tradition. A less damning version is retailed at *Cal.* 1.2-2, but it is clear from both references that Suetonius is very hostile to Piso (cf. *Cal.* 3.3; *Vit.* 2.3). Dio openly alleges murder (Dio 57.18.9). See also Vell. 2.130.3; Jos. *AJ* 18.54. Tacitus has a more balanced approach (*Ann.* 3.14; 19). Piso had been a notoriously cruel proconsul of Africa (Sen. *De Ira* 1.19.3 [between 5 BC-AD 2]), and later became governor of Spain in AD 9-10 (Tac. *Ann.* 3.13; see G. Alföldy [1969] 10; Syme, *ES* 8 [1969] 125-33). For further details see *PIR*² C 287; D.C.A. Shotter, *Historia* 23 (1974) 229-45; W. Eck, *EA* 15 (1990) 139-46. The recently discovered *Senatus Consultum de Cn. Pisone patre* has provided important new insights into the relationship between Tiberius, Piso and Germanicus. See W. Eck, *Cahiers du Centre, G. Glotz* 4 (1993) 189-208.

huius criminis reum putant quidam mandata prolaturum: for the story of the *occulta mandata* see Tac. *Ann.* 3.16.

suspicionem confirmauit...liberis Germanici...afflictis: it is not surprising that suspicions were later strengthened by the treatment of Agrippina and her children. However, it is clear that the tradition contains a great deal of speculation over imperial attitudes and dynastic preferences.

53-54 *Saeuitia* towards Agrippina and her children

53.1

si non dominaris, **inquit,** *filiola, iniuriam te accipere existimas?*: the bad relationship between Agrippina and Tiberius is said to have developed as a result of her suspicions over the cause of the death of Germanicus. Tacitus associates this outburst with a confrontation between Tiberius and Agrippina at the time of the fall of her cousin Claudia Pulchra in AD 26 (Tac. *Ann.* 4.52.3ff.). Tacitus says that the line was Greek (*Graeco uersu*), and some ingenuity has been exercised on identifying the Greek original. In the event Claudia and her lover Furnius were condemned for adultery alone and the treason charge was dropped. See Seager (1972) 201.

inter cenam porrecta a se poma gustare, non ausam etiam uocare desiit:
Suetonius records the story of the apple, expanded by Tacitus (*Ann.* 4.54),
with a variant that Seianus had sent false friends warning her of the danger of
poison. This surely apocryphal tale is accepted as historical by Seager (1972)
201.

53.2
calumniatus modo ad statuam Augusti modo ad exercitus confugere uelle:
Suetonius appears here to be confused over the charges against Nero and
Agrippina; for the charges compare the letter of Tiberius at Tac. *Ann.* 5.3,
where the emphasis is on charges of immorality. Tacitus insists that the fall of
Agrippina did not occur until after the death of Liuia in AD 29 (for her death
before June, see Levick [1976] 276 n. 108), but see Suet. *Cal.* 10.1 and Lindsay
(1993) ad loc. Elsewhere Tacitus expands on the points made by Suetonius
here, although he never accepts them as the actual charges laid by the emperor.
He says that agents were suborned by Seianus to encourage Agrippina and
Nero to flee to the armies in Germany or to clasp the statue of the Divine
Augustus in the forum, demanding the protection of the Senate and people
(Tac. *Ann.* 4.67.6). While neither of these measures was adopted, Tacitus
suggests that they were charged with having thought of acting on them, and
it seems clear that he means that the moral charges laid were a substitute for
charges of a political nature. On the idea that there was a conspiracy by
Agrippina see R.S. Rogers, *TAPhA* 62 (1931) 141-68. For discussion see D.
Hennig (1975) 91ff.

Pandateriam relegauit...oculum per centurionem...excussit: note the high
rank of the guards placed over imperial renegades. The story of the flogging
leading to loss of an eye during her exile on Pandateria is only found here.

mori inedia destinanti: according to Suetonius she engaged in self starvation,
which was followed by forced feeding. See also Tac. *Ann.* 6.25; Dio 58.22.4-5;
both sources suggest the possibility of murder rather than suicide.

natalem eius inter nefastos referendum suasisset: on her birthday as day
of ill omen, compare Tacitus, who says that it was the day of her death which
was to be celebrated annually with a thanksgiving. Coincidentally the date of
her death, 18th October, fell on the same day as the fall of Seianus two years
earlier (Tac. *Ann.* 6.25.3-5). Agrippina's birthday was on or before October
26th, and in contradiction to Suetonius it continued to be celebrated by the
Arval brothers. See *EJ*[2] p. 54; *AFA* p. xlix n.1. Tacitus is to be preferred. The
effect of the hostile measure would be to indicate her status as an enemy of

the state, if it was in fact ever carried through. See A. Bernecker (1981) 7.

imputauit etiam quod non laqueo strangulatam in Gemonias abiecerit: although Suetonius seems sensationalist in his story of the boast of clemency in not exposing her on the *Gemoniae*, Tacitus also retails this strand of the tradition (Tac. *Ann.* 6.25).

proque tali clementia interponi decretum...quo...Capitolino Ioui donum ex auro sacraretur: on the prominence given to the *clementia* of Tiberius see Levick (1976) 87. Valerius Maximus treats the virtue at 5.1. For Tacitean allusions to the *clementia* of Tiberius see Levick (1976) 252 n. 20. For the golden gift to Capitoline Jupiter compare Livy 3.55.7; A. Bernecker (1981) 23 n. 1. It may have been in conjunction with this celebration of the *clementia* of Tiberius in AD 33 that *dupondii* were issued to the *moderatio* and *clementia* of Tiberius. The date will then be between AD 34-7. See H. Gesche, *JNG* 21 (1971) 37-80. Sutherland in his discussion demonstrating that the two issues constituted a twin, die-linked series, placed them in AD 22-23 (see Tac. *Ann.* 3.51; 3.56) – still a powerful argument, which does not involve the issue commemorating the disreputable circumstances of Agrippina's death (*JRS* 28 [1938] 129-40). Levick in *The Ancient Historian and his Materials* (1975) 123-37 accepts AD 16 as the date for IMP VIII on the basis of Tac. *Ann.* 2.18.2, and associates the celebration of *clementia* with his handling of the case of Libo Drusus. Over the date of IMP VIII she agrees with the conclusive arguments of H. Gesche, *Chiron* 2 (1972) 339-48, but Sutherland had already in 1938 shown how discrepancies of this sort might arise on coinage. The options were reassessed by Sutherland in *NC* 139 (1979) 21-25, reinforcing arguments for AD 22-23.

54.1

Neronem et Drusum, patribus conscriptis commendauit: for the recommendation of Nero and Drusus to the Senate see Tac. *Ann.* 4.8. Their assumption of the *toga uirilis* was in each case celebrated with a *congiarium* (Tac. *Ann.* 3.29; *CIL* XIV.244 [Nero]; Tac. *Ann.* 4.4 [Drusus]). The amount was 60 denarii. See D. van Berchem (1939) 145-46. Nero was granted the right to stand for office five years before the normal age, and his brother received the same concession, one which had previously been granted to their father Germanicus (Suet. *Cal.* 1.1), and was now coming to be usual for imperial princes. See D. Hennig (1969) 44 n. 17; E. Meise (1969) 64f.

ut comperit ineunte anno...uota suscepta: their inclusion in New Year celebrations receives a hostile emphasis in Tac. *Ann.* 4.17 [AD 24], where it is made clear that Tiberius did not authorise the honour and suspected the machinations of Agrippina. For the date, 3rd January, see Dig. 50.16.233.1 (Gaius). As Seager points out this actually shows how effectively Seianus was undermining Agrippina's position ([1972] 188). Any favour to Agrippina's family was now construed as an attack on the emperor's position. This interpretation is valid regardless of whether Seianus was operating on his own or Tiberius' behalf. Compare 61.1 below.

54.2

ex eo patefacta interiore animi sui nota...criminationibus obnoxios reddidit: Suetonius openly claims that it was Tiberius himself who used false charges and hostile spies against Nero and Drusus. The role of Seianus is deliberately diminished (cf. Tac. *Ann.* 4.70-71).

accusauit per litteras...iudicatos hostis fame necauit: for the declaration as public enemies see also Suet. *Cal.* 7. This was a method for the Senate to express its disapproval of the brothers in the absence of a formal trial. See A.W. Lintott (1968) 155ff; Levick (1976) 169-70.

Neronem in insula Pontia: Caligula was later to retrieve the remains of his mother and brother from Pandateria and Pontia respectively (Suet. *Cal.* 15.1). Suetonius alleges that the bodies were ill-treated, which lead to difficulties for Caligula in collecting their remains. Nero had been forced to suicide/murdered when Seianus was already under suspicion (Suet. *Tib.* 61.1). Perhaps the date was soon after the expiry of Seianus' consulship (Levick [1976] 175).

Drusum in ima parte Palatii: Drusus is supposed to have resorted to eating the stuffing from his mattress. Because of his strength he is said to have lived on for nine days (Tac. *Ann.* 6.23). See further on 65.2.

ei carnifex...uncos ostentaret: on the *carnifex* see 61.5.

sic reliquias dispersas, ut uix quandoque colligi possent: see Suet. *Cal.* 15.1; Dio 59.3.5 for the retrieval of their remains early in the reign of Caligula.

55 *Saeuitia* towards his *consilium*

uiginti...depoposcerat uelut consiliarios in negotiis publicis: on the Augustan *consilium* see Suet. *Aug.* 35.2; Dio 53.21.4; 56.28.2; cf. Dio 57.7.3 for the Tiberian arrangement, but with excessive emphasis on Tiberius following Augustan precedent. Suetonius notes that the Tiberian group of 20 counsellors was formed from his *ueteres amici ac familiares*, and that their function gradually moved away from the Augustan model. They came to be imperial advisors, and not as under Augustus a group set up to prepare business for the Senate. As Crook points out speculation enables us to reconstruct part of this group ([1955] 36-39). This is assisted by the Suetonian observation that Seianus dragged several leading advisors to ruin in his wake. Leading equestrians such as Seius Strabo and C. Turranius were the first after Tiberius to take the oath, and can be presumed to form part of this inner circle (Tac. *Ann*. 1.7.3). Cossus Cornelius Lentulus is specifically known to have been an intimate and trustworthy confidant (Sen. *Ep*. 83.15). Clearly many of the leading figures known from Tacitus will have been included. For discussion of the function of the *consilium* see also Levick [1976] 92-3.

The *consilium* was apparently sent with Drusus to deal with the mutiny in Pannonia (Tac. *Ann*. 1.24; 27.1). Amongst their number was Seianus, whose uncle Blaesus was governor there. There was nothing radical in the operation of the *consilium* in the early years of Tiberius when he was following guidelines set down by his predecessor, but the advisory role gradually evolved. This development went further when the emperor moved first to Campania in AD 26 and on to Capri in AD 27. It appears that much official business was hereafter conducted by letters to the senate after a preliminary discussion with an intimate group of close advisors. There is some persuasive suggestion that the group became even more select at this stage (Dio 60.4.3; Crook, op.cit. 38).

Aelium Seianum...non tam beneuolentia prouexerat: Suetonius includes in this passage an assessment of Tiberius' use of Seianus as a tool. Tiberius' motive is said to have been to ensure that his true grandson reached the throne (cf. Seager [1972] 180). For bibliography on Seinaus and further assessment of Tiberius' motives see 61.1.

horum...uix duos anne tres...alium alia de causa perculit: exaggeration is implicit in such a statement. However, we know of a selection of victims including Cn. Piso in AD 20, Vistilius (Tac. *Ann*. 6.9.2ff.), Vescularius Flaccus and Julius Marinus (Tac. *Ann*. 6.10.2).

56 *Saeuitia* towards Greek *conuictores*

Nihilo lenior in conuictores Graeculos: it seems to be standard feature of the *uituperatio* against the emperors that they are cruel to all those who are close to them. Here the targets are his fellow *conuictores*. Tiberius retired to Capri with a retinue which included a number of Greeks devoted to the liberal arts (Tac. *Ann.* 4.58). For the composition of his retinue see G.W. Houston, *Greece and Rome* 32 [1985] 179-96.

Xenonem quendam..relegauit Cinariam: this Xeno, who was relegated to Cinaria because of a suspected reference to the emperor's retreat to Rhodes, is not otherwise known. See *PIR*[1] X 2.

Seleucum grammaticum...ad mortem compulit: the *grammaticus* Seleucus met with grief (a forced suicide) because he was asking the imperial *ministri* about the emperor's reading habits, and coming prepared. This shows a negative side of imperial control over taste. Clearly anticipating imperial interests represents a serious affront to imperial dignity. On Seleucus (only here) see *PIR*[1] S 254. On teasing of *grammatici* see also 70, and M.L. Clarke (1971) 24; M. Billerbeck, *Greece and Rome* 37 (1990) 191-203, esp. 196.

57 Early signs of *saeuitia*

57.1
Saeua ac lenta natura: compare Tac. *Ann.* 3.48.3: *intenta...pericula sordidamque et praepotentem senectam*; Jos. *AJ* 18.226. The emphasis on early *saeuitia* appears to be an attempt to retrieve the integrity of the characterisation.

Theodorus Gadareus rhetoricae praeceptor: Tiberius had been a pupil of Theodorus as a boy, as suggested by the present passage (see Stegemann, *RE* V A col. 1847f.[1934]; cf. Damascius *Vit. Isid.* 64 [p. 94, Zintzen], quoting Plutarch), and later may have visited him on Rhodes when returning from Armenia in 20 BC (11.1 above; Quintilian 3.1.17). He cannot have met him during his period of retirement on Rhodes after 6 BC. See Bowersock (1965) 35 n. 5. On Theodorus see Suda s.v. Θεόδωρος; G.M.A. Grube, *AJPh* 80 (1959) 337-65. For his influence on the rhetorical style of Tiberius see Sen. *Suas.* 3.7. Tiberius is said to have acquired the nickname Theodoreus for this reason.

πηλὸν αἵματι πεφυραμένον: this story also appears in a fragment of Dio, although unattributed (Dio 58 fr. 1).

57.2

scurram...ad supplicium imperauit: the same story also appears in Dio with minor variations (Dio 57.14.1-2). For the possibility that the anecdote reflects Vergil's version of the death of Priam, who is said to have been taunted by his assailant Pyrrhus to go and report on the villainy of Pyrrhus to the assassin's father Achilles (Verg. *Aen.* 2.535-50), see A. Turner, *CPh* 38 (1943) 261. The anecdote is also of interest in that it shows that the emperor was believed to have the power of summary execution. See Levick (1976) 122; 180.

in senatu Pompeio cuidam equiti R. quiddam perneganti: this is further anecdotal evidence illustrating Tiberian *saeuitia*, in this instance over the fate of a Roman knight, Pompeius. See Tac. *Ann.* 6.14 for his fall in AD 32 on a charge of conspiracy in the wake of the fall of Seianus (*PIR*[1] P 440). Some authorities believe that Suetonius was using the *acta senatus* here. See introduction **26-27**.

58-59 Attitudes to treason and slander

58

sub idem tempus consulente praetore...*exercendas esse leges* respondit: this is a reference to an enquiry by Pompeius Macer in AD 15 about whether charges of *maiestas* were to be heard in the praetor's court under the new emperor (Tac. *Ann.* 1.72.3ff., who reports the same words. See Levick [1976] 191; Goodyear [1981] 152). Suetonius is very casual over dates here since the fall of Pompeius took place in AD 32, hardly *sub idem tempus* as an event in AD 15. Tiberius had been advised by Augustus to be lenient over libellous attacks. See R.S. Rogers (1935) 7ff.

statuae quidam Augusti caput dempserat, ut alterius imponeret: a reference to the case of M. Granius Marcellus, a governor of Bithynia who was charged with both *maiestas* and extortion in AD 15. Tiberius himself made a notorious intervention to secure the acquittal of the defendant on the *maiestas* charge (Tac. *Ann.* 1.74). There seems to be no foundation to Suetonian allegations of the use of torture and execution in this case. See R.S. Rogers (1935) 172-73; R. Katzoff, *AJPh* 92 (1971) 680-84; R.A. Bauman (1974) 79-80; Goodyear (1981) 162. The charge *De Repetundis* was handed over to a board of *recuperatores* (Tac. loc. cit.).

perit...is qui honorem...eodem die...quo...Augusto: see Bauman (1974) 80-81.

59

Multa...specie grauitatis ac morum corrigendorum: on the role of *curator morum* and the imperial attitude to the position compare RG 6; Suet. *Aug.* 27; Dio 54.10.5 on the position under Augustus. On the whole area as a major Roman concern see E. Baltrusch (1989), esp. 133ff. for the active intervention of Augustus. Measures mentioned at 35.2 above suggest that Tiberius took just as direct an interest in the area.

nonnulli uersiculis...denuntiarent mala: Suetonius here gives a sample of satires on the emperor. These cannot be accurately dated. See Goodyear (1981) 153. Attacks of this sort on the emperor apparently had some currency under Augustus (Tac. *Ann.* 4.34.5). Suetonius notes that Augustus did not bother to trace the authors of hostile pamphlets (Suet. *Aug.* 55; cf. Dio 55.27.1; 56.27.1), but this is contradicted by Tacitus who says that Augustus was the first to proceed against libellous documents under the law of treason. See Bauman (1974) 27f. Tiberius is said to have been patient in the early years of his principate (28 above; cf. Tac. *Ann.* 1.72.4, on his early exasperation over anonymous verses which highlighted his cruelty, his arrogance, and the tensions with his mother).

Lampoons did cause their authors trouble under Tiberius; see Tac. *Ann.* 6.39 on Sextius Paconianus, strangled in prison (cf. 6.3 for Paconianus as Seianus' instrument against Caligula). Authorship of libellous pamphlets is also given as an alternative explanation for the fall of Sextus Vestilius. See Tac. *Ann.* 6.9.

As Levick points out the lampoons provide some kind of corrective to the overdrawn enthusiasm for Tiberius exhibited by Velleius. He claims that there was massive rejoicing on Tiberius' return from Rhodes and subsequent adoption, as well as a popular demand that he should be awarded the Pannonian command in AD 6 (Vell. 2.103.1ff; 104.3f; 111.2). The second of these couplets which questions Tiberius' right to even equestrian status may reflect contemporary bitterness over his indifference to popular feeling. See Levick [1976] 118.

Fastidit uinum...tam bibit...quam bibit ante merum: for the allegations of drunkenness see 42.1.

59.2

oderint, dum probent: this line has a link with the picture in the last lampoon of Tiberius as a Sulla. Compare Suet. *Cal.* 30.1: *oderint dum metuant*, a line written of Atreus in the age of Sulla with political overtones. See Lindsay (1993) ad loc.

60-64 Cruelty and terror

60

piscatori...agenti grandem mullum...perfricari...iussit: these stories of *saeuitia* associated with Capri exemplify Tiberius' dislike of intrusions into his *tranquillitas*. He is said to have discouraged visitors by an edict *ne quis quietem eius inrumperet* (Tac. *Ann.* 4.67.1). The story of the fisherman exemplies a point made by Tacitus, namely that the island of Capri was hard of access without attracting the attention of sentries. See Tac. *Ann.* 4.67. On the emperor's predilection for mullet see 34 above. A less discreditable variant story about Tiberius and a mullet is provided by Seneca (*Ep.* 95.42).

militem...ob subreptum...pauonem capite puniit: notice the exotic bird chosen for this example of imperial *saeuitia* (cf. Suet. *Cal.* 22.3; 57.4). Criticism of extravagance is implicit in the example.

lectica...uepribus impedita...primarum cohortium cen-turionum...paene ad necem uerberauit: again there is implied criticism of luxury. Conveyance in a litter was for the wealthy and especially for wealthy women (cf. Suet. *Cal.* 43).

61.1

primo matris, deinde nepotum et nurus, postremo Seiani familiares atque etiam notos persequeretur: the theme is once again that the emperor has no natural feelings for those closest to him.

commentario, quem de uita sua...composuit: this *commentarius* appears not to have been the work favoured by the emperor Domitian, who would pore over Tiberius' day-books (Suet. *Dom.* 20: *commentarii.* On *commentarii* see E.M. Wightman in *The Ancient Historian and his Materials* [1975] 98f.). See introduction 32.

Seianum se punisse, quod comperisset furere aduersus liberos Ger-manici: as Suetonius points out, this is a thin excuse, and the fact that Tiberius continued to act against Drusus in particular after the fall of Seianus suggests that the emperor had had a significant role in the initial fall from grace (cf. Levick [1976] 173). There is an extensive bibliography on the career of Seianus, and a select bibliography is appended:

F. Adams, 'The consular brothers of Sejanus' *AJPh* 76 (1955) 70-76.

M.-P. Arnaud-Lindet, '"Crimen Seiani" : sur quelques vers de Juvénal' *RHD* 58 (1980) 411-21.

H.W. Bird, 'L. Aelius Seianus and his political significance' *Latomus* 28 (1969) 61-98.

——'L. Aelius Seianus: further observations' *Latomus* 29 (1970) 1046-50.

A. Boddington, 'Sejanus. Whose conspiracy?' *AJPh* 84 (1963) 1-16.

M. Corbier, 'La famille de Séjan à Volsinii: la dédicace des Seii, *curatores aquae*' *MEFRA* 95 (1983) 719-56.

——'De Volusinii a Sestinum: *cura aquae* et évergétisme municipal de l'eau en Italie' *REL* 62 (1984) 236-74 [Corbier in these two articles reestablished the relevance of *CIL* XI 7285 = *ILS* 8996 to the family history of Seianus, as well as providing a useful discussion of their municipal context].

D. Hennig, *L. Aelius Seianus* (Vestigia 21, Munich, Beck, 1975)[a useful general treatment].

J. Nicols, 'Antonia and Sejanus' *Historia* 24 (1975) 48-58.

R. Sealey, 'The political attachments of L. Aelius Seianus' *Phoenix* 15 (1961) 97-114.

G.V. Sumner, 'The family connections of L. Aelius Seianus' *Phoenix* 19 (1965) 134-45.

61.2

genera, uelut exemplaria saeuitiae, enumerare sat erit: segments on imperial *saeuitia* are also very pronounced in the lives of tyrants such as Caligula and Nero. See Suet. *Cal.* 26-35; *Nero* 26-39, on which see K.R. Bradley (1978) 153. Emphasis here is on his disregard for both social and religious conventions.

accusati damnatique multi cum liberis atque etiam a liberis suis: compare Suet. *Cal.* 27.4, which airs the idea that the tyrant Caligula liked to torture fathers by forcing them to view the execution of their sons .

interdictum ne capite damnatos propinqui lugerent: Seager reminds us that mourning for a victim of a *maiestas* charge could take on a political dimension ([1972] 228-9). A prohibition of this sort is referred to in the Digest, but without a date (3.2.11.3). Tacitus claims that Vitia, the mother of Fufius Geminus was put to death because she had mourned her son, perhaps under this legislation (*Ann.* 6.10 [AD 32]). For doubts see Seager (1972) 228. Suetonius is likely to be generalising from the single instance of Vitia here.

61.3

decreta accusatoribus praecipua praemia, nonnumquam et testibus: for a full list of those prosecuted and the results of their cases see the summary in Rogers (1935) 206-11.

nemini...fides abrogata. omne crimen pro capitali receptum: these are typical Suetonian exaggerations.

obiectum est poetae, quod in tragoedia Agamemnonem probris lacessisset: Tacitus and Dio make it clear that this play was the Atreus of Mamercus Scaurus (Tac. *Ann.* 6.29.5f.; Dio 58.24.3-5). In it there was advice to a subject to endure the folly of the reigning monarch. Tiberius is supposed to have recognised himself as Atreus, and to have said he would make Scaurus Ajax (Dio 58.24.4). In fact the charges against Scaurus were adultery with Liuia Julia and magical rites (Tac. *Ann.* 6.29.6 [AD 34], naming his accusers as Seruilius and Cornelius), although Dio follows the Suetonian approach that his downfall was the literary work (Dio 58.24.3; cf. Sen. *Suas.* 2.22, who says he was accused of *maiestas* by one Tuscus. Perhaps this was the *cognomen* of one of the individuals named by Tacitus). The case is discussed by Rogers (1935) 151-4; Bauman (1974) 126-28.

obiectum et historico, quod Brutum Cassiumque ultimos Romanorum dixisset: on the posthumous reputation of Brutus and Cassius see E. Rawson in *Past Perspectives* (ed. Moxon, Smart and Woodman) (1986) 101-19. Suetonius here refers to the lost history of Cremutius Cordus, who got into trouble with Tiberius during AD 25 (for fragments of his history see *HRR* II CXIII-CXV; 87-90). Tacitus names his accusers as Satrius Secundus and Pinarius Natta, who were creatures of Seianus. The opposition of Cordus to the advancement of Seianus may have lain behind the charges actually brought (see Levick [1976] 164), but this is not of any interest to Suetonius, who is concerned to enumerate Tiberian atrocities. Cordus is credited by Tacitus with a powerful defence of *libertas*, which was followed by death by starvation (Tac. *Ann.* 4.34-5). The speech itself appears to be a Tacitean invention, and there is dispute over whether the history was in fact the main charge against Cordus (see Marsh [1931] 290ff.; Rogers [1935] 86ff.). Notice the unfounded implication in Suetonius that Cordus was executed. His books were burned, but some copies survived, preserved by his daughter Marcia, and subsequently published (Tac. *Ann.* 4..34-5; Sen. *Cons. Ad Marc.* 1.3; 22.4; Dio 57.24.2ff.). One of Caligula's first acts is said to have been to allow these works to circulated again (Suet. *Cal.* 16.1). But rehabilitation of Cordus had perhaps been allowed soon after the fall of Seianus. See J.

Bellemore, *CQ* 42 (1992) 219-34. For a general discussion of censorship at Rome see F.H. Cramer, *Journal of the History of Ideas* 6 (1945) 157-96.

ante aliquot annos etiam Augusto audiente: cf. Dio 57.24.3. Although Suetonius structures his comment to suggest that Tiberius adopted a hostile policy to numerous authors, it is clear that the specifics deal with the case of Cremutius Cordus.

61.4

citati...partim se domi uulnerauerunt...partim...uenenum hauserunt: both points illustrate the anxiety of defendants, a subject also broached by Tacitus (*Ann.* 2.29.2; 4.28.2; 6.3.3). The latter point generalises Tac. *Ann.* 6.40.1, the case of Vibulenus Agrippa, who in AD 36 swallowed poison in the Senate house during his trial (cf. Dio 58.21.2 {Vibullius]).

nemo punitorum non in Gemonias abiectus...uiginti uno die: again there may be some generalisation of specific instances; in AD 28 Titius Sabinus' body had been exposed the Gemonian steps before being cast in the Tiber (Dio 58.1.3; Plin. *NH* 8.145). On the *immensa strages* which took place in AD 33 in response to the fall of Seianus see Tac. *Ann.* 6.19.2ff. and the *Fasti Ostienses* (*EJ*[2] p. 43 = *Inscr. Ital.* 13.1.1898f: *complures*). Some of those prosecuted at this stage survived the process (Tac. *Ann.* 5.8.4 [Pomponius Secundus]; 6.3.4 [Sextius Paconianus, executed later in the reign: Tac. *Ann.* 6.39.1]). Discussed by Seager (1972) 232; Levick (1976) 207.

61.5

quia...nefas esset uirgines strangulari, uitiatae prius a carnifice: generalising from the case of Seianus' daughter, Junilla (Tac. *Ann.* 5.9.3; Dio 58.12.5; cf. *EJ*[2] p. 42 on the date). The *carnifex* was considered so polluted that he was not allowed to reside within the city. See Plaut. *Pseud.* 332; Cic. *Pro C. Rab.* 5.15. The *carnifex* is usefully discussed by J.-M. David, in *Du Châtiment dans la Cite: Supplices Corporels et Peine de Mort dans le Monde Antique* (1984) 144.

cum audisset unum e reis, Carnulum nomine, anticipasse eam, exclamauerit: Carnulum me euasit: the case is only recorded here: see *PIR*[2] C 443; Rogers (1935) 174, who links this circumstantial case with the theme of Tiberian *diritas*.

in recognoscendis custodiis: Caligula is also said to have exhibited *saeuitia* in a decision over the fate of prisoners with his famous command to execute *a caluo ad caluum* (Suet. *Cal.* 27.1).

61.6

annalibus suis uir consularis inseruit: the historian has been identified by some authorities as Seruilius Nonianus, the consular historian, who took a hostile line towards the emperor. See R. Syme (1958) 277. Tacitus claims Paconius as an innocent victim (Tac. *Ann.* 16.29.2-3). On Seruilius Nonianus see further Syme (1970) 91-109.

interrogatum...a quodam nano...cur Paconius...uiueret: M. Paconius had assisted Mam. Scaurus and two other satellites of Seianus, Bruttedius Niger and Iunius Otho, in an attack on the proconsul of Asia, C. Silanus, accused of *repetundae* in AD 22 (Tac. *Ann.* 3.66-9; see *PIR^1* P 15). The man said to have been used by Seianus as his agent against Caligula, Sextius Paconianus, may have been a relative (Tac. *Ann.* 6.3). He is unlikely to have been his adoptive son, since a son is known: Q. Paconius Agrippinus, an imperial opponent under Nero (*PIR^1* P 16; Tac. *Ann.* 16.28: *accusati ut paterni in principes odii heredis*; cf. Levick [1976] 214). M. Paconius appears to have fallen in the wake of Seianus on a charge of *maiestas*. See Rogers (1935) 169.

62.1

saeuitiam exacerbatus indicio de morte filii sui Drusi: the story that Liuilla in partnership with Seianus poisoned Drusus is accepted, and is made a catalyst for cruelties as well as an obsession with the case. See also Tac. *Ann.* 4.1ff; Dio (Xiph.) 57.22; 58.11.6. Tacitus tells us that it was not until after the fall of Seianus in AD 31 that rumour of a plot by Liuia Julia and Seianus gained currency. The story is questionable, and may have been invented by Caligula. See Lindsay (1993a) 84-88. The death of Liuilla is obscured by legendary elements. Dio has her preserved by Tiberius because of his regard for Antonia, but later starved by Antonia herself (Dio 58.11.7). A suspect example of imperial arbitrariness is appended to the story, in which Tiberius is supposed to have tortured a man he mistakenly believed was a witness, and then executed him to cover his error. If so, how did the tale reach Suetonius? See also Balsdon CR 65 (1951) 75; Meise (1969) 55ff.; 63ff.

62.2

ostenditur locus Capreis, unde damnatos...praecipitari coram se in mare iubebat: Suetonius may imply that he has himself visited the island (*ostenditur*). That trials resulting in execution took place in front of the emperor at Capri is known from the cases of Vescularius Atticus and Julius Marinus (Tac. *Ann.* 6.10.2). But this passage appears to be part of the speculation about imperial activities on the island.

contis atque remis elidente cadauera: compare the account of cruelty to spectators during the episode at Baiae under Caligula (Suet. *Cal.* 32.1: *cum multos e litore inuitasset ad se, repente omnis praecipitauit, quosdam gubernacula apprehendentes contis remisque detrusit in mare*).

62.3

Thrasyllus...differre quaedam spe longioris uitae compulisset: Suetonius follows the tradition that Thrasyllus had a major role in postponing further deaths. Tiberius had always had robust health (Suet. *Tib.* 68), and according to Dio Thrasyllus convinced the emperor that he would live for a further 10 years, and therefore need not hasten to destroy his enemies (Dio 58.27.1ff.). On Thrasyllus, who died a year before the emperor, see 14.4 above; Tac. *Ann.* 6.20-21; A.H. Krappe, *AJPh* 48 (1927) 359-66; R.P. Oliver, *ICS* 5 (1980)130-48; H.A.S. Tarrant (1993) 7-17.

cum et Gaium suspectum haberet et Tiberium ut ex adulterio conceptum aspernaretur: the story that he planned to kill both Gemellus and Caligula is found only here and is inherently implausible. There is quite extensive variation in the sources over Tiberian plans. Philo says that he favoured Gemellus (*Leg.* 24f), in substantial agreeement with Josephus who says, however, that Agrippa 1 backed Caligula (Jos. *AJ* 18.188; 211f.; 219). Suetonius himself elsewhere says that Tiberius preferred Gemellus (*Cal.* 19.3). Dio believed that he was supporting Caligula (Dio 58.23.1ff.). For further analysis see Meise (1969) 53. The story that Gemellus was born of an adulterous relationship may have been fostered by Caligula in an attempt to justify his exclusion from the succession.

felicem Priamum uocabat: the Tiberian quotation to the effect that Priam had been lucky in survivng all his progeny appears to be another element from the apocrypha about the emperor's attitude to the succession. A variant appears at Dio 58.23.4.

63.1

non modo inuisus...sed...quoque...contumeliis obnoxius uixerit: the following examples are intended to show how the emperor lived in constant fear of reprisals.

haruspices secreto ac sine testibus consuli uetuit: perhaps this was related to the banishment of astrologers in AD 19 (36 above). Dio claims that an oracle was delivered in this year which resulted in imperial investigation into the Sybilline books (Dio 57.18.4-5). Notice also Tiberius' refusal to allow consultation of the Sybilline books about a flood of the Tiber, as reported by Tac. *Ann.* 1.76.1 (AD 15). Augustus had already edited them (Suet. *Aug.* 31.1; Dio 54.17.2), but Tiberius clearly still felt that they were a political liability. Later in the reign he was concerned to prevent the circulation of suspect examples of this source (Tac. *Ann.* 6.12.2 [AD 32]). The *quindecimuiri sacris faciundis* had responsibility for keeping their contents secret, as well as for voting on the authenticity of suspect prophecies. Tiberius intervened at this time to ensure that in future the Senate followed this procedure which had been put in place by Augustus in 12 BC. For discussion see H.W. Parke (1988) 142.

uicina uero urbi oracula etiam dis[s]icere conatus est, sed maiestate Praenestinarum sortium territus destitit: the *sortes Praenestinae* were a collection of slips of oak marked with words in an archaic alphabet and kept in an olive wood box. The ceremony is little understood, but a young boy (*sortilegus*) would draw one of these lots out at random. The oracle was still in existence in the 4th century AD. See *PECS* s.v. Praeneste. For a full account of the temple of Fortuna at Praeneste see G. Gullini (1953). It can be appreciated that the emperor might have wanted to break the power of local oracles, but we have no control over this anecdotal evidence.

63.2

unum et alterum consulares oblatis prouinciis...detinuit: Aelius Lamia and Lucius Arruntius represent the known cases of this procedure. Explanation in terms of Tiberius' fear of the power of the individuals has met with some currency, both in antiquity (Tac. *Hist.* 2.65.2; here) and in the eyes of modern commentators. This is because the name of Arruntius is raised in connection with the *capaces imperii* in AD 14 (Tac. *Ann.* 1.13.1-2; W. Orth [1970] 89). It is clear that both figures were of sufficient ancestry and influence to represent a serious challenge to the emperor if they were to oppose him, but this is unlikely to explain Tiberius' conduct. Literary sources raise two further possible reasons for keeping these individuals at Rome: either passivity (Tac. *Ann.* 1.80.3; Suet. *Tib.* 41) or hypocrisy (Dio 58.19.5). But the emperor himself provided a precedent for the use of legates in the management of the provinces, a system adopted by Augustus in the so-called imperial provinces. It is worth considering the possibility that Tiberius was engaged in an innovative extension of this principle to senatorial provinces. That he should have introduced it in the case of powerful and senior senators can be seen as a reflection of his own snobberies, rather than reaction to their perceived reliability. The untraditional approach was not continued after Tiberius' death, and its unacceptability to the Senatorial order may sufficiently explain later hostile interpretations of it. However, this interpretation has not met with favour from modern scholars: see Levick [1976]127f; J.B. Campbell [1984] 341-43; the latter suggests that the very senior Arruntius and Aelius Lamia themselves actively sought the status and prestige of these posts without the burden of carrying out their duties on the spot.

Tacitus views the treatment of Aelius Lamia (PIR^2 A 200) in a manner hostile to Tiberius, as does Dio Cassius (Tac. *Ann*. 6.27.2; Dio 58. 19.5). Lamia had earlier been active in the war against Tacfarinas, and had been in charge in Africa perhaps in AD 15-16 (Tac. *Ann*. 4.13.3; U. Vogel-Weidemann [1982] 17-21; B.E. Thomasson II [1960] 21f.). His appointment to Syria ended in AD 32 when he was appointed as successor to Piso the Pontifex as city prefect (Dio 58.19.5), but he was dead by the end of AD 33 (Tac. *Ann*. 6.27.2). The city prefecture was probably a reward for loyalty at the time of the fall of Seianus (see 48.2 note). His legate in Syria, Pacuuius, is said to have been there for long enough to make it his own (Sen. *Ep*. 12.8).

Tacitus claims that on the death of Pomponius Flaccus in Syria, the emperor overlooked Arruntius when filling the post. This was the man whom he had prevented from going to his allotted Spain for ten years (Tac. *Ann*. 6.27.3 [AD 33]; PIR^2 A 1130). Some two years earlier, however, at the time of the fall of Seianus, the emperor had intervened to prevent the prosecution of Arruntius by the praetorian prefect on unspecified charges (Dio 58.8.3), and it is clear that the Tacitean account is highly tendentious. We have to understand that Tacitus is putting himself in the shoes of the outstanding Senatorial Arruntius and imagining the slight he would feel in not being considered worthy of this senior command. Moreover chronological problems emerge from the Tacitean claim that Arruntius was not awarded Spain until AD 23. Dio's account of his problems with Seianus mentions a ten year tenure at that point (i.e. AD 21-31), and may be correct.

Notice also that Tacitus mentions the murder of L. Calpurnius Piso, a man described as *praetor prouinciae* in Spain (Hispania Citerior) in AD 25 (Tac. *Ann*. 4.45.1). He was perhaps a man of praetorian rank, rather than a praetorian governor, and engaged in the type of role subordinate to Arruntius which Suetonius mentions in the present passage, and thus not operating as an imperial legate. See W. Orth (1970) 84f. He could be the man who put in hand considerable road works in the province (on which see Levick [1976] 131).

64

nurum ac nepotes...catenatos...mouit: the movement of the exiled Agrippina and Nero in closed litters under military escort shows that Tiberius was concerned about them as a focus for opposition. From Suetonius' point of view it was only natural that a tyrant should be hated, and consequently in a constant state of terror, as outlined in 63 above.

65 The crushing of Seianus

65.1

Seainum res nouas molientem: was Seianus plotted against or plotting? Several sources imply that the emperor's life was under threat. Of modern authorities only Rogers seems to have accepted this approach (Rogers [1935] 110 n.345, citing ancient evidence for his approach; contrast Marsh [1931] 304ff.; Seager [1972] 216 thinks Seianus may have engaged in a last act of desperation after realising that he had lost imperial support; Levick [1976] 173 thought that an attack on heirs to the dynasty would be construed as an attack on the emperor). What seems unquestionable is that the emperor himself promoted the view that he was victim of a plot. The official view emerges in the citation of his letter to the Senate below. For bibliography on Seianus see 61.1 above.

natalem eius...et imagines aureas coli passim uiderat: after Tiberius had granted priesthoods to Caligula, Seianus and his sons, proconsular power of uncertain extent was also granted to Seianus by the Senate (Dio 58.7.4f.). For the celebration of his birthday see Dio 58.2.7; worship of his images, Dio 58.4.4; Juv. 10.62; ultimately Tiberius did place a ban on sacrifices to mortal men (Dio 58.8.4). Following the fall of Seianus the Senate in AD 31 decreed that oaths should only be taken in the name of the emperor (Dio 58.12.6). But each phase of this process only served to underline how difficult it was for the emperor to curtail growth in this area.

collegam sibi assumpsit in quinto consulatu: he was elected to the consulship for AD 31 with Tiberius as his colleague (*EJ*[2] 50a; *ILS* 6044 = *EJ*[2] 53; *EJ*[2] 358a; Tac. *Ann.* 6.8.6; Dio 57.20.2; 58.4.3; 6.2; 8.3).

deinde spe affinitatis ac tribuniciae potestatis deceptum: the betrothal of Seianus to an imperial princess was now announced (Dio 58.3.9 = Zonaras 11.2: τῇ τοῦ Δρούσου θυγατρί; Tac. *Ann.* 5.6.2 (*generum*); 6.27.1 (on the subsequent marriage of the daughter of Drusus to Rubellius Blandus in AD 33). The Tacitean term *gener* might suggest that Liuilla was the woman he was to marry, but if the marriage was to have dynastic significance, and the chance of an heir, the younger daughter of Drusus would be more plausible. There had been an earlier refusal of permission for Seianus to marry the mother (Tac. *Ann.* 4.39-41, although the authenticity of this private correspondence is suspect), but that had been in AD 25. Some 8 years later the daughter would have been a better prospect. Suetonius implies that Seianus never actually married whichever woman (*spe affinitatis*). See R. Syme, *AJPh* 103 (1982) 62-85. On the award of tribunician power to Seianus see Dio 58. 9.2; 10.3.

mitterent alterum e consulibus, qui se...perduceret: Levick notes the whining tone of self pity illustrated by this passage and by a well known inscription (*ILS* 6044 = *EJ*^{2} 53). See Levick (1976) 201. The consuls at the time of the fall of Seianus were L. Fulcinius Trio, who had been one of Seianus' partisans, and P. Memmius Regulus, who was sent to escort Tiberius to Rome, but rebuffed by the emperor on arrival (Dio 58.10.3). This is the only extant segment of the letter (cf. Juv. 10.71).

65.2
tumultumque metuens Drusum nepotem...solui...ducemque constitui praeceperat: this unlikely tradition is also relayed by Tacitus (*tradidere quidam*) and Dio in their discussion of the subsequent fate of Drusus. He is said to have died in a dungeon in the palace still unrehabilitated in AD 33 (Suet. *Tib.* 54.2; Tac. *Ann.* 6.23; Dio 58.13.1). Drusus had managed to distance himself from the problems of his mother and brother, and in fact is said to have been used by Seianus against Nero (Tac. *Ann.* 4.60.4). Drusus was married to Aemilia Lepida, probably as late as AD 29 (see Furneaux on Tac. *Ann.* 6.40.4), and Dio says that she intrigued with Seianus against her husband (Dio 58.3.8). Drusus' demise was signalled by his return from Capri to Rome in AD 30 (64 above), where formal charges were laid against him by Cassius Seuerus, and he was pronounced public enemy (Dio 58.3.8; Suet. *Tib.* 54; *Cal.* 7).

aptatis etiam nauibus ad...fugam: Dio also says that Tiberius was prepared for flight because he expected Seianus to seize the city and attack him on Capri (Dio 58.13.1).

oppressa coniuratione...non egressus est uilla, quae uocatur Ionis: this is an exaggeration, since we know that he crossed over to the mainland early in AD 32 (Tac. *Ann.* 6.1).

66-67 Unease and self-reproach

66

Vrebant insuper anxiam mentem uaria undique conuicia...per libellos in orchestra positos: these *libelli* were thus intended for Senatorial consumption, since it appears that Senators from the late Republic onwards had seats not merely in the front rows, but within the *orchestra* itself. See E. Rawson, *PBSR* 55 (1987) 107. Suetonius refers here to insults primarily caused by the bad relationship with the Senate as a result of the *maiestas* trials.

Artabani Parthorum regis laceratus est litteris: there is clearly considerable exaggeration in Suetonius' version of this letter (see Anderson, *CAH* 10 747ff.). Nevertheless the Parthian king was perhaps overconfident since there had been no major military activity in the East since the death of Germanicus. For analysis see Seager (1972) 240-43. On Artabanus' contrasting view of Germanicus see also Suet. *Cal.* 5. For Vitellius and relations between Parthia and Rome after AD 35 see Jos. *AJ* 18.96-105; Plin. *NH* 15.83; 15.91; Tac. *Ann.* 6.31-7; Dio 58.26.1ff. The letter is also discussed by A. Bernecker (1981) 80ff., who notes that there is a remarkable correspondence betweeen the vices highlighted by Artabanus (*parricidia, caedes ignauia, luxuria*), and those outlined by Suetonius, after his initial statement about Tiberian viciousness at 42 above. On Vitellius see further in A. Garzetti, *Studi in Onore di R. Paribeni - A. Calderini* I (1956) 211-29. Artabanus is treated by U. Kahrstedt (1950).

67.1

semet ipse pertaesus...professus est: Suetonius proceeds to quote the beginnings of a letter through which (like Tacitus) he claims to demonstrate the despair of the emperor (cf. Tac. *Ann.* 6.6). R.S. Rogers notes that the words come from the beginning of the letter in which Tiberius dissuaded the Senate from convicting M. Cotta Messallinus (Rogers [1935] 134), and Levick reminds us that Tiberius enjoyed teasing the Senate (Tac. *Ann.* 6.2.5f; Levick [1976] 201-2). Her suggestion that Tiberius is making a literary allusion is tempting. See also Seager (1972) 226. This is another example of a letter which Suetonius is likely to have encountered in the *acta senatus*. See R.J.A. Talbert (1984) 324. See introduction **28**.

67.2

Existimant quidam...eum...prospexisse: on the pride of Tiberius in his own insight, and the significance of this material in the tradition see Levick (1976) 85.

patris patriae appellationem: refused in AD 15. See Tac. *Ann.* 1.72. Augustus had not taken the honour until 2 BC (RG 35.1), and Tiberius may have avoided the title for reasons other than *ciuilitas*. See further 26 above and Goodyear (1981) 138.

ne in acta sua iuraretur: see above 26.2; we are here given what is alleged to be the emperor's excuse for this unwillingness: *sed exempli causa cauendum esse, ne se senatus in acta cuiusquam obligaret, quia aliquo casu mutari posset* (67.3). Suetonius may have obtained the evidence from the *acta senatus*. See introduction **26-27**.

67.3

similem sui futurum nec umquam mutaturum mores suos, quam diu sanae mentis fuisset: Seager notes the irony of these words ([1972] 142).

67.4

Si quando...dubitaueris: this statement gives a very full impression of Tiberius' attitude to honours. We can compare this with the Gytheum decree (*EJ*^{2} 102) and Tac. *Ann.* 4.37-8.

68 Physical appearance

Personal descriptions in Plutarch and Suetonius assist in the moral presentation of character. With Tiberius the usual presentation is thoroughly evident. While the general description of his physical strength is clearly not unfavourable, his left handedness is undoubtedly a negative trait, often associated in the ancient world with perversion and homosexuality (see G. Maranon [1956] 50-51). The strength attributed to his left hand is actually exemplified in such a way as to suggest an interest in pederasty. Suetonius attributes to the emperor outbreaks of pimples on an otherwise clear complexion which seems to be a morally significant comment (cf. Plut. *Sulla* 2). The hereditary trait of wearing his hair at the back over the nape of his neck is itemised to remind us of his unfortunate ancestry. His capacity for seeing in the dark is a sinister feature. In the description of his gait and bearing there is a suggestion of Claudian arrogance, which is heightened by the process of quoting it as a physical rather than a moral defect. We are led to understand that even Augustus suspected his stepson of such inherent arrogance.

For the entire description compare Tac. *Ann.* 4.57: *erant qui crederent in senectute corporis quoque habitum pudori fuisse; quippe illi praegracilis et incurua proceritas, nudus capillo uertex, ulcerosa facies, ac plerumque medicaminibus interstincta.* Syme suggests that the emperor himself may have suffered from the *mentagra* which first entered Italy in the middle years of Tiberius' principate (Plin. *NH* 26.3; see 34.2 above). This would explain the eruptions on his face described by Tacitus (loc. cit.).

On the Suetonian portraits see E.C. Evans, *HSCPh* 46 (1935) 43-84; *TAPhA* 72 (1941) 96-108; J. Coussin, *REL* 31 (1953) 234-56. For further analysis of what Suetonius intends to convey to his audience about Tiberius see Bernecker (1981) 70ff. If we knew more of Suetonius' lost work *De Vitiis corporalibus*, this might have shown elements of the ancestry of his descriptions of members of the imperial family. The περὶ βλασφημιῶν shows the biographer's interest in physiognomy, since several of the terms are defined from this viewpoint. For the evidence from this source see J. Taillardat (1967).

Iconography

Portraits of Tiberius may not have been very numerous since he is said to have been discouraging on the subject (cf. 26.1 above). There is no sign of standarised types on the same scale as under Augustus. See J.D. Brecken-ridge, *ANRW* 2.12.2 (1981) 487. For a full discussion of images of Tiberius see L. Polacco (1955). Some detect signs of the withdrawn character of Tiberius in his iconography. See Breckenridge, op.cit. 487.

68.1

corpore amplo atque robusto: this was considered a sign of courage. As E.C. Evans points out, the mixture of positive and negative traits in the personal description of Tiberius correspond to the virtues and vices of his character (*HSCPh* 46 [1935] 68).

latus ab umeris...ceteris aequalis et congruens: Suetonius takes a direct interest in good proportions of the human body. Tiberius is not accorded the gross peculiarities of a Caligula. These are positive traits indicating a courageous and just man. Compare Suet. *Cal.* 50.1; E.C. Evans, *HSCPh* 46 (1935) 63-4.

sinistra manu: see introductory comments to 68.1.

68.2

colore...candido: pallor was a sign of lust, and also fearfulness, according to the physiognomists. See J. Coussin, *REL* 31 (1953) 249-50. This reinforces other tyrannical attributes accorded to Tiberius.

facie honesta, in qua tamen crebri...tumores: on these eruptions compare Tac. *Ann.* 4.57.

praegrandibus oculis: on coins and statues of the emperor surviving today the eyes are often given unusual treatment, as noted by Woodman (1977) 98, commenting on Vell. 2.94.2: *uisuque praetulerat principem.* Portraits often show his eyes with a distinct upward cast. The ability to see in the dark must be intended as a sinister trapping.

68.3

incedebat ceruice rigida et obstipa: the stiffness of Tiberius is a reminder of Claudian haughtiness. Suetonius does not fail to remind us by introducing the reaction of Augustus.

68.4

ualitudine prosperrima usus est: this section corresponds to section 50.2 of the life of Caligula. On Tiberius' robust health and the contrast with Augustus see Levick (1976) 209-10. Thrasyllus is said to have convinced him near the end of his life in AD 36 that he would live for a further ten years, and thus to have preserved certain accused from the death penalty (Suet. *Tib.* 62.3; Dio 57. 27.3).

69 Attitude to religion

Circa deos ac religiones neglegentior: neglect of religion is here blamed on Tiberius' astrological beliefs. Levick suspects the influence of Stoicism ([1976] 231 n. 37). However, Tiberius' obsessive preoccupation with Roman tradition and his duties as *Pontifex Maximus* may suggest that Suetonius exaggerates the extent to which he ignored religion. There seems to have been a feeling that the fatalism of astrology was incompatible with belief in the gods, and this may have influenced Suetonius.

addictus mathematicae: this interest can be presumed to have developed during his second stay on Rhodes, under the influence of Thrasyllus (cf. 14.4 above; Tac. *Ann.* 6.20.3; Dio 55.11; 57.15.7ff.; 58.27.1). For a brief account of the importance of astrology in the early empire see R.M. Ogilvie (1969) 54ff.; for more detail see F.H. Cramer (1954).

tonitura...praeter modum expauescebat: compare Caligula who was also frightened by thunder, a feature of his personality attributed by Suetonius to his mental health (Suet. *Cal.* 51.1). In the case of Tiberius Suetonius emphasises this fear of thunder as an attribute of a man much given to astrology.

numquam non coronam lauream capite gestauit: on superstitions related to laurel wreaths see *D & S* s.v. *corona*. The laurel wreath had been reserved for the triumph perhaps because of its perceived purificatory qualities - its capacity to efface the traces of blood spilt. Here Tiberius' gesture is intended to avert the malevolence represented by thunder sent down by the gods.

70 Literary pursuits

70.1

Artes liberales utriusque generis...coluit: attainment in the *liberales disciplinae* is highly regarded by Suetonius (see Suet. *Aug.* 84.1). These included rhetoric, philosophy, music, poetry and jurisprudence (Cic. *De Or.* 3.32,127). Here he emphasises Tiberius' proficiency in both Greek and Latin studies. On the educational and cultural background of Tiberius see Syme (1986) 346-66. On his literary interests see F. Goodyear, *ANRW* 2.32.1 (1984) 603-10.

in oratione Latina secutus est Coruinum Messalam: Levick notes the very favourable press given to his son by Velleius, a sign of continuing imperial good-will (2.112.1; Levick [1976] 43). Tiberius' teacher, M. Valerius Messalla Coruinus, was consul in 31 BC, and probably assisted the early development of Tiberius' legal career after his assumption of the *toga uirilis*. Coruinus was an advocate of the plain style, and was at the centre of a poetic circle as patron in the early Augustan years. The circle included both Tibullus and Valgius Rufus. See *PIR*[1] V 90; C. Davies, *Greece and Rome* 20 (1973) 25ff.; Syme (1986) 359. Suetonius appears to exaggerate the age difference between Tiberius and Coruinus (*quem senem adulescens obseruauerat*). In reality only twenty-two years separated the two. See J. Carcopino, *Rev. Phil.* 62 (1946) 96-117; Syme (1986) 355.

adfectatione et morositate nimia obscurabat stilum: Tiberius became notorious for the obscurity of his speech (Tac. *Ann.* 1.11.4: *etiam in rebus quas non occuleret, seu natura siue adsuetudine, suspensa semper et obscura uerba*; 33.4: *Tiberi sermone uultu, adrogantibus et obscuris*), as well as for archaising tendencies (Suet. *Aug.* 86.2: *nec Tiberio parcit et exoletas interdum et reconditas uoces aucupanti*). Wordiness is also mentioned (Juv. 10.71; Tac. *Ann.* 3.51.2). It was also claimed that he was deliberately ambiguous in his speech (Tac. *Ann.* 13.3.5). There is some exaggeration of the picture in Dio Cassius (57.1ff.). Pedantry is another accusation (*De Gramm.* 22: *sermonis Latini exactor molestissimus*). For his vocabulary see N.P. Miller, *AJPh* 89 (1968) 1-19. His philological intertests are now discussed by M. Billerbeck, *Greece and Rome* 37 (1990) 191-203.

aliquanto ex tempore quam a cura praestantior haberetur: the classic passage on imperial skill in oratory is Tac. *Ann.* 13.3, where he criticises Nero's failure in the area. Tacitus, despite his comments on Tiberian ambiguity, admits that the emperor had considerable attainments. See 13.3.5: *Tiberius artem quoque callebat qua uerba expenderet, tum ualidus sensibus aut consulto ambiguus.* Caligula was also noteworthy for his skill in speaking off the cuff (Jos. *AJ* 19.208; see Lindsay [1993] 159).

70.2
composuit...conquestio de morte L. Caesaris: the death of Lucius took place on 20th August AD 2 at Massilia (see Vell. 2.102.3; Dio 55.10a.9; *Fasti Antiates* = *EJ*² p.51; *ILS* 139 = *EJ*² 68). The date of Tiberius' composition must have been soon after this.

fecit et Graeca poemata imitatus Euphorionem et Rhianum et Parthenium: on Tiberius' Greek studies see Levick (1976) 16-18; J.P. Adams, *AJPh* 100 (1979) 462f. What is noteworthy is not merely the emperor's taste for Alexandrian poets, but his lack of interest in the earliest exponents, Callimachus and Apollonius. See Syme (1986) 350. However, both Rhianus and Euphorion were first generation descendants of the school. Parthenius had a more recent currency; each of these authors represented a scholarly fashion current a generation earlier, in the last years of the Republic, and this may give an insight into the emperor's disposition.

Euphorion was the author of *epyllia* and epic poems well known to Catullus and Cornelius Gallus. His subject matter included the Trojan cycle and other Greek myths, and he was known for his abstruseness. Note Cicero's mockery in his description of Roman Alexandrian poets as *cantores Euphorionis* (Cic. *Tusc.* 3.45). Stewart emphasies Euphorion's interest in the obscure and the monstrous, providing a link with Tiberius' baroque artistic predilections (*JRS*

67 [1977] 85). There are themes in common between Euphorion and the Sperlonga sculptures created by the Rhodian artists.

Rhianus, like Euphorion, was an epigramist of third century date, and again a Homeric scholar with wide-ranging knowledge of Greek mythology, and probably an obsession with Homeric geography. He wrote at least five epics on such themes, and had produced a notable edition of Homer. See R. Pfeiffer (1968) 148f.

Parthenius was active in the first century BC as an elegist, and himself under the influence of Euphorion and Callimachus. Heluius Cinna, Cornelius Gallus and Vergil numbered amongst his acquaintance. Most of the surviving fragments derive from Stephanus of Byzantium and cover grammatical, mythological and geographical themes. This makes it hard to determine exactly what his poetry was like. For analysis of his importance see N.B. Crowther, *Mnemosyne* 29 (1976) 65-71. See also W.V. Clausen, *GRBS* 5 (1964) 187ff.

scripta...et imagines publicis bibliothecis...dedicauit: imperial taste is the issue here. Suetonius commonly criticises imperial attitudes to literature and intellectual matters, and in this way assists the characterisation of his subject. See Lindsay (1993) 12. We can contrast the difficult Tiberius and his abstruse tastes with the allegation that the iconoclast Caligula wanted to throw Vergil and Livy out of the public libraries at Rome (Suet. *Cal.* 34.2).

ob hoc plerique...multa de his ediderunt: none of this secondary literature is known today (cf. R. Pfeiffer (1968) 150 [Euphorion]; 148f. [Rhianus]; 272 [Parthenius]).

70.3

grammaticos...quaestionibus experiebatur: Nero carried on Tiberian traditions, and liked to invite philosophers to dinner and amuse himself with their wrangles (Tac. *Ann.* 14.16.2), a sport carried further by Hadrian who used to tease *grammatici* with *quaestiones* of the sort mentioned here (HA *Hadr.* 16.8; 20.2). Juvenal satirises the life of the *grammaticus*, who is portrayed as obsessed with pedantic *quaestiones*, although his are all based on Vergil (Juv. 7.233-6; cf. Philippus *Anth. Pal.* XI.321 [on whether the Cyclops kept dogs]; 347 [the fathers of Proteus and Pygmalion]). Those who solved such questions were called λυτικοί, according to Athenaeus (Athen. 11.493e-494a). Seneca disapproved of this aspect of the *artes liberales* (*De Brevitate Vitae* 13.2: *Graecorum iste morbus*), and provides other stories about Homeric obsessions (see Sen. *Ep.* 27.5.; 88.5-8 [on Homeric detail]; 88.37 [on the lengthy disquisitions of Arius Didymus]: these passages are discussed by C.D.N. Costa [1988] 193; 201). Discussions about mythological subjects may also have been favoured by Tiberius. See Plut. *De defectu oraculorum* 18, discussed by Syme (1986) 351, n. 38.

quo...die post excessum Augusti curiam intrauit...ture quidem ac uino uerum sine tibicine supplicauit: Suetonius uses this story as another example of Tiberius' obsession with early Greek history deriving from the Homeric tradition. There are variant stories on how exactly Androgeus, the son of Minos and Pasiphae, met his end. What is important here is how Minos and later Tiberius handled their grief. Flutes (as well as various percussion instruments) were commonly associated with funerary rites, and have a link with primitive ideas about transition. See R. Needham, *Man* n.s. 2 (1967) 606-14; R. Huntington & P. Metcalf (1979) 46-50. Their omission on this occasion may have been intended to heighten mourning over a premature departure. If the story has any foundation, it reinforces the picture of Tiberius as a staunch traditionalist over matters of religious observance.

71 Attitude to Greek language

sermone Graeco...non tamen usque quaque usus est abstinuitque maxime in senatu: on Tiberius as a purist about the speaking of Latin in Latin contexts see M. Dubuisson (1986) 109-20; M. Billerbeck, *Greece and Rome* 37 (1990) 191-203, esp. 196-7.

Three examples are used by Suetonius to illustrate this point. The first case is an apology for his own usage of the Greek term monopoly (cf. 30 above), the second is an objection to an intrusive Greek term in a decree (cf. Dio 57. 17.1-3: his own use of a Greek word in an edict), and the third shows his insistence on the use of Latin evidence in a Roman court. Dio also mentions a centurion brought into the Senate to testify in AD 16, who was refused permission to give his evidence in Greek (Dio 57.15.3). Levick thinks this must have been at the trial of Libo, since no other Senatorial trial is known in that year (Levick [1976] 153). These examples seem to have been drawn by the biographer from the *acta senatus*. See introduction **26-27**.

72 Attempts at a return from retirement

72.1
Bis omnino...Romam redire conatus: Suetonius lists only two occasions when Tiberius attempted to return to Rome, The first is dated to early AD 32

(cf. Tac. *Ann.* 6.1.1f.), and the second to the last weeks of his life. But Syme points out that there was an excursion to Latium in AD 33 at the time of the marriages of his granddaughters; he stayed there for some months and came within 30 stades of the capital (Tac. *Ann.* 6. 15.3; Dio 58.21.1; see Syme, *Athenaeum* 61 [1983] 23). It is clear that he spent quite a lot of time in Campania during his years on Capri. See list in Bernecker (1981) 103 n. 2. Some exaggeration of Tiberius' reclusiveness may have entered the sources as a result of his earlier retreat to Rhodes.

semel triremi usque ad proximos naumachiae hortos: for the location of the *naumachia Augusti* near S. Cosimato on the right bank of the Tiber see Platner/Ashby (1929) 357. It had been constructed by Augustus in 2 BC and was used for sham naval combats at the time of the dedication of the temple of Mars Ultor. See RG 23; Vell. 2.100; Tac. *Ann.* 12.56; Suet. *Aug.* 43; Dio 66.25.

disposita statione per ripas Tiberis: an interesting detail on Tiberius' increased emphasis on personal security. Suetonius introduces this to highlight Tiberius' paranoia, but it may nevertheless be authentic.

72.2
erat...serpens draco...monitus est ut uim multitudinis caueret: Levick suggests that astrology may have been used to keep the emperor out of the city (Levick [1976] 217). This would suggest a politically naive Tiberius, which is hard to credit. A. Stewart relates the story of the pet snake to Tiberius' interest in the contorted and brutal products of Hellenistic art such as the Laocoon and the Sperlonga sculptures (*JRS* 67 [1977] 84).

rediens...Campaniam Asturae in languorem incidit: Suetonius gives the most detailed account of his final perambulations. See also Suet. *Cal.* 12.2; Tac. *Ann.* 6.50; Jos. *AJ* 18.205ff; Dio 58.28. Levick 218-9.

72.3
Misenum usque deuectus nihil ex ordine cotidiano praetermitteret: Tiberius had a villa at Misenum, which had once been in the possession of Lucullus. See 73 below.

Chariclen medicum...existimans temptatas ab eo uenas...recumbere hortatus est: the legendary story of Charicles trying Tiberius' pulse at Misenum is also found in Tacitus in nearly identical guise, although in Tacitus it is associated with advice to Macro to make preparations for the accession of Caligula (Tac. *Ann.* 6.50). For Charicles and possible references to his remedies in Galen see *PIR*² C 710.

in medio triclinio astante lictore singulos ualere dicentis appellaret: another interesting detail on imperial security.

73 Return from retirement and death

73.1

cum in actis senatus legisset dimissos...de quibus...nihil aliud quam nominatos ab indice scripserat: on the *acta senatus* see full discussion in Talbert (1984) 322-34. A ban on their publication had been issued by Augustus, but they seem nevertheless to have been available for consultation, at least by those in high office (Suet. *Aug.* 36). The present passage may suggest that they again became available in published form under Tiberius (cf. Dio 57.23.2). Suetonius makes it clear that this episode occurred in the period immediately before the death of Tiberius in AD 37. Levick suspects that the Suetonian version is a garbled reaction to Tacitus' account of the trial of Albucilla. Tacitus claims that the emperor knew nothing of the charges against her (Tac. *Ann.* 6.47.4; cf. Dio 58.27.3; Levick [1976] 289 n.131). However, it may be that the Suetonian version is totally unhistorical and forms part of the dramatisation of the death of the emperor. It is thus intended to highlight his loss of grip in the last stages before death.

obiit in uilla Lucullana: Misenum, like the rest of the region on the bay of Naples, had become a favoured site for the villas of the wealthy during the last century of the Republic. The villa in which Tiberius died may have belonged to Marius before it was taken over and extended by Lucullus. Tiberius had later acquired it (Tac. *Ann.* 6.50.2; Suet. *Cal.* 12.2; 13). See E. Badian, *JRS* 63 (1973) 121-32; J. D'Arms (1970) 23-7, 86.

octauo et septuagesimo aetatis anno, tertio et uicesimo imperii, XVII. Kal. Ap. Cn. Acerronio Proculo C. Pontio Nigr<in>o conss: Tiberius died on 16th March, as Suetonius notes. Dio incorrectly gives the date as ten days later (*Fasti Ostienses*, *EJ*² p. 43 = *Inscr. Ital.* 13.1 no. 5; Tac. *Ann.* 6.50; Dio 58.28.5).

73.2

Sunt qui putent uenenum ei a Gaio datum lentum atque tabificum: as I have pointed out in the commentary on the Caligula there is little likelihood that Tiberius died under suspicious circumstances given his age (78). Legendary elements, including the tale that Charicles anticipated his death after taking his pulse, have shrouded the story. Suetonius canvasses 4 different versions of his death: (1) Poisoned (also at *Cal*. 12.2). (2) Starved (here; cf. Tac. *Ann*. 6.50; Dio 58.28.1-5). (3) Smothered after he revived during an attempt to remove his ring (here; also at *Cal*. 12.2; cf. Tac. & Dio). (4) The present passage has a suspect item from the elder Seneca. In this contemporary account Tiberius took off the ring of his own volition as though to hand it to a successor. He then returned it to his finger, clenched his fist, and remained motionless for a long time. His attendants left, and eventually he got up and collapsed dead. The elder Seneca had died before his son's exile in AD 41, and this could be a version acceptable to Caligula. Notice its elimination of all suggestion of foul play. The passage provides a not implausible end for Tiberius, but its value as a record is impugned by the possibility that it reflects Caligulan propaganda. Contrast Seager (1972) 244f.; Levick (1976) 218f.; Fairweather (1981) 15 n. 50. On the Tacitean evidence see E. Keitel, *Hermes* 109 (1981) 206-14, highlighting ironic contrasts between the last years and deaths of Tiberius and Claudius. For the now lost epitaph of Tiberius see *ILS* 164.

74 Omens relating to the death of Tiberius

Three omens immediately preceded Tiberius' death. There is the usual build up to a climax. The first is his dream that a statue brought from Temenos to be erected in the library of the temple of Augustus spoke to him telling him that he would never dedicate it. This episode could have a hint of divine vengeance about it, representing a divine response to his hubris in moving the statue. One can compare the clearer case of the statue of Olympian Zeus which Memmius Regulus was to move for Caligula (Suet. *Cal*. 22.2; 57.1). Utterances from such sources were commonly interpreted as messages from the gods (see Krauss [1930] 161ff; cf. Lindsay [1993] 164-5). The second omen was the thunderbolt which hit the Capri lighthouse a few days before his death, usually interpreted as evidence of Jupiter's wrath (Krauss [1930] 46f.). Finally embers from his evening fire at Misenum blazed up unexpectedly as a symptom of change. Notice here that this may relate to the omen reported at Suet. *Tib*. 19 (q.v.).

The employment of omens in Suetonius as part of the moral assessment of his subject has been investigated by B. Mouchova (1968) 34-42; H. Gugel (1977) 45-49. As Gugel points out it makes sense for the man whose ancestor suffered a serious reverse after despising the omen of the chickens refusing their food (*Tib*. 2.2) to have an ambiguous response to omens (cf. *Tib*. 14.2-4; 69).

Apollinem Temenitem...aduectum Syracusis: Tiberius had continued to be interested in art until the end of his life. According to Pliny amongst his particular sculptural interests was Lysippus' Apoxyomenos (*NH* 34.62), and Dio claims that he employed his *trib. pot.* when on his way to Rhodes in 6 BC to compel the Parians to sell him a statue of Vesta for the temple of Concord in Rome (Dio 55.9.6). His interests were in Hellenistic art rather than in the classicism of Augustus. On paintings included by him in the temple of Augustus see 47 above. For his tastes see also 44.2. Remnants of the temple of Apollo Temenites are thought to have been found in the district of ancient Syracuse known as Neapolis, to the West of the theatre. See *PECS* s.v. Syracuse.

ut in bibliotheca templi noui poneretur: on the library built in connection with the temple of Augustus see Platner/Ashby (1929) 84. Pliny notes a colossal bronze statue of Apollo some fifty feet tall in this library (Plin. *NH* 34.43). On the temple of Augustus see 47 above.

Phari...Capreis concidit: there is known to have been a lighthouse on the Eastern promontory of the island. See *PECS* s.v. Capreae.

75 Reactions to the death of Tiberius

This section has parallels in other Suetonian lives. Contrast especially reactions to the death of Germanicus as recorded at Suet. *Cal*. 5-6.

75.1

laetatus est populus...*Tiberium in Tiberim!* clamitarent: the death of Tiberius provides Suetonius with an opportunity to demonstrate his unpopularity, which is emphasised through this popular catch-cry. This incidentally represents a response to his perceived haughtiness, and lack of concern over popular interests. The Tiber was an approved destination for the corpses of state enemies. Compare the plans of the tyrannicides for the body of Julius Caesar (Suet. *Caes*. 82; F. Vittinghof [1936] 43ff.). Popular zeal for turning the tables on Tiberius is depicted. He is to receive the punishment he has been inflicting on those accused of *maiestas*.

Gemonias cadaueri minarentur: suggestions that his body should be flung from the Gemonian steps perhaps represent a suitable popular revenge, based on his earlier treatment of Seianus. The revenge motive was also strong in the popular mind because of those sentenced to death whose stay of execution was to expire on the very day of Tiberius' death. According to Suetonius these people were nevertheless executed by their gaolers who cast them onto the Gemonian steps because no other avenue of appeal existed (75.2). The continuation of the regime beyond the grave was alleged by his detractors, who are supposed to have heckled as his funeral cortège left Misenum. Such a view of the last stages of the Tiberian regime was perhaps encouraged by Caligula and Macro who could not fail to benefit from an unfavourable review of the predecessor.

75.3

creuit igitur inuidia, quasi etiam post mortem tyranni saeuitia permanente: Suetonius reinforces earlier points about the tyrannical status of Tiberius.

conclamantibus plerisque Atellam...semiustilandum: the heckling about taking him to the amphitheatre at Atella for a half-burning is of interest. This relates to his perceived tyrannical status. It was notorious that a tyrant's body could not be totally consumed by the flames (see Cic. *Phil.* 2.89-91 for Cicero's vituperation against Antony's handling of Caesar's funeral). This is presumably because he was considered polluted. Plutarch has a similar moralistic story about Sulla, when he relates that Sulla was lucky that the rain held off for long enough for his body to be entirely consumed (Plut. *Sulla* 38.3). For some brief comments see G. Kennedy, *Quarterly Journal of Speech* 54 (1968) 100-101. For Tiberius' unpopularity with the plebs see Levick (1976) 121; Yavetz (1969) 108ff.

corpus...Romam per milites deportatum est: see Suet. *Cal.* 13; *Fasti Ostienses, Inscr. Ital.* 13.1.190f. = EJ^2 p. 43: *XVII k. Apr. Ti. Caesar Misen[i] excessit. IIII k. Apr. corpus in urbe perlatum per mili[t.] III non. Apr. f(unere) p(ublico) e(latus) e(st)*. This shows that he died on 16th March and was conveyed slowly to the city, reaching Rome on the night of March 28-29th. Cremation was on April 3rd. Compare Suet. *Aug.* 100.2.

crematumque publico funere: on the *funus publicum* see F. Vollmer, *Jahrb. für class. Philol.* Suppl. Bd XIX (1892-3) 319-64. The funeral *laudatio* was delivered by Caligula (Dio 58.28.5).

76 The will of Tiberius

Testamentum duplex...fecerat: this short discussion of the will of Tiberius matches the like discussion in the life of Augustus, which is, however, far more detailed (Suet. *Aug.* 101). It purports to give a history of Tiberius' testamentary arrangements, which are said to have included a will written some two years earlier, and an identical copy in the hand of a freedman. A peculiar statement to the effect that both these documents had been signed and sealed by witnesses of the lowest class is appended. This has some connection with Suetonius' characterisation of Tiberius as a debauchee, and hence associating with unsuitable types, but is more plausibly explained as a calumny invented by Caligula to justify the invalidation of the will (cf. E. Champlin [1992] 76). As we are told at Suet. *Cal.* 14.1 the will was swiftly invalidated, and had contained a provision that Gemellus should be joint heir with Caligula. Dio mistakenly believed that they were to be joint heirs to the principate (Dio 59.1f.). For full discussion see Lindsay (1993a) 84-88.

On the frequency of revisions of wills see E. Champlin (1991) 67. This version, written some two years before the emperor's death, was not the first. Tiberius had made a point of reading his will in 6 BC before his retirement to Rhodes, perhaps hoping to quash hostile rumours about his intentions (Dio 55.9.8).

Amongst more important acquisitions for Caligula were the slaves of his predecessor, representing as they did continuity from one emperor to another. Caligula acquired his *cubicularius* Helicon in this way. See G. Boulvert (1974) 21. Boulvert doubts whether any partition of the slaves between Caligula and Gemellus his co-heir would have taken place in any event, since he notes that Claudius in turn inherited the slaves of Caligula because of his accession as emperor, and not for reasons related to private law (op.cit. 25). It is important to appreciate that the emperor's will is not a private document, as suggested by D. Timpe (1962) 71f. It is clearly to be perceived as dynastic. See Levick (1976) 210.

Caligula demanded deification for Tiberius as well as other honours formerly granted to Augustus (Dio 59.3.7). Naturally this was a move designed to benefit himself, and not the memory of Tiberius. In the event he had to be satisfied with the state funeral on April 3rd which gave him an opportunity to deliver a funeral oration with an important political slant in his own favour (Suet. *Cal.* 10.1; 15.1; Dio 58.28.5; 59.3.8).

reliquit...nepotes substituitque in uicem: Tiberius left equal shares to his grandsons. Although Caligula was older, Tiberius Gemellus had important standing as the son of Drusus. The proviso for mutual substitutions was a standard procedure covering the possibility of mortality. In some cases with private wills a special friend might be named as a substitute heir as a recognition of their status, rather than with any serious intention that they should inherit. See Champlin (1991) 146-7.

dedit et legata plerisque: on Claudius' lowly status in this pecking order see Suet. *Claud.* 6.2.

inter quos uirginibus Vestalibus: Augustus had set the precedent for unrestricted legacies to individual groups (Suet. *Aug.* 101). These very expensive manifestations of imperial *liberalitas* appear to have been distributed at the funeral (see Champlin [1991] 157), although Caligula is portrayed by Dio buying popularity with the soldiers during inspections at drill (59.2.1ff.). Notice the donation to the Vestal Virgins. Augustus had entrusted his will to the Vestals for safe-keeping (Suet. *Aug.* 101), and Tiberius may have followed suit. Vestals had special status in relation to inheritances, with an emphasis on their isolation from their original family. They could not inherit from a close relative who had died intestate, and their own property would revert to the state if they were to die intestate (Aul. Gell. *NA* 1.12.18). For discussion of the status of Vestal Virgins see M. Beard, *JRS* 70 (1980) 12-27, esp. 21 on inheritances.

et militibus uniuersis plebeique Romanae uiritim: from the *Fasti Ostienses* it is known that Caligula gave out 75 denarii = HS 300 to the people on 1st June AD 37, and a similar sum on 19th July (*Inscr. Ital.* 13.1, tab. LXIX; cf. Suet. *Cal.* 17.2, with Lindsay [1993] ad loc.). One of these *congiaria* represented the HS 45 million Tiberius had left to the people (the other was probably in honour of the *tirocinium* of Caligula, delayed since AD 31). Thus he was anticipating 150,000 recipients (see Van Berchem [1939] 146-47). We may suspect that in the event these acts of liberality were used by Caligula to celebrate events in his own career rather than to commemorate his predecessor.

etiam separatim uicorum magistris: on these officials see the analysis of J.-M. Flambard, *Ktèma* 6 [1981 (1983)] 143-66. The *uici* of Rome itself appear not to number amongst the primitive territorial divisions of the city. Pliny for the year of Vespasian's censorship in AD 73 gives a total of 265 (Plin. *NH* 3.66), and this is thought to enumerate subdivisions of the territorial reorganisation of Augustus, when he instituted the 14 regions

(Suet. *Aug.* 30). There were also *uici* in municipalities outside of Rome, but it seems unlikely on numerical grounds that Tiberius extended his largesse beyond the city.

Bibliography

Abel, E., 'Were the Jews banished from Rome in AD 19?' *REJ* 127 (1968) 383-6.

Adams, F., 'The consular brothers of Sejanus' *AJPh* 76 (1955) 70-76.

Adams, J.P., review of B.Levick, *Tiberius the Politician AJPh* 100 (1979) 460-65.

Alföldy, A., 'Die Ausgestaltung des monarchischen Zeremoniells am römischen Kaiserhofe' *MDAI (R)* 49 (1934) 1-118.

——'Insignien und Tracht der römischen Kaiser' *MDAI (R)* 50 (1935) 1-171.

Alfoldi, A., *Early Rome and the Latins* (Ann Arbor, 1963).

Alföldy, G., *Noricum* (London, Routledge, 1974).

——'La politique provinciale de Tibère' *Latomus* 24 (1965) 824-44.

——*Fasti Hispanienses* (Wiesbaden, Steiner, 1969).

Allen, W., 'The death of Agrippa Postumus' *TAPhA* 78 (1947) 131-9.

Arkenberg, J.S., 'Licinii Murenae, Terentii Varrones, and Varrones Murenae' *Historia* 42 (1993) 327-51; 471-91.

Arnaud-Lindet, M.-P., '<Crimen Seiani>: sur quelques vers de Juvénal' *RHD* 58 (1980) 411-21.

Badian, E., 'The quaestorship of Tiberius Nero' *Mnemosyne* 27 (1974) 160-72.

——'The Thessalian clients of Tiberius Nero' *CR* 24 (1974) 186

Baladié, R., *Le Péloponnèse de Strabon* (Paris, Les Belles Lettres, 1980).

Baldwin, B., 'The acta diurna' *Chiron* 9 (1979) 189-203.

——*Suetonius* (Amsterdam, Hakkert, 1983).

Baltrusch, E., *Regimen Morum* (Vestigia 41, Munich, Beck, 1989).

Barnes, T.D., 'The victories of Augustus' *JRS* 64 (1974) 21-26.

Barrett, A.A., *Caligula: The Corruption of Power* (London, Batsford, 1989).

——'Caligula and the client kings' *CQ* 40 (1990) 284-86.

Bastianini, G., 'Lista dei prefetti d'Egitto dal 30ª al 299ᵖ' *ZPE* 17 (1975) 263-328.

Bauman, R., 'Criminal prosecutions by the aediles' *Latomus* 33 (1974) 245-64.

——*Impietas in Principem* (Munich, Beck, 1974).

Baurain, C., 'Suetone et l'inscription d'Hippone' *LEC* 44 (1976) 124-44.

Beard, M., 'The sexual status of Vestal Virgins' *JRS* 70 (1980) 12-27.

Beard, M., & North, J. (eds), *Pagan Priests* (London, Duckworth, 1990).

Beaujeu, J., 'Le <mare rubrum> de Tacite' *REL* 38 (1960) 200-35.

Bellemore, J., 'The dating of Seneca's *Ad Marciam De Consolatione*' *CQ* 42 (1992) 219-34.

Benediktson, D.T., 'A survey of Suetonius scholarship, 1938-1987' *CW* 86 (1993) 377-447.

Benner, M., *The Emperor Says: Studies in the Rhetorical Style in Edicts of the Early Empire* (Göteborg, 1975).

Berchem, D. van, *Les distributions de blé et de l'argent à la plèbe romaine sous l'empire* (Geneva, 1939).

Bernecker, A., *Zur Tiberius-Uberlieferung der Jahre 26-37 n. Chr.* (Bonn, Habelt, 1981).

Berthet, J.-F., 'La Culture Homérique des Césars d'après Suétone' *REL* 56 (1978) 314-34.

Berthold, R.M., *Rhodes in the Hellenistic Age* (Cornell, 1984).

Billerbeck, M., 'Philology at the imperial court' *Greece and Rome* 37 (1990) 191-203.

Birch, R.A., 'The correspondence of Augustus: some notes on Suetonius, Tiberius 21.4-7' *CQ* 31 (1981) 155-61.

Bird, H.W., 'L. Aelius Seianus and his political significance' *Latomus* 28 (1969) 61-98.

——'L. Aelius Seianus: further observations' *Latomus* 29 (1970) 1046-50.

Birley, A.R., *The Fasti of Roman Britain* (Oxford, 1981).

——review of recent work on Suetonius, *JRS* 74 (1984) 245-51.

Blake, M.E., *Roman construction in Italy from Tiberius through the Flavians* (Washington D.C., 1959).

Boatwright, M., 'The "*Ara Ditis-Ustrinum*" of Hadrian" in the Western Campus Martius and other problematic Roman *ustrina*' *AJA* 89 [1985] 485-97.

Boddington, A., 'Sejanus. Whose conspiracy?' *AJPh* 84 (1963) 1-16.

Boulvert, G., *Esclaves et Affranchis Impériaux sous le Haut-Empire romain: rôle politique et administratif* (Naples, Lugli, 1970).

——*Domestique et Fonctionnaire sous le Haut-Empire Romain* (Paris, Les Belles Lettres, 1974).

Bourne, E., 'Augustus as a Letter-Writer' *TAPhA* 49 (1918) 53-66.

Bourne, F.C., *The public works of the Julio-Claudians and Flavians* (Princeton, 1946).

Bowersock, G.W., *Augustus and the Greek World* (Oxford, 1965).

——'Suetonius and Trajan' *Hommages à Marcel Renard I* (1969) 119-25.

Bowersock, G.W., *Roman Arabia* (Harvard, 1983).

Boyce, A.A., 'The origin of *ornamenta triumphalia*' *CPh* 37 (1942) 130-41.

Bradley, K.R., 'The composition of Suetonius' *Caesares* again' *JIES* 1 (1973) 257-63.

——*Suetonius' Life of Nero: An Historical Commentary* (Collection Latomus 157, 1978).

——'The rediscovery of Suetonius' *CPh* 80 (1985) 254-65.

Breckenridge, J.D., 'Imperial Portraiture: Augustus to Gallienus' *ANRW* 2.12.2 (1981) 477-512.

Bringmann, K., 'Zur Tiberiusbiographie Suetons', *RhM* 114 (1971) 268-85.

Briscoe, J., *A Commentary on Livy Books XXXIV-XXXVII* (Oxford, 1981).

——'The grandson of Hortensius' *ZPE* 95 (1993) 249-50.

Brunt, P.A., 'Charges of provincial maladministration under the early principate' *Historia* 10 (1961) 189-223.

——'C. Fabricius Tuscus and an Augustan dilectus' *ZPE* 13 (1974) 161-85.

——'Lex de imperio Vespasiani' *JRS* 67 [1977] 95-116.

——'Evidence given under torture in the principate' *ZRG* 97 (1980) 256-65.

Buttrey, T.V., 'The *spintriae* as a historical source' *NC* 1973 52-63.

Campbell, J.B., *The Emperor and the Roman Army, 31 BC-AD 235* (Oxford, 1984).

Carcopino, J., *Le Culte de Cybèle et d'Atthis* (Paris, 1944).

——'La véritable Julie' *Revue de Paris* 65 (February 1958) 66-80.

——'Notes biographiques sur M. Valerius Messala Corvinus (64 av. J.-C. -8 ap. J.-C.)' *Rev. Phil.* 62 (1946) 96-117.

Carney, T.F., 'How Suetonius' lives reflect on Hadrian' *PACA* 11 (1968) 7-21.

Carter, J.M., *Suetonius Augustus* (Bristol Classical Press, 1982)

Castagnoli , F., *Roma antica: Profilo urbanistico* (Rome, Jouvence, 1978).

Cazzaniga, I., 'De Atalantae Tabula Parrahasiana' *ASNP* 4 (1974) 1301-6.

Champlin. E., *Final Judgments* (California, 1991).

Charlesworth, M.P., 'Tiberius and the death of Augustus' *AJPh* 44 (1923) 145-57.

——'Liuia and Tanaquil' *CR* 41 (1927) 55-7.

——'The refusal of divine honours: an Augustan formula' *PBSR* 15 (1939) 1-10.

Chastagnol, A., '*Latus Clavus et Adlectio*: L'accès des hommes nouveaux au sénat romain sous le haut-empire' *RHD* 53 (1975) 375-94.

Chilton, C.W., '*The Roman law of treason under the early principate*' *JRS* 45 (1955) 73-81.

Chowen, R.H., 'The problem of Hadrian's visits to North Africa' *CJ* 65 (1969-70) 323-4.

Cizek, E., *Structures et Idéologie dans les Vies des Douze Césars de Suétone* (Paris, Les Belles Lettres, 1977).

Clarke, M.L., *Higher Education in the Ancient World* (London, Routledge, 1971).

Clausen, W.V., 'Callimachus and Latin poetry' *GRBS* 5 (1964) 181-96.

Cochran, L.R., 'Suetonius' conception of imperial character', *Biography* 3 (1980) 189-201.

Coninck, L. de, 'Les sources documentaires de Suétone, "Les XII Césars"', *ANRW* 2.33.5 (1991) 3675-3700.

Conticello, B. and Andreae, B., 'Die Skulpturen von Sperlonga' *Antike Plastik* 14 (1974).

Corbett , P.E., *The Roman Law of Marriage* (Oxford, 1930).

Corbier, M., 'La famille de Séjan à Volsinii: la dédicace des Seii, *curatores aquae*' *MEFRA* 95 (1983) 719-56.

—— 'De Volusinii a Sestinum: *cura aquae* et évergétisme municipal de l'eau en Italie' *REL* 62 (1984) 236-74.

——'La descendance d'Hortensius et de Marcia' *MEFRA* 103 (1991) 655-701.

Costa, C.D.N. (ed.), *Seneca: 17 letters* (Warminster, Aris & Phillips, 1988).

Cotton, H.M., 'Military tribunates and the exercise of patronage' *Chiron* 11 (1981) 229-38.

Coussin, J., 'Suétone physiognomiste dans les vies des XII Césars' *REL* 31 (1953) 234-56.

Cramer, F.H., 'Bookburning and censorship in ancient Rome' *Journal of the History of Ideas* 6 (1945) 157-96.

——*Astrology in Roman Law and Politics* (Philadelphia, 1954).

Crook, J.A., *Consilium Principis* (Cambridge, 1955).

——'Suetonius *Ab epistulis*' *PCPhS* n.s. 4 (1956-7) 18-22.

Crowther, N.B., 'Parthenius and Roman poetry' *Mnemosyne* 29 (1976) 65-71.

Dack, E. van't, 'A studiis, a bibliothecis' *Historia* 12 (11963) 177-84.

Daly, L.J., 'The report of Varro Murena's death (Dio 54.3.5)' *Klio* 65 (1983) 245-61.

——'Augustus and the murder of Varro Murena (cos. 23 BC' *Klio* 66 (1984) 157-69.

D'Arms, J.H., *Romans on the Bay of Naples* (Harvard, 1970).

David, J.-M., 'Du *Comitium* à la roche Tarpeienne. Sur certains rituels d'exécution capitale sous la République, les règnes d' Auguste et de Tibère in *Du Châtiment dans la Cite: Supplices Corporels et Peine de Mort dans le Monde Antique* (Rome, 1984).

Davies, C., 'Poetry in the Circle of Messalla' *Greece and Rome* 20 (1973) 25-35.

Davies, O., *Roman Mines in Europe* (Oxford, 1935).

Debevoise, N., *A Political History of Parthia* (Chicago, 1938).

Degrassi, A., *I Fasti consolari* (Rome, 1952).

Detweiler, R., 'Historical perspectives on the death of Agrippa Postumus' *CJ* 65 (1969-70) 289-95.

Dionisotti, A.C., 'Nepos and the generals' *JRS* 78 (1988) 35-49.

Dixon, S., *The Roman Mother* (London, Routledge, 1988).

Döpp, S., 'Zum Aufbau des Tiberius-Vita Suetons', *Hermes* 100 (1972) 444-60.

Dobiás, J., 'King Maroboduus as a Politician' *Klio* 38 (1960) 155-66.

Dorey, T.A. (ed.), *Latin Biography* (London, Routledge, 1967)

Du Four, M.J., C. *Suetonii Tranquilli Vita Tiberii: Chapters 1 to XXIII* (Philadelphia, 1941).

Dubuisson, M., 'Purisme et politique: Suétone, Tibère et le grec au Sénate', *Hommages à Josef Veremans* (Brussels 1986) 109-20.

Dunkle, J.R., 'The rhetorical tyrant in Roman historiography' *CW* 65 (1971) 12.-20.

——'The Greek tyrant and Roman political invective of the late Republic' *TAPhA* 98 (1967) 151-71.

Eck, W., 'Jahres- und Provinzialfasten der senatorischen Staathalter von 69/70 bis 138/139' *Chiron* 12 (1982) 281-362.

——'Cn. Calpurnius Piso, cos. ord 7 v. Chr. und die Lex Portorii provinciae Asiae' *EA* 15 (1990) 139-46.

——'Marcius Hortalis, *nobilis iuuenis*, und seine Söhne' *ZPE* 95 (1993) 251-60.

——'Das s.c. de Cn. Pisone patre und seine Publikation in der Baetica' *Cahiers du Centre G. Glotz* 4 (1993) 189-208.

Eck, W. and Fernández, F., 'Sex. Marius in einem Hospitiumsvertrag aus der Baetica' *ZPE* 85 (1991) 217-22.

Erkell, H., *Augustus, Felicitas, Fortuna. Lateinische Wortstudien* (Göteborg, Elander, 1952).

Evans, E.C., 'Roman descriptions of personal appearance in history and biography' *HSCPh* 46 (1935) 43-84.

——'The study of physiognomy in the second century AD' *TAPhA* 72 (1941) 96-108.

Fairweather, J., *Seneca the Elder* (Cambridge, 1981).

Fishwick, D.,*The imperial cult in the Latin West: studies in the ruler cult of the western provinces of the Roman Empire* (3 vols, Leiden, Brill, 1987).

Fiske, G.C., 'The politics of the patrician Claudii' *HSCPh* 13 (1902) 1-59.

Flambard, J.-M.,'Collegia compitalicia: phenomène associatif, cadres territoriaux et cadres civiques dans le monde romain à l'époque républicaine' *Ktèma* 6 [1981 (1983)] 143-66.

Flory, M.B., 'Abducta Neroni uxor: the historiographical tradition of the marriage of Octavian and Livia' *TAPhA* 118 (1988) 343-59.

Frank, T., 'The financial crisis of 33 AD' *AJPh* 56 (1935) 336-41.

Fraschetti, A., 'La *Tabula Hebana, la Tabula Siarensis* e il *iustitium* per la morte di Germanico' *MEFRA* 100 (1988) 867-89.

Frier, B.W., *Landlords and Tenants in Imperial Rome* (Princeton, 1980).

Gabba, E., 'The Perusine War and Triumviral Italy' *HSCPh* 75 (1971) 139-60.

Garnsey, P.D.A., *Social Status and Legal Privilege in the Roman Empire* (Oxford, 1970).

Garzetti, A., 'La Data dell'Incontro all'Eufrate di Artabano III e L. Vitellio, Legato di Siria' *Studi in Onore di R. Paribeni - A. Calderini* I (1956) 211-29.

Gascou, J., 'Nouvelles données chronologiques sur la carrière de Suétone' *Latomus* 37 (1978) 436-44.

——*Suétone historien* (Rome, Ecole française de Rome, 1984).

Geiger, J., 'M. Hortensius M.f. Q.n. Hortalus' *CQ* 20 (1970)132-4.

——*Cornelius Nepos and Ancient Political Biography* (Stuttgart, Steiner, 1985).

Gesche, H., 'Datierung und Deutung der CLEMENTIAE - MODERATIONI - Dupondien des Tiberius' *Jahrbuch für Numismatik und Geldgeschichte* 21 (1971) 37-80.

——'Die Datierung der 8. imperatorischen Akklamation des Tiberius' *Chiron* 2 (1972) 339-48.

Gill, C., 'The question of character-development: Plutarch and Tacitus' *CQ* 33 (1983) 469-87.

González, J., and Fernández, F., 'Tabula Siarensis' *Iura* 32 (1981) [1985] 1-36 [with photographs].

González, J., '*Tabula Siarensis, Fortunales Siarenses et municipia civium Romanorum*' *ZPE* 55 (1984) 55-100 [with full text].

González, J., and Arce, J., (eds), *Estudios sobre la tabula Siarensis* (Madrid, 1988)

Goodyear, F.R.D., *The Annals of Tacitus, Vol. 1* (Cambridge, 1972).

——*The Annals of Tacitus, Vol. 2* (Cambridge, 1981).

——'Tiberius and Gaius: their influence and views on literature' *ANRW* 2.32.1 (1984) 603-10.

Goudineau, C., 'Note sur la fondation de Lyon' *Gallia* 44 (1986) 171-3.

Grant, M., *Aspects of the Principate of Tiberius* (New York, 1950) = (1950a).

——*Roman Anniversary Issues* (Cambridge, 1950) = (1950b).

Grether, G., 'Liuia and the Roman imperial cult' *AJPh* 67 (1946) 222-52.

Grimal, P., *Les Jardins Romains* (Paris, Presses Universitaires, 1969).

Grube, G.M.A., 'Theodorus of Gadara' *AJPh* 80 (1959) 337-65.

Guarino, A., 'I *gladiatores* e l'*auctoramentum*' *Labeo* 29 (1983) 7-24.

Gugel, H., *Studien zur biographischen Technik Suetons* (Vienna, Bohlau, 1977).

Guia, M., 'Sulla biografia suetoniana di Tiberio: tradizione e struttura', *Athenaeum* 56 (1978) 329-45

_____ 'Tiberio simulatore nella tradizione storica pretacitiana', *Athenaeum* 53 (1975) 352-63 .

Gullini, G., *Il santuario della Fortuna Primigenia a Palestrina* (2 vols, Rome, 1953).

Gwatkin, W.E., 'Cappadocia as a Roman Procuratorial Province' *University of Missouri Studies* 5 (1930) 1-66.

Hallett, J.P., 'Morigerari: Suetonius, *Tiberius* 44' *AC* 47 [1978] 196-200

Harris, W.V., *War and Imperialism in Republican Rome* (Oxford, 1979)

Hayne, L., 'The Last of the Aemilii Lepidi' *AC* 42 (1973) 497-507.

Heidel, W.A., 'Why were the Jews banished from Italy in AD 19?' *AJPh* 41 (1920) 38-47.

Hennig, D., L. *Aelius Seianus* (Vestigia 21, Munich, Beck, 1975).

Hermann, P., *Der römische Kaisereid* (Göttingen, Vandenhoek & Ruprecht, 1968).

Heurgon, J., 'L'inscription de Tibère à Bavai' *AC* 17 (1948) 323-30.

Hinard, F., *Les proscriptions de la Rome républicaine* (Ecole française de Rome, 1985).

Hohl, E., 'Primum facinus noui principatus' *Hermes* 70 (1935) 350-55.

Holleman, A.W.J., 'Considerations about the tomb of the Claudians at Cerveteri' *Historia* 33 (1984) 504-8

Holleman, A.W.J.,'The First Claudian at Rome' *Historia* 35 (1986) 377-8.

Horsfall, N., *Cornelius Nepos: A selection including the lives of Cato and Atticus* (Oxford, 1989).

Houston, G.W., 'Tiberius on Capri' *G & R* 32 (1985) 179-96.

Huntington, R., & Metcalf, P., *Celebrations of Death* (Cambridge, 1979).

Hurley, D.W., 'Gaius Caligula in the Germanicus tradition' *AJPh* 110 (1989) 316-38.

Iacopi, G., *L'Antro di Tiberio a Sperlonga* (Rome, 1963).

Instinsky, H.U., 'Augustus und die Adoption des Tiberius' *Hermes* 94 (1966) 324-43.

Jameson, S., '22 or 23?' *Historia* 18 (1969) 204-29.

—— 'Augustus and Agrippa Postumus' *Historia* 24 (1975) 287-314.

Jones, A.H.M., *Studies in Roman Law and Government* (Oxford, 1960).

——*Cities of the Eastern Roman Provinces* (2nd ed., Oxford, 1971).

——'Towards a chronology of Plutarch's works' *JRS* 56 (1966) 61-74; Jones,

——*Plutarch and Rome* (Harvard, 1971).

Kahrstedt, U., *Artabanos III und seine Erben* (Berne, Francke, 1950).

Kampff, G., 'Three Senate meetings in the early principate' *Phoenix* 17 (1963) 25-58.

Katzoff, R., 'Tacitus, Annales, 1.74: the case of Granius Marcellus' *AJPh* 92 (1971) 680-84.

Kavanagh, B.J., 'The Admission of the Claudian Family to Rome' *AHB* 4.6 (1990) 129-32.

Keitel, E., 'Tacitus on the deaths of Tiberius and Claudius' *Hermes* 109 (1981) 206-14.

Kennedy, G., 'Antony's speech at Caesar's funeral' *Quarterly Journal of Speech* 54 (1968) 99-106.

Kleiner, F.S., 'An extraordinary posthumous honor for Livia' *Athenaeum* 68 (1990) 508-14.

Kloft, H., *Liberalitas Principis* (Vienna, 1970).

Koenen, L., 'Die "Laudatio funebris" des Augustus für Agrippa auf einem neuen Papyrus' *ZPE* 5 (1970) 217-83.

Koestermann, E., 'Der pannonisch-dalmatische Krieg 6-9 n. Chr.' *Hermes* 81 (1953) 345-78.

——'Die Majestätsprozesse unter Tiberius' *Historia* 4 (1955) 72-106.

Krappe, A.H., 'Tiberius and Thrasyllus' *AJPh* 48 (1927) 359-66.

Krauss, F.B., *An Interpretation of the Omens, Portents, and Prodigies Recorded by Livy, Tacitus and Suetonius* (Philadelphia, 1930).

Krause, C., and Morsch, G. (eds), *Domus Tiberiana: Nuove Ricerche - Studi di Restauro* (Zurich, 1985).

Lafon, X., 'La voie litorale Sperlonga-Gaeta-Formia' *MEFRA* 91 (1979) 399-419.

Latte, K., *Römische Religionsgeschichte* (Munich, 1960).

Lebek, W.D., 'Schwierige Stellen der *Tabula Siarensis*' *ZPE* 66 (1986) 31-48.

—— 'Die drei Ehrenbogen für Germanicus: Tab. siar. frg. I 9-34; *CIL* VI 31199 a 2-17' *ZPE* 67 (1987) 129-48.

—— 'Kleinere Ergänzungsprobleme in der Tabula Siarensis' *ZPE* 70 (1987) 57-62.

—— '*Consensus universorum civium*: Tab. Siar. frg. II col. b. 21-27' *ZPE* 72 (1988) 235-40.

—— 'Die circensischen Ehrungen für Germanicus und das Referat des Tacitus im Lichte von Tab. Siar. frg. II col. C 2-11' *ZPE* 73 (1988) 249-74.

—— 'Tab. siar. frg. I 25-28; frg. II col. A 7-8 und einige Liviusstellen' *ZPE* 73 (1988) 281-84.

—— 'Augustalspiele und Landestrauer (Tab. Siar. frg. II col. A 11-14)' *ZPE* 75 (1988) 59-70.

—— '*Sub edicto suo proponere*: Tab. siar. frg. II col. B 12 und Suet. Aug. 89.2' *ZPE* 77 (1989) 39-41.

—— 'Die Mainzer Ehrungen für Germanicus, den alteren Drusus und Domitian (Tab. Siar. frg. I 26-34; Suet. *Claud.* 1,3)' *ZPE* 78 (1989) 45-82.

—— 'Der proconsulat des Germanicus und die auctoritas des Senats: Tab. Siar. frg. I 22-24' *ZPE* 87 (1991) 103-24.

—— 'Standeswürde und Berufsverbot unter Tiberius: Das SC der Tabula Larinas' *ZPE* 81 (1990) 37-96.

—— 'Das SC der Tabula Larinas: Rittermusterung und andere Probleme' *ZPE* 85 (1991) 41-70.

Lehmann, K., 'A Roman poet visits a museum' *Hesperia* 14 (1945) 259-69.

Leo, F., *Die griechisch-romische Biographie nach ihrer litterarischen Form* (Leipzig, 1901).

Levick, B.M., 'The Beginning of Tiberius' Career' *CQ* 21 (1971) 478-86

—— 'Atrox fortuna' *CR* 22 (1972) 309-11.

—— 'Abdication and Agrippa Postumus' *Historia* 21 (1972) 674-97.

—— 'Tiberius retirement to Rhodes in 6 BC' *Latomus* 31 (1972) 779-813.

—— (ed.) *The Ancient Historian and his Materials* (Westmead, Farnborough 1975).

—— 'Mercy and moderation on the coinage of Tiberius' in *The Ancient Historian and his Materials* [ed. B.M. Levick] (Westmead, Farnborough 1975).

—— *Tiberius the Politician* (London, Thames and Hudson, 1976).

—— 'Poena legis maiestatis' *Historia* 28 (1979) 358-79.

—— 'The Senatus Consultum from Larinum' *JRS* 73 (1983) 97-115.

Lewis, J.D., 'Primum facinus noui principatus' *Auckland Classical Essays in honour of E.M. Blaicklock* (1970) 165-84.

Lewis, R.G., 'Suetonius' *Caesares* and their literary antecedents' *ANRW* 2.33.5 (1991) 3623-3674.

Linderski, J., 'The mother of Livia Augusta and the Aufidii Lurcones of the Republic' *Historia* 23 (1974) 463-80.

——'Julia in Regium' *ZPE* 72 (1988) 181-200.

Lindsay, H.M., 'Observations on the career of Tiberius Gemellus', *Festschrift for R.G. Tanner: Prudentia Supplement* (1993) 84-88 (cited as Lindsay [1993a]).

——*Suetonius Caligula* (Bristol Classical Press, 1993) (cited as Lindsay [1993]).

——'Suetonius as *ab epistulis* to Hadrian and the early history of the imperial correspondence' *Historia* 43 (1994) 454-68.

——'Suetonius on the character of Horace' *AUMLA* 83 (1995) 69-82.

Lintott, A.W., *Violence in Republican Rome* (Oxford, 1968).

Lounsbury, R.C., *The Arts of Suetonius* (New York, Lang, 1987).

Luce, T.J., & Woodman, A. J. (eds), *Tacitus and the Tacitean Tradition* (Princeton, N.J., 1993).

Macev, A., *Essai sur Suétone* (Paris, 1900).

Magie, D., 'Augustus' War in Spain (26-25 BC)' *CPh* 15 (1920) 323-39.

——'The mission of Agrippa to the Orient in 23 BC' *CPh* 3 (1908) 145-52.

Malcovati, H, *Operum Fragmenta Imperatoris Caesaris Augusti* (Paravia, 1928).

Maranon, G., *Tiberius: A Study in Resentment* (London, Hollis and Carter, 1956).

Marec, E., and Pflaum, H.-G., 'Nouvelle inscription sur la carrière de Suétone, l'historien' *CRAI* (1952) 76-85.

Marsh, F.B., *The Reign of Tiberius* (Oxford, 1931).

Marx, F.A., 'Tacitus und die literatur der *exitus illustrium virorum*' *Philologus* 92 (1937) 83-103.

Maxfield, V., *The Military Decorations of the Roman Army* (London, Batsford, 1981).

McDougall, I., 'The reputation of Appius Claudius Pulcher, cos. 143 BC' *Hermes* 120 (1992) 452-60.

McGinn, T.A.J., 'The SC from Larinum and the repression of adultery at Rome' *ZPE* 93 (1992) 273-95.

Meise, E., *Untersuchungen zur Geschichte der julisch-claudischen Dynastie* (Vestigia 10, Munich, Beck, 1969).

Merrill, E.T., 'The Expulsion of the Jews from Rome under Tiberius' *CPh* 14 (1919) 365-72.

Millar, F., *A Study of Cassius Dio* (Oxford, 1964).

——'The emperor, the Senate and the provinces' *JRS* 56 (1966) 156-66.

——*The Emperor in the Roman World* (London, Duckworth, 1977).

——'Cornelius Nepos, "Atticus" and the Roman Revolution' *Greece and Rome* 35 (1988) 40-55.

Miller, N.P., 'Tiberius speaks' *AJPh* 89 (1968) 1-19.

Mitford, T.B., 'A Cypriot oath of allegiance to Tiberius' *JRS* 50 (1960) 75-79.

Mócsy, A., *Pannonia and Upper Moesia* (London, Routledge, 1974)

Moehring, H.R., 'The persecution of the Jews and the adherents of the Isis cult at Rome AD 19' *Novum Testamentum* 3 (1959) 293-304.

Mogenet, J., 'La conjuration de Clemens' *AC* 23 (1954) 321-30.

Moles, J.L., 'Nepos and Biography' *CR* 39 (1989) 229-33.

Momigliano, A., *The Development of Greek Biography* (Harvard, 1971).

Mommsen, Th., 'Die römischen Eigennamen' *RhM* 15 (1860) 169-210.

Montevecchi, O., 'Osservazioni sulla lettera di Tiberio ai Giteati' *Epigraphica* 7 (1945) 104-108.

Mouchova, B., *Studie zu kaiserbiographien Suetons* (Prague, 1968).

Moxon, I.S., Smart, J.D., Woodman, A.J. (eds), *Past Perspectives: Studies in Greek and Roman Historical Writing* (Cambridge, 1986).

Murison, C., 'Tiberius, Vitellius and the *spintriae*' *AHB* 1,4 {1987] 97-9.

——*Suetonius: Galba, Otho, Vitellius* (Bristol Classical Press, 1992).

Nash, E., *Pictorial Dictionary of Ancient Rome* (2 vols, New York, Praeger, 1961-62).

Needham, R., 'Percussion and transition' *Man* n.s. 2 (1967) 606-14.

Newbold, R., 'Social tension at Rome in the early years of Tiberius' reign' *Athenaeum* 52 (1974) 110-43.

——'Suetonius' boundaries' *Latomus* 43 (1984) 118-32.

Nicolet, C., 'La Tabula Sirensis, la *lex de imperio Vespasiani*, et le *jus relationis* de l'empereur au sénat' *MEFRA* 100 (1988) 827-66.

Nicols, J., 'Antonia and Sejanus' *Historia* 24 (1975) 48-58.

Noy, D., 'Wicked stepmothers in Roman society and imagination' *Journal of Family History* 16 (1991) 345-62.

Oakley, S.P., 'Single Combat in the Roman Republic' *CQ* 35 (1985) 392-410.

Ogilvie, R.M., *A Commentary on Livy Books 1-5* (Oxford, 1965).

——*The Romans and their Gods* (London, Chatto and Windus, 1969).

Oliver, R.P., 'Did Tacitus finish the *Annales*?' *ICS* 2 (1977) 289-314.

——'Tacitus - Librarian?' *CQ* 29 (1979) 223-4.

——'Thrasyllus in Tacitus (ANN. 6.21)' *ICS* 5 (1980)130-48.

Orth, W., *Die Provinzialpolitik des Tiberius* (Munich, 1970).

Pallottino, M., 'L'ermeneutica etrusca tra due documenti-chiave' *Studi Etruschi* 37 (1969) 79-91.

Pani, M., *Roma e i Re d'Oriente da Augusto a Tiberio* (Bari, Adriatica Editrice, 1974).

Pappano, A.E., 'Agrippa Postumus' *CPh* 36 (1941) 30-45.

Parke, H.W., *Sibyls and Sibylline Prophecy in Classical Antiquity* [ed. B.C. McGing] (London, Routledge, 1988).

Parker, H.M.D., *The Roman Legions* (Oxford, 1928).

Parker, E.R. 'The Education of Heirs in the Julio-Claudian Family' *AJPh* 67 (1946) 29-50.

Pekary, T., 'Tiberius und der Tempel der Concordia in Rom' *MDAI* (R) 73/4 (1966-7) 105-33.

Pfeiffer, R., *History of Classical Scholarship* (Oxford, 1968)

Pippidi, D.M., 'La date de l'*Ara numinis Augusti* de Rome' *REL* 10 (1933) 435-56.

Platner, S.B., and Ashby, T., *A Topographical Dictionary of Rome* (Oxford, 1929).

Polacco, L., *Il Volto di Tiberio: Saggio di critica iconografica* (Rome, 1955).

Potter, D.S., 'The *Tabula Siarensis*, Tiberius, the senate and the Eastern boundary of the Roman empire' *ZPE* 64 (1987) 269-76.

Poulsen, B., 'The Dioscuri and ruler ideology' *Symbolae Osloenses* 66 (1991) 119-46.

Powell, G., 'The Praetorian Guard' *History Today* 18 (1968) 858-66.

Prévost, M.-H., *Les Adoptions politiques à Rome sous la république et le principat* (Paris, Sirey, 1949).

Price, S.R.F., 'Between man and god: sacrifice in the Roman imperial cult' *JRS* 70 (1980) 28-43.

——*Rituals and Power: The Roman imperial cult in Asia Minor* (Cambridge, 1984).

——'Gods and emperors: the Greek language of the Roman imperial cult' *JHS* 104 (1984) 79-95.

Purcell, N., 'The apparitores: a study in social mobility' *PBSR* 38 (1983) 125-73.

Purcell, N., 'Liuia and the womanhood of Rome' *PCPhS* 32 (1986) 78-105.

Rau, R., 'Zur Geschichte des pannonisch-dalmatischen Krieges der Jahre 6-9 n. Chr.' *Klio* 19 (1925) 313-46.

Rawson, E., 'The Eastern clientelae of Clodius and the Claudii' *Historia* 22 (1973) 219-39.

——'Cassius and Brutus: the memory of the Liberators' in *Past Perspectives: Studies in Greek and Roman Historical Writing* [I.S. Moxon, J.D. Smart, A.J. Woodman (eds)] (Cambridge, 1986) 101-19.

——'Discrimina ordinum: the Lex Julia theatralis' *PBSR* 55 (1987) 83-113.

Reed, N., 'Some neglected evidence on the early career of Tacitus' *CQ* 26 (1976) 309-12.

Reinhold, M., *Marcus Agrippa* (New York, Humphrey 1933).

——'Marcus Agrippa's son-in-law P. Quinctilius Varus' *CPh* 67 [1972] 119-21.

Richmond, I.A., 'The relation of the praetorian camp to Aurelian's wall of Rome' *PBSR* 10 (1927) 12-22.

Ritter, H.W.'Liuias Erhebung zur Augusta' *Chiron* 2 (1972) 313-38.

Roddaz, J.-M., 'Lucius Antonius' *Historia* 37 (1988) 317-46.

Rodewald, C., *Money in the Age of Tiberius* (Manchester U.P., 1976).

Rogers, R.S., 'The conspiracy of Agrippina' *TAPhA* 62 (1931) 141-68.

——*Criminal Trials and Criminal Legislation under Tiberius* (American Philological Association, 1935).

——*Studies in the Reign of Tiberius* (Baltimore, 1943).

——'Treason in the early empire' *JRS* 49 (1959) 90-94.

Rogers, R.S., 'Ateius Capito and Tiberius' *Synteleia V. Arangio-Ruiz* I (1964) 123-27.

——'The death of Julia and Gracchus, AD 14' *TAPhA* 98 (1967) 383-90.

Romer, F.E., 'A numismatic date for the departure of C. Caesar?' *TAPhA* 108 (1978) 187-202.

——'Gaius Caesar's military diplomacy in the East' *TAPhA* 109 (1979) 199-214.

Sage, M.M., 'Tacitus and the accession of Tiberius' *Ancient Society* 12/13 (1982/3) 293-321.

Sande, S. and Zahle, J., 'Der Tempel der Dioskuren auf dem Forum Romanum' in *Kaiser Augustus und die verlorene Republik* (Berlin, 1988) 213-24.

Sattler, P., 'Julia und Tiberius' *Studien aus dem Gebiet der alten Geschichte* (1962) 1-36 = *Augustus* (ed. W. Schmitthenner) [1969] 486-530.

Scheid, J., 'Scribonia Caesaris et les Julio-Claudiens' *MEFRA* 87 (1975) 349-75.

Schmitthenner, W., 'Augustus' spanischer Feldzug und der Kampf um den Prinzipat' *Historia* 11 (1962) 29-85.

——*Oktavian und das Testament Casars* (2nd ed. 1973).

Schnurr, C., 'The *lex Julia theatralis* of Augustus' *LCM* 17.10 (1992) 147-60.

Schwartz, J., 'Recherches sur les dernières années du règne d'Auguste (4-14)' *Rev. Phil.* 19 (1945) 21-90.

——'Préfets d'Egypte sous Tibère et Caligula' *ZPE* 48 (1982) 189-92.

Scobie, A., 'Spectator security and comfort at gladiatorial games' *Nikephoros* 1 (1988) 191-243.

Scott, K., 'Greek and Roman honorific months' *YCS* 2 (1931) 201-78.

——'The significance of statues in precious metals in emperor worship' *TAPhA* 62 (1931) 101-23.

——'The *diritas* of Tiberius' *AJPh* 53 (1932) 139-51.

——'Tiberius' refusal of the title "Augustus"' *CPh* 27 (1932) 43-50.

Seager, R., 'The return of the standards in 20 BC' *LCM* 2 (1977) 201-2.

——'"Populares" in Livy and the Livian tradition' *CQ* 27 (1977) 377-90.

——*Tiberius* (London, Methuen, 1972).

Sealey, R., 'The political attachments of L. Aelius Seianus' *Phoenix* 15 (1961) 97-114.

Shaw-Smith, R., 'A letter from Augustus to Tiberius' *Greece and Rome* 18 (1971) 213-14.

Sherwin-White, A.N., 'The Roman citizenship: a survey of its development into a world franchise' *ANRW* I.2 (1972) 23-58.

Shotter, D.C.A., 'Tiberius' part in the trial of Aemilia Lepida' *Historia* 15 (1966) 312-17.

——'Cn. Calpurnius Piso, legate of Syria' *Historia* 23 (1974) 229-45.

——*Tiberius Caesar* (London, Routledge, 1992).

Shuckburgh, E.S., *C. Suetonii Tranquilli Divus Augustus* (Oxford, 1896).

Simpson, C.J., 'The original site of the Fasti Capitolini' *Historia* 42 (1993) 61-81.

Skutsch, O., *The Annals of Q. Ennius* (Oxford, 1985).

Smallwood, E.M., 'Some notes on the Jews under Tiberius' *Latomus* 15 (1956) 314-29.

——*The Jews under Roman Rule* (Leiden, Brill, 1976).

Stanton, G.R., '*Cunctando restituit rem*: the tradition about Tiberius' *Antichthon* 5 (1971) 49-56.

Steidle, W., *Sueton und die antike Biographie* (2nd ed., Munich, 1963).

Stevenson,T.R., 'The ideal benefactor and the father analogy in Greek and Roman thought' *CQ* 42 (1992) 421-36.

Stewart, A.F., 'To entertain an emperor: Sperlonga, Laokoon and Tiberius at the dinner-table' *JRS* 67 (1977) 76-90.

Stockton, D., 'Primus and Murena' *Historia* 14 (1965) 18-40.

Stuart, D.R., *Epochs of Greek and Roman Biography* (California, 1928).

Sullivan, R.D., 'Thrace in the Eastern Dynastic network' *ANRW* 2.7.1 (1980) 186-211.

Sullivan, R.D., 'The Dynasty of Cappadocia' *ANRW* 2.7.2 (1980) 1125-68.

Sumner, G.V., 'The family connections of L. Aelius Seianus' *Phoenix* 19 (1965) 134-45.

——'Germanicus and Drusus Caesar' *Latomus* 26 (1967) 413-35.

——'Varrones Murenae' *HSCPh* 82 (1978) 187-95.

Suolahti, J., 'Claudia insons. Why was a fine imposed on Claudia Ap. f. in 246 BC?' *Arctos* 11 (1977) 133-51.

——'M. Claudius Glicia, qui scriba fuerat, dictator' *Arctos* 10 (1976) 97-103.

Sutherland, C.H.V., *Coinage in Roman imperial policy 31 BC-AD 68* (Oxford, 1951).

——The Emperor and the Coinage: Julio-Claudian Studies (London, 1976).

——'The *Clementiae and Moderationi* dupondii of Tiberius: more thoughts on the chronology' *NC* 139 (1979) 21-25.

Swain, S., 'Character change in Plutarch' *Phoenix* 43 (1989) 62-8.

Swan, M., 'The consular fasti of 23 BC and the conspiracy of Varro Murena' *HSCPh* 70 (1966) 235-47.

Syme, R., 'Some notes on the legions under Augustus' *JRS* 23 (1933) 14-33.

——'The Spanish War of Augustus (26-25 BC)' *AJPh* 55 (1934) 293-337.

——*The Roman Revolution* (Oxford, 1939).

——*Tacitus* (2 vols, Oxford, 1958).

——'Consulates in absence' *JRS* 48 (1958) 1-9.

——'Imperator Caesar: a study in nomenclature' *Historia* 7 (1958) 172-185.

——'A governor of Tarraconensis' *ES* 8 (1969) 125-33.

——'Domitius Corbulo' *JRS* 60 (1970) 27-39.

——*Ten Studies in Tacitus* (Oxford, 1970).

——'The travels of Suetonius Tranquillus' *Hermes* 109 (1981) 105-17.

——'Biographers of the Caesars' *MH* 37 (1980) 104-128.

——'The marriage of Rubellius Blandus' *AJPh* 103 (1982) 62-85.

——'Clues to testamentary adoption' *Tituli* 4 (1982 [1984]) 397-410 = *Roman Papers* IV (1988) 159-73.

——'The year 33 in Tacitus and Dio' *Athenaeum* 61 (1983) 3-23.

——*The Augustan Aristocracy* (Oxford, 1986).

——'Diet on Capri' *Athenaeum* 67 (1989) 261-72.

Taillardat, J., *Peri blasphemion, Peri paidion, extraits byzantins* (Paris, 1967).

Talbert, R.J.A., *The Senate of Imperial Rome* (Princeton, 1984).

Tarrant, H., *Thrasyllan Platonism* (Cornell, 1993).

Tarver, J.C., *Tiberius the Tyrant* (London, 1902).

Taylor, L.R., 'Seuiri Equitum Romanorum and municipal *seuiri*: a study in pre-military training among the Romans' *JRS* 14 (1924) 158-71.

——'Tiberius' refusals of divine honours' *TAPhA* 60 (1929) 87-101.

——*The Divinity of the Roman Emperor* (Middleton, Connecticut, 1931).

Thomasson, B.E., *Die Statthalter der römischen Provinzen Nordafricas von Augustus bis Diocletianus* (Lund, 1960).

Timpe, D., *Untersuchungen zur Kontinuität des frühen Prinzipats* (Wiesbaden, Steiner, 1962).

Townend, G.B., 'The Hippo inscription and the career of Suetonius' *Historia* 10 (1961) 99-109.

——'The post of *ab epistulis* in the second century' *Historia* 10 (1961) 375-81.

——'The trial of Aemilia Lepida in AD 20' *Latomus* 21 (1962) 484-93.

——'Suetonius and his influence' in T.A. Dorey (ed.) *Latin Biography* (London, Routledge, 1967).

Treggiari, S., *Roman Marriage: Iusti Coniuges from the Time of Cicero to the Time of Ulpian* (Oxford, 1991).

Turner, A., 'A Vergilian anecdote in Suetonius and Dio' *CPh* 38 (1943) 261.

Ustinsky, H.U., 'Augustus und die adoption des Tiberius' *Hermes* 94 (1966) 324-43.

Vanoni, L.C., 'Rivista di epigrafia etrusca' *Studi Etruschi* 37 (1969) 317-23.

Vasaly, A., 'Personality and power: Livy's depiction of the Appii Claudii in the first pentad' *TAPhA* 117 (1987) 203-226.

Ville, G., *La gladiature en Occident des origines à la mort de Domitien* (Paris, de Boccard, 1982).

Viljamaa, 'Suetonius on Roman Teachers of Grammar' *ANRW* 2.33.5 (1991) 3826-51.

Vittinghof, F., *Der Staatsfeind in der römischen Kaiserzeit* (Berlin, 1936)

Vogel-Weidemann, U., *Die Statthalter von Africa und Asia in den Jahren 14-68 n. Chr: eine Untersuchung zum Verhältnis Princeps und Senat* (Bonn, Habelt, 1982).

Vollmer, F., 'De funere publico Romanorum' *Jahrb. für class. Philol.* Suppl. Bd. XIX (1892-3) 319-64.

Wallace-Hadrill, A.F., 'The emperor and his virtues' *Historia* 30 (1981) 298-325.

——'Ciuilis Princeps: Between citizen and king' *JRS* 72 (1982) 32-48.

——*Suetonius: The Scholar and his Caesars* (London, Duckworth 1983).

——'Suetonius as Historian' *CR* 36 (1986) 243-5.

Wardle, D., 'Caligula and the client kings' *CQ* 42 (1992) 437-43.

Wardman, A.E., *Rome's Debt to Greece* (London, Elek, 1976).

Weeber, K.-W., 'Troiae Lusus' *Ancient Society* 5 (1974) 171-96.

Weingärtner, D.G., *Die Agyptenreise des Germanicus* (Bonn, Habelt, 1969).

Weinrib, E.J., 'The family connections of M. Livius Drusus Libo' *HSCPh* 72 [1967] 247-78.

Weinstock, S., *Divus Julius* (Oxford, 1971).

Weller, J.A., 'Tacitus and Tiberius' Rhodian exile' *Phoenix* 12 (1958) 31--5.

Wellesley, K., 'The *dies imperii* of Tiberius' *JRS* 57 (1967) 23-30.

Wells, C., *The German Policy of Augustus* (Oxford, 1972).

Wightman, E.M., 'Priscae Gallorum Memoriae: some comments on sources for a history of Gaul' in *The Ancient Historian and his Materials* (1975) 93-107.

Wilkes, J.J., 'The military achievement of Augustus in Europe with special reference to Illyricum' *University of Birmingham Historical Journal* 10 (1965-6) 1-27.

——*Dalmatia* (London, Routledge 1969).

——'Julio-Claudian historians' *CW* 65 (1972) 177-92; 197-203.

Williams, M.H., 'The Expulsion of the Jews from Rome in AD 19' *Latomus* 48 (1989) 765-84.

Wiseman, T.P., *Clio's Cosmetics* (Leicester, 1979).

——'The mother of Livia Augusta' *Historia* 14 (1965) 333-4.

——*Death of an Emperor* (Exeter, 1991).

Wissowa, G., 'Neue Bruchstücke des römischen Festkalenders' *Hermes* 51 (1923) 369-93.

Wissowa, G., *Religion und Kultus der Römer* (Munich, 1971).

Woodman, A.J., *Velleius Paterculus: The Tiberian Narrative* (2.94-131) (Cambridge, 1977).

——*Velleius Paterculus: The Caesarian and Augustan Narrative* (2.41-93) (Cambridge, 1983).

Zetzel, J.E.G., 'New light on Gaius Caesar's Eastern campaigns' *GRBS* 11 (1970) 259-66.